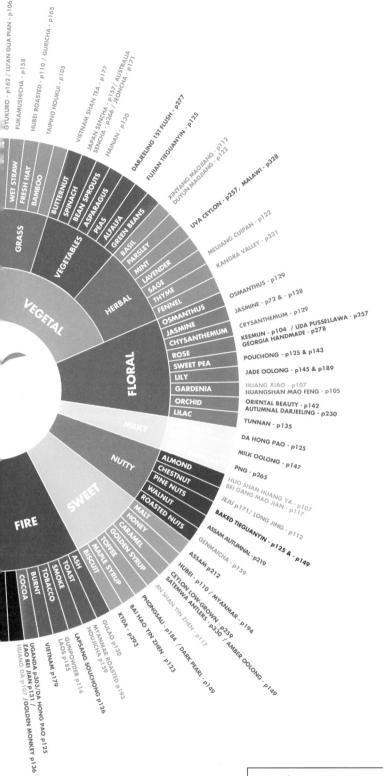

GYUKURO - p162 / LU'AN GUA PIAN - p106
FUKAMUSHICHA - p158
HUBEI ROASTED - p110 / GURICHA - p165
TAIPING HOUKUI - p105
VIETNAM SHAN TEA - P177
JAPAN SENCHA - P157/ AUSTRALIA
SENCHA - P226 / JEONCHA - P171
HAINAN - p226 / p130
DARJEELING 1ST FLUSH - P277
FUJIAN TIEGUANYIN - p125
XINYANG MAOJIANG - p112
DUYUN MAOJIANG - p122
UVA CEYLON - p257, MALAWI - p328
MEIJIANG CUIPAN - p122
KANGRA VALLEY - p231
OSMANTHUS - p129
JASMINE - p72 & - p128
CRYSANTHEMUM - p129
KEEMUN - p104 / UDA PUSSELLAWA - p257
GEORGIA HANDMADE - p278
POUCHONG - p125 & p143
JADE OOLONG - p145 & p189
HUANG XIAO - p107
HUANGSHAN MAO FENG - p105
ORIENTAL BEAUTY - p142
AUTUMNAL DARJEELING - p230
YUNNAN - p135
DA HONG PAO - p125
MILK OOLONG - p147
PNG - p265
HUO SHAN HUANG YA - p107
BEI GANG MAO JIAN - p117
JEJU p171/ LONG JING - p112
BAKED TIEGUANYIN - p125 & - p149
ASSAM AUTUMNAL - P219
GENMAICHA - p159
ASSAM p212
HUBEI - p110 / MYANMAR - p194
CEYLON LOW-GROWN - P239
SATEMWA ANTLERS - p330 / AMBER OOLONG - p149
JIN SHAN YIN ZHEN - p117
PHONGSALI - P184 / DARK PEARL - p149
BAI HAO YIN ZHEN - p123
KTDA - P293
GULAO p130
MYANMAR ROASTED p193
HOUJICHA p159
PHONGSALI - P293
GUNPOWDER p114
LAOS p185
LAPSANG SOUCHONG p126
VIETNAM p179
ZAO BEI JIAN p131 /
HUANG DA p107 /GOLDEN MONKEY p136
UGANDA p303/DA HONG PAO p125

WET STRAW
FRESH HAY
BAMBOO
GRASS
BUTTERNUT
SPINACH
BEAN SPROUTS
ASPARAGUS
PEAS
VEGETABLES
ALFALFA
GREEN BEANS
BASIL
PARSLEY
HERBAL
MINT
LAVENDER
SAGE
THYME
FENNEL
VEGETAL
OSMANTHUS
JASMINE
CHYSANTHEMUM
FLORAL
ROSE
SWEET PEA
LILY
GARDENIA
ORCHID
LILAC
MILKY
NUTTY
ALMOND
CHESTNUT
PINE NUTS
WALNUT
ROASTED NUTS
SWEET
MALT
HONEY
CARAMEL
TOFFEE
GOLDEN SYRUP
MAPLE SYRUP
BISCUIT
FIRE
ASH
TOAST
SMOKE
TOBACCO
BURNT
COCOA

This flavour wheel is designed to assist readers in identifying teas
that may appeal based upon their characteristic flavour profile. It
is to be noted that many teas may show facets of a number of the
flavour descriptors so can be located in multiple areas on the
wheel. A particular tea's propensity to represent the exact flavour
it is linked to above will depend upon a number of factors related
to terroir and manufacture, so this should be regarded as a
directional guide.
The teas around the outer rim are all featured within The World Tea
Encyclopedia, the flavour wheel at the centre is reproduced with
kind permission of the Australian Tea Masters.

THE WORLD TEA ENCYCLOPAEDIA

THE WORLD TEA ENCYCLOPAEDIA

The world of tea explored and explained from bush to brew

Will Battle

Matador
9 Priory Business Park,
Wistow Road, Kibworth Beauchamp,
Leicestershire. LE8 0RX
Tel: 0116 279 2299
Email: books@troubador.co.uk
Web: www.troubador.co.uk/matador
Twitter: @matadorbooks

ISBN 978 1785893 131

British Library Cataloguing in Publication Data.
A catalogue record for this book is available from the British Library.

Typeset in 12pt Aldine401 BT by Troubador Publishing Ltd, Leicester, UK

Matador is an imprint of Troubador Publishing Ltd

For Henry and Sophie

CONTENTS

INTRODUCTION

Tea is drunk by more of the world's people than any other beverage apart from water. Its influence is felt right across the planet and in every strata of society. For most of us in the West, though, it remains a staple product, often uncomfortable with its place in the world as it fights off the ostensibly sexier challenges from the coffee and soft drinks corners.

It need not be so. The world of tea is a glorious one, redolent with variety and opportunity; the self-evident blessings of a naturally conceived product should be the answer to our fear of what is regularly hidden in today's ingredients lists. Even the best tea is outstanding value when compared to any alternative, and there is a tea for everyone if only they know how to discover it.

One of tea's great features is its accessibility to all. Eminent gardens produce tea that is lavishly packaged for the most exclusive of London retailers just as it may end up in a five-pence teabag. In this book we try to celebrate tea's democratic characteristic by acknowledging that it is not the format (teabags or loose tea) that defines a great tea, it is the start point – the tea itself.

Camellia sinensis, the tea bush, is the hero of this book. The origins in which it grows, the landscapes and climate that influence it and the artisans who craft it into its myriad forms are its supporting dramatis personae. The world boasts myriad teas, most of them lying undiscovered by Western cultures still rooted in the view that tea comes from a tissue bag at breakfast or 4pm. Even the tea in a breakfast teabag can be sublime or undrinkable.

The World Tea Encyclopaedia aims to shed light on this wealth of variety, and to debunk the snobbishness and doctrine that can scare off newcomers from the joys of connoisseurship. What is out there? Where does it come from? How do others drink it? What makes it so special? How does it taste? How can we get the best from our teas?

Hopefully this book will feed its readers with a new world of tea-drinking enjoyment and opportunity. The knowledge to upgrade the teabag, to know what to seek online, to brave a journey to the local tea shop, to submit to curiosity and jump into a world of discovery, or better still, to visit the countries and people that lovingly produce it.

As Ralph W. Sockman said, 'The larger the island of knowledge, the longer the shoreline of wonder.'

A NOTE ON MAPS AND NOMENCLATURE

The maps in this book are designed as an accompaniment to the text rather than as an aid to navigation. Accordingly we have tried to avoid the inclusion of excessive detail such as roads or villages where this may distract from or confuse cartographical renderings of tea-producing regions.

Some maps comprise larger-scale renderings of extended areas, and where this is the case we have tried to follow a rule of labelling regions or districts in white, whilst multiple gardens or factories belonging to a group are labelled in red with the name of the group. On smaller-scale maps, individual gardens or factories are labelled in red.

In East Asian producing countries such as China and Taiwan, producing areas are named by style and/or standard number following the manner in which they are sold.

In producing countries to the west of China, whether the tea is smallholder or plantation, the factory would sell the tea under a particular name known as a *selling mark*, occasionally even multiple selling marks. Sometimes the name of the selling mark is the same as that of the factory and estate, but frequently a different selling mark is used which may bear no relation to the name of the factory or estate. Constraints of space on the maps mean we cannot list the multiple selling marks and have named only the factory.

Tea gardens and the factories that produce tea come in many shapes and sizes. Some regions tend to contain more large estates in which a plantation and factory are under the same ownership. Other areas are dominated by smallholdings that can be anything from a handful of bushes in a kitchen garden, to multiple hectares of tea interspersed with any number of crops, whether maize, rubber, bananas, rice or forest. This patchwork nature of land use can create problems when marking areas of tea, but we have continued to show such areas as tea producers even if other crops are also cultivated there.

There are estimated to be more than ten thousand tea gardens in the world. In some especially large producing regions such as Assam, Sri Lanka or Kenya we have struck a balance between detail and usability, meaning that only the better producers are included. We have defined *better* both objectively as well as subjectively through reference to auction prices combined with historical experience of what quality a garden is capable of producing, or that producer's position in the global speciality industry.

GENDER

Where we have described the activities of individuals on tea estates and in factories, they have been listed in the masculine. In this case it is purely for reasons of textual flow and brevity and not intended as a personal observation upon gender issues in the tea industry.

Part 1

GROWING AND MAKING TEA

THE TEA GARDEN

Family

Genus

Species

Variety, or *jat*

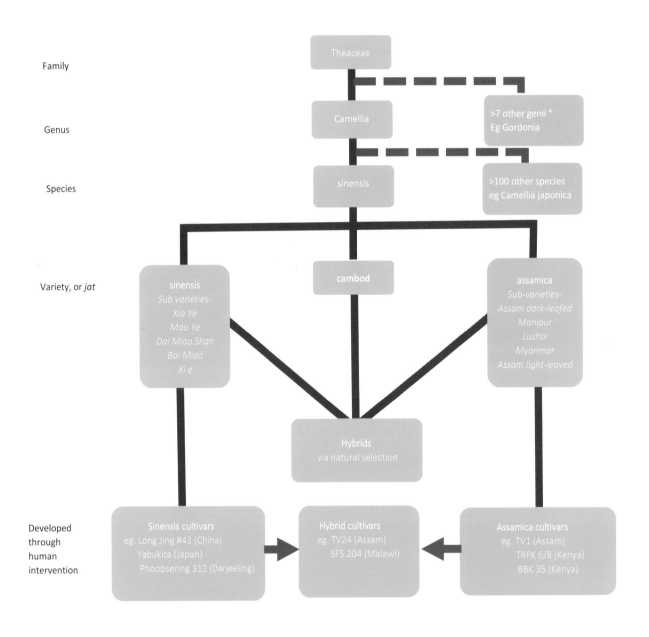

Theaceae

Camellia

>7 other genii [4]
Eg Gordonia

sinensis

>100 other species
eg Camellia japonica

sinensis
Sub varieties-
Xia Ye
Mao Ye
Dai Miao Shan
Bai Miao
Xi e

cambod

assamica
Sub-varieties-
Assam dark-leafed
Manipur
Lushai
Myanmar
Assam light-leafed

Hybrids
via natural selection

Developed
through
human
intervention

Sinensis cultivars
eg. Long Jing #43 (China)
Yabukita (Japan)
Phoobsering 312 (Darjeeling)

Hybrid cultivars
eg. TV24 (Assam)
SFS 204 (Malawi)

Assamica cultivars
eg. TV1 (Assam)
TRFK 6/8 (Kenya)
BBK 35 (Kenya)

TEA (*CAMELLIA SINENSIS*) IS a species of evergreen perennial plant from the family *Theaceae*. In the Linnaean classification the genus is *Camellia* and the species is *sinensis*. The family resemblance in the lush, deep green, mildly serrated leaf of a tea bush is evident in any garden camellia, whilst its supposed Chinese origin is also suggested in its name, *sinensis*. The tea plant is generally regarded to have hailed from the borderlands area where China and Laos meet, but it flourishes anywhere it can find well-drained, acidic to neutral soils, rainfall of over 1,300 millimetres per year, and tropical or subtropical temperatures. Rainfall permitting, *Camellia sinensis* is in fact quite adaptable. Bushes in the Caucasus and parts of China can tolerate periodic snow so long as the mercury does not drop below freezing for extended periods, whilst the steamier year-round warmth closer to the Equator provides a test of endurance characterised by extended periods of extreme heat.

The plant we refer to as a tea bush is considered to come from one of two major varieties. West of China these are often known as *jats*. The China jat, *Camellia sinensis var. sinensis*, is a narrow-leafed plant more often planted at higher altitudes or in slightly cooler producing countries. If left unpruned then *sinensis* plants can develop to 2 or 3 metres in height.

The Assam jat *Camellia sinensis var. assamica*, often also curtailed to *Camellia assamica*, is a broad-leafed bush that tends to thrive in the hotter corners of the tea world. Left unpruned, *assamica* can reach heights of 15 to 20 metres. This is also the same variety found in parts of Yunnan, where the planters refer to it as *Da Ye* (or 'large leaf'), whilst in Sri Lanka it is known as 'white jat'.

Other subspecies are occasionally glimpsed. *Camellia assamica ssp. lasiocalyx (known as the Cambod)*[1] represents a taxonomic middle ground between *assamica* and *sinensis* but is not widely seen in commercial plantations.

Although Western tea experts usually talk of these main varieties, there are parts of China where the bush demonstrates such unique characteristics that to group it into *sinensis* or *assamica* seems bold. China specialist Michael Adams identified up to five further variants, termed *xia ye* (narrow leaf), *mao ye* (hairy leaf), *dai miao shan* (big mountain bud), *bai mao* or *da bai* (big hairy white bud or big white) and *xi e* (small sepals).[2] It is a moot point whether these variants can be taxonomically grouped within a variety such as *sinensis* or form sub-varieties in their own right,

A nursery in Malawi.

Tea needs ample rainfall to flourish; here in Hainan it is showing signs of drought-related stress.

but what is important to remember is that there is widespread diversity in the plant material and this has a profound effect on the potential tea that is produced.

Some Assam and Yunnan planters would also differentiate between varieties of the Assam subspecies. Different shades and sizes of leaf are ascribed to Manipuri, Myanmarese or Mizoram provenance, such that a planter may be overheard talking of a *Lushai* plant (which boasts exceptionally broad leaves), when actually this is just another variety of *Camellia assamica*.

CULTIVARS

So far, so simple. Until around 1970, most tea was planted from seed. Estates maintained unpruned tea trees whose specific purpose was to exhaust

TEA SEEDLINGS AVAILABLE
1. TN 14/3   6.   31/8
2. 18 U   7. ST·306/1 (PURPLE TEA
3. C 12   8. 371/3
4. EJULU   9. D 99/10
5 A·H·P 15/10

Cultivar tea plants on sale to local smallholders in Kenya.

themselves in the generation of tea seeds for onward planting in nurseries. Some tea is in fact still planted in this way, but the majority of gardens now elect to make use of cuttings to develop bushes that exhibit one or more desirable characteristic.

Much of the tea now consumed comes from bushes that have been specifically developed to give the tea-maker exactly the style of tea that the market wants. Such bushes, formerly known as clones but now increasingly termed cultivars where the term *clone* can bring unwelcome associations, can potentially yield five times what could have been achieved in the past from seedling bushes, and often of much better quality to boot. So how do researchers go about developing a cultivar?

Plant breeding is a technical science requiring of immense patience, large resources of land and labour, deep pockets and even deeper foresight and botanical expertise. The start point is often to make small volumes of tea from potentially interesting 'mother bushes' in pilot factories. These trials will reveal certain bushes that show some potential, possibly because they are especially vigorous, because they have been the last bush standing during a period of drought, or maybe because they produce tea that exhibits

TEA TREES

Tea trees can develop from bushes for less noble reasons. Any visit to Uganda in the years following the Amin regime would reveal numerous plantations that had been permitted to grow into mini-forests, and there remain a number of gardens in Mozambique that are yet to be rehabilitated following the civil war that ended in the 1990s. This is certainly not the domain of the 'single tree artisan', and where this has happened there is no alternative but to prune back to the trunk much like a coppice, and allow the bush to regenerate from its base.

an especially appealing liquor, or one of any other number of characteristics that a planter may approve of.

If the stars are in alignment and an appealing tea is produced from a vigorous bush that survives dry weather successfully, then the next step for the plant breeder is to take a number of cuttings from the plant that has demonstrated such potential in order to replicate the success on a larger scale. Trial areas are set aside in model gardens, permitting potentially useful cultivars to develop to maturity. More advanced developments can then ensue which may involve the grafting of useful scions onto rootstocks with favoured characteristics. Alternatively, favoured cultivars can be isolated together and encouraged to pollinate with the result that so-called 'polyclonal' seeds are reproduced.

Whatever the means, long-term assessment of the viability of the plant is a prerequisite, without which assurance few farmers would be prepared to commit their land for the fifty-year or more productive life of the modern tea bush.

Breeders will be interested in a number of characteristics which, depending upon the likely market, will assume greater or lesser importance. In Taiwan the preference may be for a bush that yields a seductive floral aroma when processed as an oolong. In Malawi a plant scientist may look to develop teas which deliver a deep red colour when made with milk, combined with some drought resistance to cope with the southerly location and increasingly long dry season wrought by climate change. In Sri Lanka or Assam, a low-grown cultivar may have a preponderance

An ancient tea tree in the valleys of Yunnan.

of tips in the made tea or resistance to the tea mosquito bug, whereas in Kenya there may be a need to target good leaf density and a bright, golden cup.

Cultivar tea fields are notable for their homogenous appearance and colour, reflecting the genetically identical plants which contrast with the more patchwork appearance of fields planted longer ago from seed. Although such genetic homogeneity always brings with it the risk of some unforeseen disease or mutation threatening the entire plantation, we should on balance welcome such cultivars. They are the path to higher yields of better quality thereby ensuring a more vibrant, healthy, local economy, and lower household food prices for the local communities arising from the land this potentially frees up for the cultivation of other crops.

PLANTING TEA

Tea plants spend a year in a shaded nursery before they can be regarded as robust and hardy enough to withstand the rigours of direct sunlight and potentially erratic rainfall. The field earmarked for the tea will usually have been planted with a break crop such as *Mana* or Guatemala grass for a couple of years in order to endow the soil with adequate nutrients and organic matter before it again plays host to tea bushes. These crops are typically ploughed in before the tea is planted out, and the break time should ensure that any typical root-borne diseases have enough time to disappear before more tea is introduced without the need to fumigate the soil with more toxic agents.

Young tea, like any infant plant, is exceedingly vulnerable to lack of rainfall and as such it will usually be planted during the cooler months when there is also an excess of available labour who would otherwise be engaged in plucking or weeding during the peak season. The hope is that the young plants will have established themselves in time for the stress of the tropical summer that will provide their first serious test of viability.

Youthful tea is more or less unproductive for at least three years. This formative period ensures that the tea establishes itself without the additional stress of regular plucking. Through skilful pruning, the planter trims the bush into the optimum shape to make maximum use of the available sunlight, and at the appropriate height to form a useful basis for plucking. This is known as the plucking table, and without this activity the bush would grow to tree height, becoming fundamentally useless to all but the most skilled climbers and monkeys.

There are a number of tea trees in Yunnan, Myanmar, Laos, Thailand and Vietnam requiring precisely this agility. Indeed, this sort of plucking has long been part of local culture, and the trees are often more part of a mixed forest than a plantation gone wild. Although such trees do little for productivity, the quality of the unique artisanal teas that 'single tree' tea masters can produce can be unparalleled. Tea produced from a distinct tree is shorn of any quality moderation accompanying larger volumes, and such teas can express their individuality in a captivating way.

Once mature, most bushes will have a productive life of around fifty to sixty years before they are uprooted and the replanting process begins again. This is on the basis of a typical well-run estate with money to invest aiming to replant about 2% of its tea each year. This is not to say that tea cannot remain productive well beyond this age. There are a number of gardens in Darjeeling with bushes well over a hundred years old, whilst in the village of Mangjing in Yunnan there exists a tea tree claimed to be 1,300 years old.[3]

MANAGING A TEA GARDEN

The activities involved in the day-to-day running of an area of tea bushes maintained for the production of tea vary depending upon the time of year and the physical location. A hillside of tea trees in Laos will require a lower level of attention than a similarly-sized area of cultivar tea maintained on the plantation model. Equatorial producers such as Kenya or Sri Lanka with year-round growth will inevitably observe a different annual cycle than seasonal origins further into the tropics.

Aside from the six-days-a-week plucking activity, the producer needs to organise teams of weeding parties to ensure that the pluckers are only returning with tea and no foreign matter. The larger plantations maintain areas of managed forest in order to ensure that they have the fuelwood to keep their boilers supplied in a sustainable way. Roads require maintenance, especially after the rainy season, drainage channels and culverts need to be cleared, and estate housing refurbished or brought up to standard.

PRUNING

The main annual activity in the garden itself is pruning (often known as *skiffing*) in which the bushes are given a deep prune every three or four years, and shallower cuts in the intervening years. This will usually take place just before the onset of cooler or dryer weather when the bush will in any case be less productive.

The visual difference between seedling tea (L) and cultivar tea (R) is clear from the air.

Pruning has both a quality and a practical motive. In the immediate year following its recovery from the attentions of the pruning knife, it yields softer, more succulent leaf that makes for better quality tea, especially tea processed in the orthodox fashion. Although the crop is compromised, quality is much improved and this is a key battleground between accountants and quality managers.

From a practical perspective, tea bushes are subject to *creep* – a gradual increase in height over the course of the year, even despite the attentions of pluckers who remove the new growth on a regular basis. If a bush is left unpruned for a number of years then it will eventually reach a height that makes plucking an impossible task.

PLUCKING

Plucking is the cornerstone of tea-making. The ostensibly simple process of removing the leaf from a bush and placing it into a receptacle is fraught with expert opinion, governmental interference, union agitation, luddite action and NGO interest. The one thing that does remain certain is the old maxim, *you can't make good tea from bad leaf, but you can make bad tea from good leaf.* This is suggestive of the importance of plucking to the whole process.

Plucking can happen in three different ways: by hand, through the use of shears, or with a mechanical harvester. In this progression from manual plucking, through shears and on to machines, one sees a progressively lower labour cost, yet also a smaller chance of selecting only the best, youngest leaf. It is the youngest leaf that is preferred because this contains the highest concentration of polyphenols and caffeine, the bodies that give the tea its characteristic taste. The older the leaf, the higher the proportion of other solids (such as crude fibre, for example) that will ultimately act to dilute the quality.

Manual plucking, here in New Zealand, for high-quality oolong tea.

PLUCKING TECHNIQUE

To replicate the plucking technique best suited to both the bush and the plucker, the hands should be placed in front of the waist, then inverted inwards so that the thumb and forefinger are bottom-most and little finger uppermost. Then with thumb and forefinger, an imaginary stalk bearing two leaves and a bud can be grasped and detached from the bush by the outward rotation of the hand accompanied by a brisk pull. Pluckers are often seen clutching long bamboo canes. These aid the pluckers in recognising how deep to pluck when placed atop the bush on the 'plucking table'.

MANUAL PLUCKING

Common sense should tell us that through the use of our own hands, we stand the best chance of plucking only that leaf which is the most tender and optimal for tea production. Hands are selective, they are gentle in the process, the bush suffers minimal trauma and they select only the good leaf, ignoring the bad leaf and any foreign matter missed by weeding parties. Better still, they remove damaged leaf and dormant buds known as *Bhanji*, thereby facilitating the growth of active shoots and stimulating productivity. Why wouldn't everyone pluck manually?

The answer lies in good old boring economics. In some parts of the world, the return an estate gets on its tea is insufficient to justify the vast amount of labour needed to revisit the same bush every seven to ten days. By way of example, no matter how hard an Argentine producer tries, there are few buyers who will ever pay more than a couple of dollars per kilo for even the best tea they can create. Under such circumstances, investing in a very expensive labour force to maintain the highest plucking standards can only be folly, and it is this that will lead the producer down the road towards mechanisation.

In contrast, for a Darjeeling producer, quality levels are so finely distinguished that the difference between an excellent tea and a merely very good one can be measured in tens of dollars per kilo. Here they cannot get away with anything other than the skilled use of hands, even if there were an appetite to risk an expensive machine with very sharp teeth on the steep and perilous slopes of the Himalayas.

SHEAR PLUCKING

Quality-minded producers struggling to obtain or afford the labour needed to pluck manually are likely to explore shear plucking. Shears are commonly seen in parts of Africa, Indonesia and South India. They represent the middle ground between manual and machine plucking. The productivity is better than manual plucking, yet with acceptable levels of leaf quality.

MACHINE PLUCKING

Machines do not discriminate on leaf and are bad for quality. Machines cause unemployment. Machines damage the bush and in the long-term reduce yields. Machines harvest foreign matter and endanger the consumer. This is one of the most contentious discussions of today's industry, which estimates that around 40% of the world's tea is plucked by machine. One day, though, almost all of the world's tea will be plucked by machine. It is an inevitability to be embraced and anticipated with relish rather than dread, because the day this happens will be the day that tea plantation workers are highly paid, skilled machine operators. Until then estates will be left with a mix of plucking methods; sometimes all three in the same garden.

Everything that has been said about manual plucking can just as easily be said in reverse about machines – they are ideally suited to high-wage economies producing cheap tea. But this does not mean that with skilful fieldwork and planting, very good tea cannot be produced from machine-plucked leaf. The overwhelming majority of Japan's tea, often of outstanding quality, is produced from machine-harvested gardens.

Plucking machines resemble giant hedge trimmers and come in numerous forms. The very

Mechanical harvesters at work in Argentina, the most automated of all tea producers.

wealthiest Japanese producers have mounted theirs on rails, the South Americans' are tractor-based, but elsewhere a machine is more usually carried by a team of three: two for the machine, one to hold the bag containing the leaf blown out of the rear of the device.

Machines can enable a producer to cut back on labour costs and invest in other areas, such as in the factory or in replanting with new quality cultivars, which are increasingly orientated around suitability for machine harvesting. Machines do not get tired at 4.30pm and maintain a regular standard all day (so the theory goes, although the operatives carrying them may tire). Most importantly of all, machines permit those operating them to be paid more, and it is for this reason that the spread of mechanisation should not be concealed and obstructed. We should be proud of the march of progress to remote rural communities all too often bypassed by technological development.

PLUCKING STANDARDS

Plucking itself can be performed to a number of potential leaf quality levels. Typically, fine plucking would aim to remove only the terminal bud and the youngest two leaves. Medium plucking may take one further or older leaf, and coarse plucking yet one leaf more. Each producer will work out the standard that suits the business best. What is for sure is that there are levels of coarse plucking and to take four leaves and a bud is as good as it gets; I have seen ten or more leaves and a bud in parts of the world purporting to produce fine speciality tea, and there is little in the way of downwards limit here.

For those making genuinely superior speciality teas you may see small sections of an estate being plucked even finer than 'fine'. For some Silver Tip manufacture, for example, the pluckers would aim only to take the bud, or at the most one leaf and a bud. Such teas are to be treasured in line with the time invested in their creation. This is an incredibly time-consuming and eye-wateringly costly business. If you take the standard calculation of 4.2 kilos of green leaf for one kilo of made tea then it is a daunting prospect to send pluckers out to pluck adequate tea to fill only a speciality tea shop tin, let alone a larger volume.

Once the leaf has been plucked it is usually weighed, both to assess the yield of the field and also

Two leaves and a bud, accepted the world over as 'good leaf'.

whether the pluckers have hit the productivity targets that trigger the payment of their bonus. It will then be sent to the factory, the aim being to get it there as quickly as possible and as cool as possible with no compression, disruption to the cell structure, or opportunity to wither before the factory manager elects to commence the processing on his own terms.

Transporting the leaf to the factory is no easy task in itself, given the difficulty of travel on often-potholed dirt roads during the rainy season. The most promising-looking hard-pan road can swiftly turn to impassable mud, whilst bridges can disappear without warning under the sudden deluges common to tea-producing regions. Under these circumstances the fact that the leaf makes it to the factory at all is a testament to the resourcefulness and skill of those who work in tea who, because of the science of plant growth, tend to see their most heavy cropping period coincide with the heaviest rainfall, and hence greatest logistical challenge.

Plucked leaf being loaded into bags for transport to the tea factory.

THE TEA FACTORY

Leaf arriving at an Indonesian tea factory; it is sent in small bags to avoid excess heat and compression.

Mechanised leaf delivery in a modern Argentine factory.

THE TEA FACTORY IS perhaps an incongruous heading under which to group the varied methods by which green leaf is transformed into any one of the six different tea types. *Factory* conjures up images of industrial processes on a grand scale, which in reality is atypical for much of the world's fine-quality tea.

A large, multi-floor building would typically play host to the black tea manufacture process, which is responsible for 70% of the world's output, but even here there is widespread variation and the Darjeeling facilities are a fraction of the size of a large Kenyan factory. Although one also finds such industrialisation in the green tea industry in China, Japan and elsewhere, it is much more the domain of the smaller craftsman. Good-quality white, green, oolong and yellow tea is more likely to have received the requisite attention to detail when it has been processed with the care and expertise that small teams of quality-minded artisans can bring.

BLACK TEA

Upon arrival in the factory, the leaf will be checked by a quality control manager to assess whether it is of the appropriate standard. The better factories are 'brands' in their own right, with buyers favouring the particular characteristics of one over another, and no one wishes to be responsible for diluting this quality through acceptance of substandard leaf. The smallholder or leaf supplier will suffer a nervous few minutes whilst he or she awaits the verdict of the factory. Leaf rejected at this stage initiates a sorry afternoon for the supplier, who will have to find a less discriminating, more desperate, or more distant factory.

WITHERING

The first stage in black tea manufacture is the wither. Withering is a process of chemical and physical preparation of leaf for rolling, and whilst visibly it appears to be a lengthy and static procedure, if it is done badly then there is no hope for the eventual quality of the tea.

Withering is accomplished by spreading the leaf upon wire mesh in long troughs through which warm or ambient air can be blown, thereby removing both surface water and actual leaf moisture. Vast amounts of space are needed in order to accomplish a successful wither given the typical ratio of 4.2kg of green leaf to 1kg of made tea. The leaf on arrival (if it has been raining, for example) may even be more than 100% moisture, expressed as the weight of water compared to the weight of leaf as it arrives. The layer of leaf sitting in the trough will be given around twelve to sixteen hours to wither and assume a more malleable quality. Withers are expressed as being *hard* or *soft*. A hard wither will result in more moisture having been removed from the leaf than a soft wither. Hard withers tend to be more common in orthodox manufacture, especially origins such as Darjeeling in the first flush. CTC manufacture by contrast requires softer withers.

This physical change in the leaf resulting purely from the loss of moisture is just half of the battle. It is the chemical wither that is responsible for creating the right constituents in the leaf to ensure that what emerges at the end of the process not only looks nice, but crucially tastes nice as well. Only time can genuinely influence the chemical wither, and tea will not be rushed. This means that the process has to last *at least* six hours. The chemical wither is initiated at the point of plucking when various biochemical changes start to take place in the leaf: proteins start to turn into amino acids and flavour compounds are formed. It is these that are responsible for the seductive grassy-flowery aromas that can be enjoyed in a tea factory.

Given the area needed to wither large volumes of green leaf, the temptation is always to cut corners during periods of high crop. If tea is badly withered then it can become unpalatable. Over-withered leaf can result in flat or earthy teas; under-withered leaf can result in the additional moisture hampering oxidation. Tasty compounds run away with liquid as leaf is twisted, and the leaf can break up or refuse to co-operate with the factory's machines. Withering is an important process to perform well, and an area of the factory in which skilled tea-makers can often be found.

Because of the logistical challenge in handling vast quantities of leaf, modern factories are increasingly looking towards technological solutions that simultaneously simplify the process, reducing the amount of space required, and enabling the use of storage bins, fans and continuous withering conveyor belts. The big test of this technology will be its application to the production of teas of the very best quality.

ROLLING

Withered leaf is introduced into a process designed to disrupt the cell structure and allow oxygen to react with enzymes in the leaf. There are a number of ways of initiating this process but the two most commonly seen are known as orthodox and Crush Tear Curl (or CTC).

ORTHODOX

Orthodox rolling, as its name suggests, is a more traditional technique that gradually squeezes and twists leaf in order to break open the cell structure. The equipment needed for this is a set of large

Continuous withering in a modern factory.

The optimum period for withering will depend on the moisture content of the leaf when it arrives at the factory, as well as factors such as ambient air temperature and humidity. Typically, though, the duration is around twelve hours, which means that in the best factories leaf plucked during the day (as all leaf is) will inevitably be manufactured at night. The generally cooler temperatures that prevail also ensure that oxidation can happen at a much more controlled speed, and makes for better quality teas. This means that many visits to tea factories will demand an early start or a late night in order to see top-quality tea being produced.

drums into which withered leaf is charged. Each drum rotates above a table set with battens, against which the leaf is twisted. The degree of the twist is governed by the amount of pressure applied from the top of the drum (the cap).

Batches will be removed periodically and run over a mesh, the smaller particles that fall through being collected. This leaf becomes known as the first *dhool*, and is removed from the rolling room for oxidation. The remainder is passed through a device known as a ball-breaker to break up clumps of leaf that can tend to form within the drum, before being rolled again to twist it further before the ball-breaking and sieving process is repeated. This way the leaf is not over-handled, and if it is ready for oxidation then that is where it goes. The difficulty with orthodox production is its batch nature, which tends to impede the efficiency of the factory and require exceptional attention and skill in order to get the best from the leaf.

An orthodox rolling machine.

Orthodox rolling is common in Asia, especially Sri Lanka, parts of India, Indonesia, Vietnam and China. It tends to result in teas with a classic twisted appearance and more mellow yet potentially more complex taste characteristics.

> *Dhool* is the Hindi word for sand or dust. It is likely that its use in tea was derived from the sight of smaller particles falling through a sieve being likened to sand.

CTC (CRUSH TEAR CURL)

Two rollers, each featuring sharp teeth, rotate against each other. As the leaf is fed into the minute gap between the teeth, it is both crushed into smaller particles and torn as a result of a differential in speed between each of the rollers. This process is usually repeated three or four times in order to achieve a regular leaf size. From here it proceeds to oxidation, usually seamlessly as on a production line, whilst orthodox tea tends to proceed in batches linked to the *dhools* taken from the rolling room.

CTC arose as a result of the teabag generation and it is fiercely debated by tea purists, many of whom assume it to be a modern-day evil. Its 1930s genesis hardly counts it as modern-day, but more crucially some consumers now actually prefer the strong, colour brews that CTC enables, especially countries that consume tea with milk, such as India and Pakistan.

OXIDATION

This is the key point in black tea manufacture, as it is for oxidation that each of the previous stages has been preparing the leaf. It is important that the leaf cells are broken down through the rolling process because this enables enzymes contained within the cells to mix with polyphenols in the presence of oxygen. Visually this is evident in the colour of the *dhool*. Over time, this is transformed from a greenish colour, through shades of yellow and copper and ultimately to a muddy brown if left unchecked and allowed to proceed for too long. The taste of the tea also changes during this process: an under-oxidised tea has greenish, metallic notes, whilst an over-oxidised tea is all earthy softness, lacking genuine briskness or length of flavour.

During oxidation a number of stages of biochemical change are taking place in the *dhool*, ultimately resulting in the conversion of polyphenols into theaflavins (TFs) and then thearubigins (TRs). A skilled tea-maker needs to retain a balance of TFs (which tend to bring brightness) and TRs (which bring strength and colour), whilst being aware of what his potential market pays most for.

A typical Japanese buyer of Nuwara Eliya 'light-bright' teas is interested in a very pale, bright liquor which clearly will have a much higher proportion of TFs. For this reason the tea-maker will only permit the tea a very short oxidation time as he knows that TFs are produced before TRs. Accordingly, in a Nuwara Eliya factory there is little evidence of any oxidation at all as the leaf passes from the rolling tables almost directly into the dryer.

Conversely, a British buyer looking for a rich, full-bodied, colour tea that will go well with milk is likely to favour a factory that has oxidised its *dhool* for longer, and therefore with sufficient time for more TFs to turn into TRs. The tricky thing is that the ambient temperature and relative humidity of

Green leaf being fed into the first CTC cut. It will undergo two or three further cuts.

Oxidation in an automated factory – the revolving tines help to mix and aerate the dhool.

the leaf can also impact on the process. Seldom are two days or nights the same in a factory, and the tea-maker needs to be on his toes to make the most of the material he has to work with.

When the tea-maker believes that the *dhool* has reached the optimum point of oxidation, he needs to stop the process and stabilise the tea.

DRYING

Because the enzyme activity that underpins tea oxidation is killed at temperatures above 35°C, subjecting the leaf to such heat is the best way of arresting the process. This is where the dryer plays its part. Drying tea is a relatively simple process to understand, but an incredibly easy process to bungle in practice. The regulation of heat in the dryer, the flow of leaf into the apparatus, and the maintenance of the equipment are all fraught with difficulty, and a minor error of judgment or process can destroy even the best lot of tea leaving the oxidation room.

The theory is that the oxidised *dhool* is fed into a heated chamber, causing the oxidation activity to cease and reducing the moisture in the leaf. As the leaf progresses through the dryer the temperature should rise progressively such that the leaf is stabilised to the point where it is at around 2%–3% moisture as it leaves the dryer. If the temperature is too hot as the tea enters the first chamber then it will either scorch, leaving the tea with a burnt character, or (in the case of CTCs) it will cause the outside of the particle to harden whilst oxidation continues inside. If the temperature is too low as the leaf enters then oxidation will continue and result in soft teas with a stewed taste.

Dryers are amongst the most expensive pieces of equipment most tea factories have to procure, and as such if there is an area in which to make savings, it is here. An Assam tea factory may receive 20 tonnes of green leaf each day in the early spring or late autumn seasons, but upwards of 100 tonnes during the monsoons. Ideally they would have the capacity to cope with this, but who invests just to cope with the ten or twelve days a year of under-capacity when there are so many other calls on one's funds? In reality there will be days when they are forced to overload their dryers, and it is

Heat is needed in the production process, especially in the dryer.

these days that can see leaf emerging with too much moisture, leading over the course of time to a musty note, just as attempts to increase the flow by turning up the temperature will lead to burnt-tasting teas.

Dryer defects are amongst the most common in tea and thankfully usually easy to spot, but I have seen glaring problems from even the most blue-blooded of tea producers. Smokiness is another common problem. It is often the result of leaks in the dryer leading to smoke contamination of a tea, although it could also be due to boiler smoke drifting into the withering area. It can be found in all teas, whether green, white, oolong or black. As it is the sort of defect that can be masked by milk and its detection is much easier to taste in some water types than others, it is illustrative of how important it is to taste a batch before buying, and to taste in a way that will allow you to detect faults rather than at consumer strength.

SORTING

Up until now, the tea has been a mix of different leaf sizes. As it emerges from the dryer this jumble of leaf is labelled 'dryer mouth' tea, containing dust, stalk, large leaf and everything in between. There is hardly a customer around who will pay for this hotchpotch, so the factory needs to remove the stalk, run the tea over a series of sieves to sort it into grades suitable for all potential customers, and ideally also winnow the tea to ensure the density of each grade is consistent.

The business of removing the stalk is dependent upon one scientific principle: that the stalk has a different static conductivity to the black leaf. This means that if an electrostatic force is applied to the dryer mouth tea, then it can potentially induce the stalk to adhere to the instrument applying the force (like strands of children's hair attracting themselves to a balloon), whilst the black tea proceeds unimpeded. In a tea factory this is done by routing tea on a conveyor belt under a number of electrostatically charged rollers, which one by one reduce the stalk content until purely black tea is all that remains.

The black tea is then sieved through a number of different meshes to create a variety of leaf grades. The stalk can be used as mulch, sold to buyers looking to get a cheap product to extract for the iced tea industry, to customers from poorer economies or poorer customers from richer economies. The Somalis and Djiboutis, for example, are enthusiastic consumers of what is labelled BMF in East Africa – Broken Mixed Fannings (occasionally known as Broken Mattress Fibre, to which it bears a close resemblance). Such teas can be brewed a number of times, thereby maximising cuppage.

There is not a leaf grade that someone won't buy; the only question a tea-maker has is who needs what the most. He should then orientate his machine settings to make more of this grade and less of the grades that are out of favour. No easy task.

Once sorted, the tea-maker would ideally wish to ensure that there is consistency of density within each leaf grade. A sieve may permit both lightweight and dense leaf particles through onto the same mesh, but these are not regarded equally by the customer who may want a denser tea that occupies less space in the caddy or the bag. In order to ensure that the density (or weight of a specific volume of tea) is consistent across each lot, the factory may winnow the tea. During this process tea will be blown by a fan through a tunnel with a number of chambers beneath it into which the tea may fall; whilst the heaviest tea will fall into the first chamber, the fan will blow the lightest tea the farthest. This gives us the fannings now applied almost universally to describe the smaller leaf sizes, but was originally a function of density.

The removal of stalk.

COMMON LEAF GRADES

Common primary (i.e. maingrade) leaf grades for Orthodox Tea
N.B The basic Sri Lankan leaf grades below are built-upon using the suffixes and prefixes listed in the bottom table.

	Indian Teas	Abbreviation	Sri Lankan Teas	Abbreviation
Largest	Special Fine Tippy Golden Flowery Orange Pekoe	SFTGFOP	Orange Pekoe A	OPA
	Fine(st) Tippy Golden Flowery Orange Pekoe	FTGFOP	Orange Pekoe	OP
	Tippy Golden Flowery Orange Pekoe	TGFOP		
	Golden Flowery Orange Pekoe	GFOP		
	Tippy Golden Broken Orange Pekoe	TGBOP	Pekoe	PEK
	Flowery Broken Orange Pekoe	FBOP		
	Broken Orange Pekoe	BOP		
	Flowery Orange Fannings	FOF	Broken Orange Pekoe Fannings	BOPF
	Golden Orange Fannings	GOF		
Smallest	Dust	D	Dust	D

Common Primary Leaf Grades for CTC Tea

	Indian Teas	Abbreviation	African Teas	Abbreviation
Largest	Broken Orange Pekoe	BOP	Broken Pekoe 1	BP1
	Broken Orange Pekoe (Small)	BOP (SM)		
	Broken Pekoe	BP		
	Broken Pekoe (Small)	BP (SM)		
	Pekoe Fannings	PF	Pekoe Fannings 1	PF1
	Pekoe Dust	PD	Pekoe Dust	PD
	Dust	D	Dust 1	D1
	Fine Dust	FD		
	Churamani Dust (North India)/	CD		
Smallest	Red Dust (South India)	RD		

In addition to the usual grades, a number of other common prefixes and suffixes are in common use depending upon origin. This is at the discretion of the producer as there is no denomination governing their useage beyond the (usually loose) guidelines of the local tea association.

Classification	Abbreviation	Description
1 (Orthodox)	1	When used in connection with Orthodox leaf grades, the suffix 1 denotes that the tea is composed of superior quality leaf, usually more well-twisted and often selected from an early dhool during the rolling process
1 (CTC-India)	1	When used in connection with Indian CTC grades, the suffix 1 denotes an inferior leaf quality containing more fibre
1 (CTC- Africa)	1	As if in direct contrast to the Indian nomenclature, when used in connection with African CTC grades, the suffix 1 denotes a superior quality maingrade. Hence a BP1 should be superior to a BP
2	2	As in Dust 2 or Fannings 2- a more fibrous version of Fannings or Fannings 1
A	A	Used in Sri Lanka to denote a less wiry more open (and usually discounted) leaf. So an OPA is a less well-twisted than an OP which itself is inferior in the same way to an OP1
Broken Mixed	BM	A mixed grade of tea containing stalk and fibre
Broken Mixed Fannings	BMF	Often seen in E-Africa, BMF can be comprised almost exclusively of stalk and fibre
China (seen on Darjeelings)	China	An FTGFOP1 China would indicate that the leaf comes from Camellia sinensis var. sinensis (China jat) seedling plants.
Clonal	Cl.	Teas from specially-developed clones may be denoted as such- especially in Darjeeling
Drier Mouth	DM	Tea emerges from the drier as an unsorted mix of tea and stalk. Strictly speaking, teas labelled DM are sold in unsorted form. As sorting involves some abrasion, the lack of handling that DM teas undergo should potentially result in a better liquoring tea with less of the bloom having been rubbed off.
Dust	D or Dust	The smallest particle size. Dust or Pekoe Dust grade teas are much sought after by consumers in Egypt and Yemen frequently selling at a premium to equivalent larger-leafed teas.
Extra Special	Ex. Sp	Always used in conjuction with Sp. To denote an attractive show of golden or silver tips so an FBOPF Ex.Sp is tippier than a FBOPF Sp.
Fannings	Fngs	A tea composed of more stalk, broadly equivalent in size to a BOPF or a PF1
Flowery	F	Teas with a substantial amount of tip may have the suffix Flowery added to the grade hence FBOPF
Golden	G	Draws attention to a higher concentration of golden tips and as such usually seen in India

Muscatel	Musc.	Denoting a specific Muscatel character on Darjeelings, usually second flush
Orange Pekoe (in USA)	OP	When labelled on packs of teabags in the USA, OP seldom bears any resemblence to the classic Ceylon OP leaf grade of the same name
Pekoe	Pek. or P	Derives from the Amoy word for the pale downy hairs found on finer tea leaves. Pekoe is used variously as a general descriptor to refer to a maingrade tea, or in Sri Lanka when used alone, it specifically denotes a more shotty style of leaf. The usual pronunciation is peck-o
Pekoe Fannings Dust or other similar combinations	PFD	A variant of drier mouth tea may be produced comprising two or more of the more useful grades- a PFD would contain PF and PD, the main teabag grades, again this reduces the amount of handling the leaf suffers.
Souchong	S	Originally used in reference to smaller grades of tea, occasionally now seen in Indonesia to denote a Drier Mouth grade
Special	Sp	This denotes an even higher quality version of a particular grade. A producer may have sorted his leaf to include more tips for example which would be a justification for the suffix
Superior Cultivar	SC	Superior Cultivars are the same as Clonals, often seen in Malawi

Sorting leaf into different leaf grades.

Tea in paper sacks.

PACKING

The tea-maker's final task is to pack the tea, formerly into plywood chests lined with foil, now most likely into paper sacks which may lack the romance and subsequent utility to removals companies, but they make a much easier prospect for shipping and handling. Chests did, however, have the advantage that the robust plywood uprights prevented the total weight of the consignment bearing down onto the bottom chest. Not so with tea sacks, where the substance inside the sack is carrying the weight. The more elevated qualities are therefore more likely to be shipped either in rigid sacks, which are more structured, or if you have paid up handsomely for a premium tea, you may even still receive a chest.

GREEN TEA

Green tea is the 'original tea'. It is green tea that Emperor Shennong is said to have discovered in 2737 BC, see p94 (or the green leaf that fell into his pot, at least). Green tea remains the overwhelmingly predominant style in China and Japan, and it accounts for a third of all of the tea produced in the world. Green tea was also the first tea to be imported into Europe, and is now again being rediscovered by consumers lured by frequent news reports suggesting many and varied health benefits.

Just its name, green tea, is at the heart of what makes the two main processes, black and green, fundamentally different. The central principle in the processing of leaf for green tea is to prevent oxidation, which puts it into an entirely different methodology to the processing of black tea. This has the visual effect of retaining the green colour in the leaf and its liquor when brewed, and the biochemical effect of maintaining the highest range of catechin polyphenols in the dry leaf. Polyphenols within green tea are known as catechins of which there are a number of sub-types depending upon the chemical structure. Catechins are important because it is they that are responsible for the principal antioxidant (or *free radical*-fighting) health impact boasted in a number of green tea health studies.

If the enzymes in the leaf are what cause oxidation, it is the deactivating of them that defines what the tea will look and taste like, and gives us the two subcategories that most tea lovers have become familiar with in one form or another: roasted (or pan-fried) and steamed (or sencha).

Withering in China for green tea processing.

ROASTED TEA (TEA PROCESSED IN THE CHINESE STYLE)

WITHERING

As with black tea manufacture, the Chinese style of green tea processing tends to require a withering stage to better prepare the leaf. If this stage is skipped then the leaf can react poorly to the pan-firing process and scorch. The better green teas may even be solar withered, a process that is common to yellow tea and fine oolong. Solar withering helps in removing some of the greenish aromas and maximises the more attractive floral fragrances we associate with fine tea.

Hand-roasting green tea in Hangzhou. The green leaf is rubbed against the hot sides of the pan to deactivate the enzymes.

PAN FIRING/PAN FRYING

If the black tea process is defined by the methodology used to break open the leaf cells (orthodox or CTC), then the green tea process is characterised by the method used to deactivate the enzymes.

In China the traditional method is to expose the leaf to direct heat in the form of a large pan or roasting vessel that would usually be heated from below by hot coals or wood, a process known locally as *sha qing*. The tea-maker introduces green leaf into the pan and (using his bare hands) alternately presses the leaf against the metal sides of the pan to heat it, before cooling the leaf by gathering it and scattering it back into the vessel from above. It only takes a trip on the tourist bus to the areas around Hangzhou where Long Jing is produced to see this happening today (albeit with electric rather than coal power).

As the leaf is heated, the enzymes are deactivated and the potential for oxidation is stopped. The hotter the temperature, the quicker the deactivation of the enzymes, but the greater the potential for the tea to develop a toasty character, one of the most distinctive of all defects and the easiest to taste. In getting this balance right between the quick deactivation of enzymes and avoiding of any toasty notes, there is

Green leaf within the roasting drum

seldom a perfect balance, with the result that many roasted green teas have either a mild yellow-gold colour indicating some small oxidative action or a modest suggestion of excess heat. Or more likely, both.

The modern industrialised versions of the pan are large heated drums into which leaf is charged and which rotate, allowing each individual leaf its moment of heat and cooling. These machines are potentially excellent at deactivating the enzymes but the control and individual touch is lacking. You can usually see the difference between handmade tea and machine-made if you look hard at the leaf (and the price). Handmade tea has a flatter, more compressed appearance as well as a smoothness that you do not see with machine-made green tea.

For a high-quality tea, no further intervention is needed; the tea is ready for sale and much the better for further lack of handling. Lower grades may proceed into a dryer to fully stabilise the product followed by further sorting steps to create a number of leaf grades suited to multiple uses.

STEAMED GREEN TEAS (OR SENCHA)

If direct conductive heat from the pan is the agent to deactivate tea leaf enzymes in the Chinese method, it is steam that is the method for the Japanese tea-making tradition. The leaf is placed in an environment in which it is subjected to steam exposure, usually a stainless steel vessel through which leaf is carried on a conveyor. As with roasting, steaming can have a profound effect on the end quality of the product. Shorter periods of exposure between twenty and thirty seconds yield teas with high astringency and strength and a clear, light yellow colour. Longer steaming of up to about two minutes leads to softer, smoother, less astringent teas, with reduced aroma and a more greenish, cloudy appearance in the cup. In general, steamed teas tend to have a more grassy taste with more sweetness but less of the bite of a roasted tea.

Green leaf being steamed in a Japanese factory.

Following on from the steaming process, which has effectively saturated the tea, it needs to be rolled and shaped into what is usually a needle style. The rolling process is typically in two stages, each of which has the effect of heating the leaf from around 28°C to around 35°C, further contributing to a gradual drying and stabilisation of the product. The shaping process, which would formerly have been done by hand, is an intricate succession of shaping, drying and polishing tasks, ensuring the leaf has lost much of its moisture before any further handling can take place that would otherwise destroy overly saturated leaf. It is here that the needle style develops as pressing and heating combine to elongate the leaf into its characteristic shape. Despite the multitude of processes the leaf has undergone, it is technically only known as 'crude tea' at the conclusion of this stage. Depending upon the producer's equipment, he may then either pack it as it is, or extract the stalk which shows as an almost fluorescent white amid the deep jade of the leaf. The leaf will then be sent to an auction for sale where it is likely to be bought by a dealer.

REFINING

Although there are increasing numbers of crude tea processors seeking to remove the middleman, the traditional model in Japan is for the dealer to then further refine the tea. He will sort it into varied leaf sizes, remove any remaining stalk through optical sorting, and carry out a final drying stage to prolong the shelf life. Only now is the tea ready for sale.

Much Japanese tea is sold in its crude form; here the stalk is visible in the broker's sample.

The buyer will then sort and polish the crude tea (L) into refined tea (R).

YELLOW TEA

Yellow tea processing is the least known and least practised tea-making style, representing significantly less than 1% of China's total production. Indeed, the methodology for making yellow tea reputedly lay lost for a century before its rediscovery in the 1970s. The yellow tea heartland is Anhui and Hunan with pockets in Sichuan and Henan, and it is seldom if ever witnessed outside of China. To make yellow tea well is a skill that remains the domain of only a very few tea masters. Because of the attention required by the process, batch sizes will remain small and demand seems destined always to exceed supply. The process is for the most part largely similar to green tea.

SOLAR WITHERING
As with some of the finer green teas, leaf destined for yellow tea will usually be withered in the sun prior to *sha qing*. This sun withering helps to develop some of the finer aromas and reduce the rawness typical to green leaf.

PAN FIRING/PAN FRYING
Yellow tea follows the same process as green tea, although frequently this is accomplished by hand, given the generally higher quality ambition for most yellow teas.

STEAMING AND SWEATING
As it emerges from the pan-frying process, the leaf usually experiences a brief exposure to steam, before which it is heaped and covered. The steam exposure helps the tea to become warm and to sweat, although depending upon the duration and success of solar withering it may be bypassed or curtailed. The heaping and sweating is key in the process: although the enzymes have been deactivated by *sha qing* there will always be some residual potential for oxidation, and it is this that occurs during the heaping. The grassy notes typical to green tea develop into a creamy, buttery sweetness.

DRYING

In order to prevent over-oxidation and loss of the delicate aromas, the leaf then needs to be dried, a process that the steaming has rendered more difficult by the moister nature of the leaf at this stage. It is typically batch dried with great care to preserve the delicate leaf appearance, and to ensure that the temperatures to which it is exposed are high enough to reduce leaf moisture and prevent further oxidation, but not so high as to kill the seductive sweetness.

Solar withering for yellow tea manufacture.

OOLONG

Oolong is often regarded as a middle ground between green and black tea, an imperfect summary of a process demanding constant attention and immense skill. Oolong is the most difficult of all of the styles to make successfully, and as such it typically commands the highest prices, if we compare oolong with its better-known green and black cousins. It also features a number of sub-variants; here we describe the typical process for ball-type oolongs.

The wicker drum in which leaf is bruised for oolong tea.

SOLAR WITHERING

After plucking, the leaf destined for oolong is scattered onto mats exposed to the sun, where it remains for around an hour as it loses its moisture and begins to chemically change. For the sensitive tea leaf, this sun-bathing is a more intense treatment than the indoor version better known in black tea manufacture. If done well, it can initiate some oxidation within the leaf without needing to breach the cell walls mechanically; if done badly – in very hot summer conditions above 40°C, for example – a degree of shade needs to be provided, lest it result in sunburn, which soon destroys the leaf.

The leaf is then moved indoors, where it is given a conventional wither on woven mats or in a withering trough. Around eight hours is sufficient, but it is the heady, pungent, floral aroma that announces when the tea is ready.

BRUISING

The characteristic of oolongs, and one that you can witness if you unfurl the leaf of a jade oolong after brewing, is the bruising of the outer edges of the leaf, whilst the centre of the leaf remains to a greater or lesser extent untouched. To bruise the leaf, the tea master will charge the tea into a large wicker basket that can be spun on its axis. This relatively gentle process, in which leaf acts upon leaf, results in the breakdown of cell walls around the periphery of the leaf and the start of oxidation.

PAN FIRING AND CLOTH BALL FORMING

The leaf is then fired at a relatively low temperature in order to control the oxidation process and reduce moisture before being compressed into a cloth ball more or less the size and weight of a medicine ball. The tea within the cloth ball is then returned for firing, a process that can start to compress the individual leaves into shotty pellets, and as a process the firing and ball-forming can be repeated up to thirty-two times. A less diligently-run factory may make a vast number of balls and leave them to sit for a few hours rather than observing the labour-heavy method preferred by the purists. It is this painstaking adherence to the process that really marks out proper oolong manufacture as the domain of the skilled tea master. Teamwork is a key element, as the individuals responsible for the cloth balls and the firing need to finish their steps at exactly the same time so that the cycle can proceed seamlessly.

DRYING, SORTING AND PACKING

When the thirty-two cycles have been completed, the tea will be dried and sorted into grades. The oolong characteristic of floral sweetness and aromatic top notes is so valuable that many producers elect to vacuum-pack their teas in order to minimise any post-manufacture oxidative activity.

BAKING

Taiwanese tea consumers are a broad church, and there is as much interest in floral, orchid-like top notes as there is in the smooth, toasty aromas resulting from the measured application of heat. It is therefore possible that a factory, having observed the processes above (although perhaps with more oxidation), will then bake their teas in an oven in order to impart some smoothness and complexity to the tea. The floral scents are lost, but in return fruity, toasty notes are generated. Such teas are much enjoyed after meals, and have a longer keeping time ahead of them.

The cloth is bundled...

... and then compressed.

... before being returned for firing.

WHITE TEA

White tea is always a contentious area, with more hot air expended on what *is* and what *isn't* white tea than almost anything else. One expert's definition is not always consistent with another's, and the name is more used and abused than any other. The best way to understand white tea manufacture is to focus on the themes common to most of the teas sold as 'white' around the world.

PLUCKING

First and foremost comes the leaf. A purist would state that the leaf should come from a *Da Bai* bush, translated as 'Big White'. As Da Bai is found mainly in Fujian province one also often finds Fujian argued as the only authentic white tea origin. The leaf of Da Bai is characterised by an abundance of tiny hairs, not only on the bud, but also on the leaves, right down to the second leaf and sometimes beyond. Ideally it should be plucked in spring when the quality is better (as it is all over China) and the downy hairs are more profuse. There are experts who argue that it is just the bud that should be plucked but this is a misnomer: for silver needle this is the case, but for lower grades of white tea, the first and sometimes second leaf are also acceptable.

Over the years all sorts of legends have sprung up about white tea. 'Plucked by virgins with golden scissors' is one of the more creative of them, although not a claim that an auditor would feel comfortable in certifying. Although this is flippant, it gets to the core of the white tea debate. Because there is no appelation or prescribed manufacture method, almost anything is possible. Who is to tell the Sri Lankan who has made his silver tips faithfully to the Fujianese style that his tea cannot be called white tea because it is not spring-plucked Chinese tea from Da Bai? Just as the later-season Da Bai teas made as two leaves and a bud are a step removed from spring crop finer plucking. White

Da Bai leaf with its characteristic coating of downy hairs.

tea is all shades of grey, and really it is up to the customer to determine where he or she is content to draw the line. Be sure to be guided by taste rather than marketing spin and you will emerge satisfied.

SOLAR WITHERING

Originally, the leaf destined for white tea would have been left outside to wither and then dry, taking the leaf directly to the point where it can be infused and with no mechanical assistance. There are still producers who will make their white tea in this old-school and distinctly non-interventionist fashion. Now it is more likely that a period of solar withering will be employed, much as in the oolong process, to initiate a small amount of oxidation before the leaf is moved inside for withering.

WITHERING

A process that in the white tea manufacture tradition can last up to thirty hours, withering is instrumental in the development of potential flavour. The leaf as it arrives from the solar withering patio may be around 75% moisture; this is scattered onto bamboo mats and placed into racks for an extended period, during which it starts to emit an intoxicating aroma. As it slowly loses moisture, the impact of the solar withering becomes clear: flavour and aromas develop that would have been impossible were the leaf brought straight inside. As the leaf moisture reaches around 60% it is moved on to drying.

DRYING

Most white tea producers will endeavour to make as much whole leaf as they can as this usually realises the best prices, especially in the East Asian markets that form the bulk of global white tea consumption. Factories will therefore try to avoid any intervention that threatens to break up the leaf, meaning the bamboo mats are tipped directly into a dryer in order to stabilise the tea. The dryer will then reduce the leaf moisture to around 3% before the leaf is removed to settle.

SORTING

Where the very best grades of white tea are sought, it is highly possible that manual picking will be used. Highly skilled, and highly patient, teams of ladies will pick out the higher value silver tips using either their fingers or expertly wielded chopsticks. This process can happen either at the original factory, or more often in a secondary location run by a merchant with more awareness of what his buyers want.

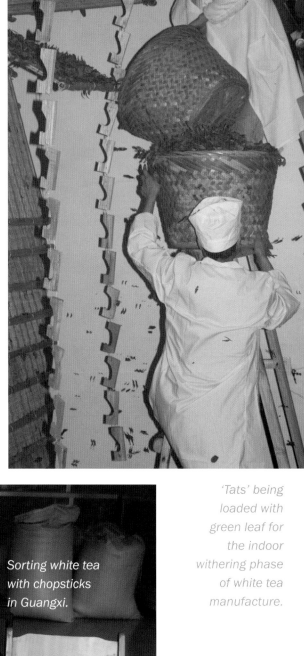

'Tats' being loaded with green leaf for the indoor withering phase of white tea manufacture.

Sorting white tea with chopsticks in Guangxi.

DARK TEA

There are a number of different subcategories of dark tea of which Pu Erh is the best known. Fu tea is another, and its process is covered in the chapter on Shaanxi, so here we concentrate on Yunnan's famous tea.

Pu Erh is processed initially as a green tea, although variations on this theme have sprung up in recent years and we can now talk about *Sheng*, meaning 'raw' or 'alive', which requires patience of the producer and deep pockets of the buyer, and *Shou*, also known as 'cooked' or 'ripe' Pu Erh, which is processed in an accelerated fashion and is more commonly seen in the West. The better and more traditional Pu Erhs are Sheng and it is these that have given the tea its global reputation as an investment, whilst the Shou yields the more earthy character that modern-day mass market Pu Erh is known for.

Large, genuinely wild, old tea trees are regarded as the optimal source of leaf for Pu Erh, but there is no consensus on plucking standard. Some consumers prefer fine plucking, whilst for many the older leaves are elemental to the flavour. Plucked leaf is laid on mats for withering, ideally solar withering if conditions permit, following which it is pan-fired to halt most of the enzyme activity; the stage referred to by the Chinese as 'kill green' or *sha qing*. This process can be more or less severe, the duration being dependent upon the tea-maker's desired end product, but the rule is that the fewer enzymes that are deactivated, the more the tea will develop and darken over its maturation.

The tea, which is referred to as *maocha* or rough tea at this stage, is then rolled and left on mats to sun-dry, after which it can follow one of two routes. Sheng Pu Erh is sorted and pressed into cakes, which will then be cellared in warm, humid locations. The relatively dry coolness that prevails at Yunnan's high altitude is unsuited to this, and the process is more likely to take place in provinces such as Guangdong, where the action of microflora such as the bacterium *Asper nigellus* can proceed in a more benign environment of heat and humidity.

The speed of maturation is a factor of the nature of the *maocha*, the tightness of compression and the conditions of storage. It is said by some that thirty years is needed in order to generate the appropriate maturation for a tea to really shine. Thirty-year plus teas are at the quality level of the tea

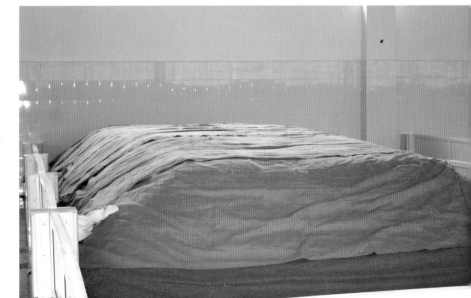

Wo Dui – maocha heaped into a pile in a Yunnan tea factory.

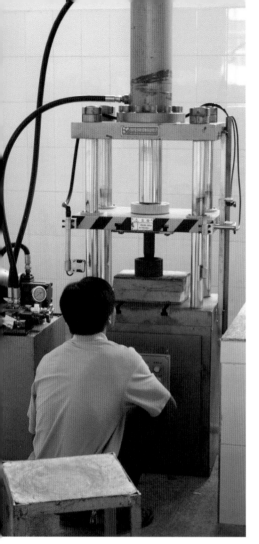

Pu Erh being compressed into cakes.

master and the price level of the oligarch, so for most consumers a more modest maturation has to be adequate. A well-matured Sheng tea will have a sweetish character with notes of overripe soft fruit and honeycomb; there are earthy characteristics but these should not be too predominant.

Shou tea is produced initially in a similar fashion to Sheng. The processes deviate from each other the moment the *maocha* is heaped into piles for a period of between six weeks and a number of months, a process known as *Wo Dui*. This process is more akin to that of cheesemaking than anything we encounter elsewhere in tea. These piles, which are regularly turned and moistened, permit the development of microbial action, ideally evenly distributed throughout the tea. Yeasts, moulds and bacteria develop in the hot and humid conditions, and the fermentation that results endows the tea with its distinctive aroma of recently dug earth. After this ripening period the tea will be given a shot of steam in order to render the leaf pliable before being pressed into shape. This can take one of any number of forms, the most commonly seen being the cake and the *tuocha* (a smaller, finger-formed dome). Although at this stage Shou is usually of a darker colour, the best tastes rather similar to a Sheng Pu Erh of modest age. It can be stored and will not deteriorate, but it is unlikely to develop further.

Recently compressed cakes await wrapping.

A variety of Pu Erh teas on sale in a Kunming tea shop.

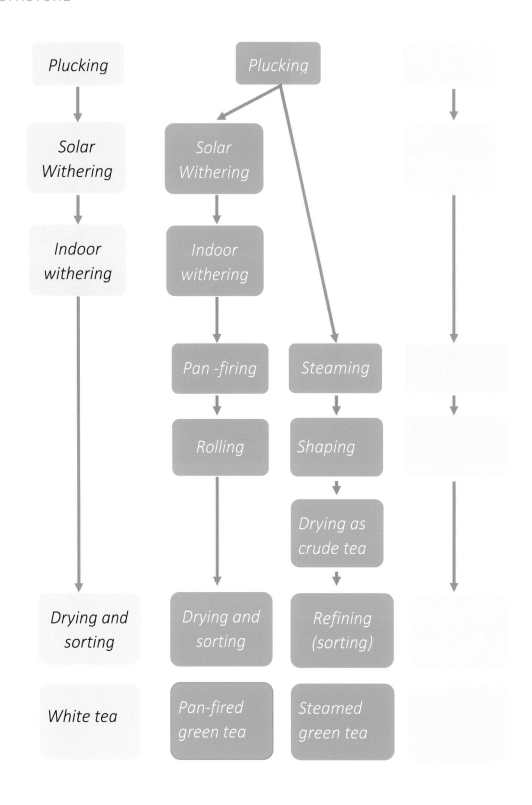

Plucking → Solar Withering → Indoor withering → Drying and sorting → White tea

Plucking → Solar Withering → Indoor withering → Pan-firing → Rolling → Drying and sorting → Pan-fired green tea

Plucking → Steaming → Shaping → Drying as crude tea → Refining (sorting) → Steamed green tea

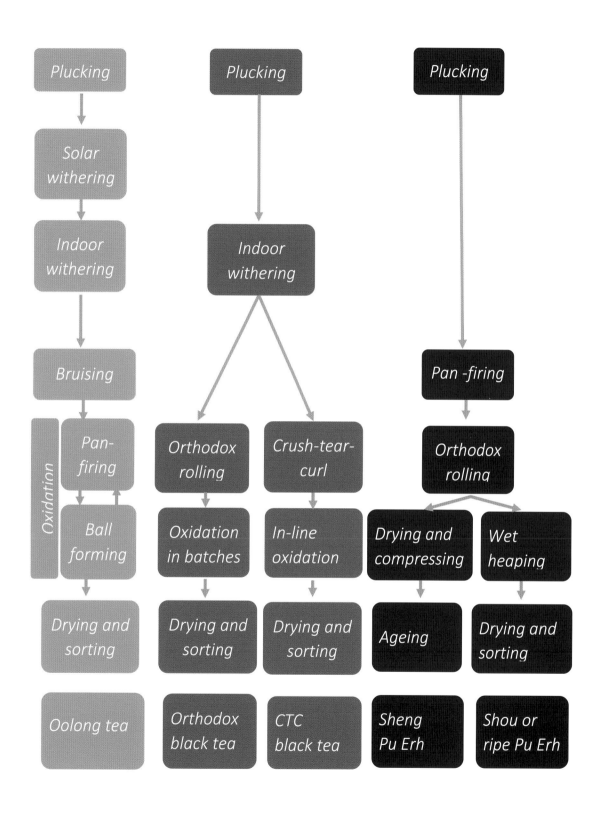

A school on a tea estate in Malawi.

SOCIAL ASPECTS OF
TEA PRODUCTION

A water pump in Malawi.

THE LONG-TERM HEALTH of tea is invested in the treatment of those who labour in it and their environment. If we cannot sustain the industry through encouraging people to work in it, and through husbanding plants in a productive environment that survives into the future, then it will wither and die.

REGIONAL VARIATION

We should avoid generalising about tea-producing communities. What is true for affluent rural Taiwan is not true for the remote valleys of Yunnan. Just as literate, well-educated South India, only a short hop from the tech hubs of Bangalore and Hyderabad, is entirely different to the conditions that prevail in the more isolated reaches of Assam or West Bengal.

There are characteristics that, to some extent, tea-producing communities tend to share across the world, especially in the plantation sector. Firstly, because of the requirement for large areas of land and labour, such communities are often more remote, where land and wages are cheaper. Secondly, the isolated location and its status as an employer of some significance often brings with it an obligation to take on the role performed by the state in more developed parts of the world with more affluent national purses, such as the provision of clinics or schools.

There are also local factors particular to the approach of the state. For example, does the government favour jobs for all at a meagre minimum wage, or an elevated wage that threatens to render employers uncompetitive unless they undertake more mechanisation, potentially leading to both rural unemployment and a tea-quality sacrifice?

There are parts of the world where the minimum wage and accompanying in-kind benefits, such as subsidised food, are barely sufficient to be regarded as a genuine living wage when all household costs are taken into account, especially those of a truly nutritious diet. Although these concerns are common to a number of industries and are shared with rural areas across much of the developing world, the collective tea industry from producer to retailer bears responsibility for their resolution within its own sphere of influence, and has taken the lead in countries such as Malawi in trying to do just that. The more responsible and concerned elements of the tea industry – producers, traders and packers, with the support of expert NGOs – are making attempts to tackle the issues pre-competitively. The best way to encourage such efforts is to check and challenge what tea packers or retailers are doing, and support those who you feel are serious about making progress.

ASSURANCE SCHEMES

The main thing that any would-be buyer of a tea can do is to verify what level of assurance the supplier claims. This applies whether the tea is loose from a specialist retailer or branded and packaged from a supermarket. Some brands have in-house proprietary schemes for establishing the conditions under which their tea has been produced, Typhoo having been the pioneers of this during the 1990s. Details of such schemes should be made clear on a website and ideally be independently audited.

On a larger pan-industry scale is a pre-competitive organisation called the Ethical Tea Partnership (in which I must declare an interest, having enjoyed an association with it for a number of years). A programme such as the ETP, which is funded by its membership, involves the monitoring of producers against a code of conduct.

Producers are obliged to show continuous improvement from one monitoring cycle to the next, and to undertake to resolve any areas of non-conformity. The code covers major areas of social and environmental concern such as health and safety, sexual harassment and gender discrimination, child labour, and human resource-related issues such as contracts or wages and benefits. The participation of a producer should be a sign that basic decent standards are being upheld and improved upon.

The ETP's merit is that it is a tea industry organisation focusing exclusively upon the product. The great expertise within the secretariat and regional staff is set to work in a productive way beyond the sometimes narrow stipulations of pure certification as identified in a restricted code of conduct. The ETP has a tried and tested convening role in co-ordinating donors and tea packers within projects that aim to improve lives, livelihoods and the general environments of tea communities, often resolving issues that it has itself uncovered.

CERTIFICATION

Major certifiers, such as Fairtrade, Rainforest Alliance (RA) and UTZ Certified, audit producers against codes of conduct which cover aspects of social and environmental impact. These certifiers derive their credibility from their multi-stakeholder boards, and from the standards they set following a rigorous process of public consultation. Although 80%–90% the same, each certifier's standard has particular areas of greater focus. Fairtrade is the most financially extreme of the certifiers in its stipulation of at least a 50 cents per kilo premium aimed at support for smallholder producing communities as well as a base price to protect the producer from market volatility. RA is characterised by a more environmental bent, whilst UTZ focuses more on farming as a business. All nonetheless have very solid and holistic provisions for the fundamental areas of social and environmental responsibility.

These codes cover a multitude of criteria against which producers will be measured. Compliance with the basics and steady improvements year on year are expected. As with the ETP, audits are carried out by independent third parties. The advantage of such certifications is that they are usually expertly monitored and the authorisation of packers to use the logo on their packs is based upon well-regulated and verified calculation of the percentage of certified tea that is included in each blend.

Certification is very effective at providing guidance to tea producers in which good practice is integrated into the daily process. This helps to enshrine ways of working that are inherently productive for the producers and yet also appropriately sustainable from a social and/or environmental perspective.

Viewed on the ground, one provision of a code could, for example, stipulate how firewood for use in the tea-factory boilers may be grown, logged and dry-stored in order to encourage responsible silviculture and efficient use of wood of the highest possible calorific value. The aims of such a focus are to minimise wood use, avoid any further encroachment into indigenous forest areas housing rare flora and fauna, and maximise the amount of land already in productive use that can be devoted to growing remunerative crops like tea or vegetables, rather than timber plantation that contributes little apart from cost to a tea factory.

In buying a tea with the certifier's stamp on it, you have a level of confidence that the packer has made efforts to ensure that producers who invest in improved social and environmental sustainability are featured in its blends. Where certification has an issue to overcome is in the perception, implied in various advertising campaigns, that it is the answer to all ills. It is not, as much as anything because it seldom resolves endemic national or regional-rural issues such as poverty, but it is an important part of the road to a better future.

THE FUTURE

In the long term, the improvement of conditions in tea-producing communities will come down to the alleviation of poverty through multiple interest groups encouraging the creation of diverse, healthy economies that present options for those growing up in such rural areas. Producers, governments, certifiers, civil society, industry, donors and the media all need to interplay in a positive way in order to make a difference to origin communities. To enable these opportunities to be created, adequate education at all levels is needed as well as appropriate employment prospects beyond just tea. These are infrastructural and macroeconomic shifts beyond any one individual entity.

One consumer cannot make all of the difference, but what concerned tea-drinkers *can* do is to take a greater interest in the responsible sourcing schemes that packers and retailers present, whether they are small, medium or multinational – enlightened social responsibility doesn't discriminate by size. Apply pressure to increase the price producers are paid by supporting responsible and progressive brands in the supermarket, the tea shop or online. Hold them to account, whether you are a customer, shareholder or have an influence via your pension fund. Ensure that their CSR activities are proportional to their net profit and resist the temptation of discounted or suspiciously cheap tea. The best and most responsible businesses will always welcome such scrutiny as a way to differentiate themselves from the laggards.

ENVIRONMENTAL ASPECTS

Tea and blue gum.

E VEN THOUGH THE GROWTH of the smallholder sector is bringing more mixed agriculture to rural communities, tea in many of its commercially viable guises remains a monoculture. Tea, and its often indispensable brother blue gum, which is the fuel of choice for many tea factories, dominates rural landscapes, especially in East Africa, and it has inevitably been responsible for a decline in biodiversity relative to the indigenous forest that existed a century ago before the advent of the pioneers. The world's growing populous cannot survive off the back of native forest, though, and tea is both lower in impact than most alternative plantation crops, and has a rapidly progressing awareness of its environmental footprint.

BIODIVERSITY

By definition, diversity will always suffer in a monoculture in comparison with native forest areas, but tea producers increasingly play their part here by encouraging the return of indigenous forest in less viable parts of the estate, leaving unsprayed margins, creating plant screens to avoid spray drift, and planting vegetative barriers that dissuade pests from entering fields. In much of Asia, shade trees are potentially useful natural providers of nitrogen, as well as an alternative environment for animal and bird life. The clearance of native forest is legally prohibited in all major tea-producing countries, so any new plantings need to come from land currently in agricultural or managed forest use.

Certification, especially by the Rainforest Alliance, has been important in this, and the recovery of previously declining species demonstrates the merits of the programme. The long-term nature of most tea plantings means that the soil remains broadly undisturbed for at least half a century at a time. Pruned stems are usually left in situ to be trodden back into the earth by pluckers over the ensuing months, and to cover fertilisers, ensuring their release of nutrients is into the soil rather than as nitrous oxide emissions into the atmosphere. Its status as a food crop ensures that farmers are more careful about the use of agrochemicals than many other non-food monocultures, a position that consumer activists and packers hold them to rigorously.

ORGANIC TEA

Organic tea gardens have existed for a number of years, Darjeeling being home to the largest concentration both out of compulsion (the residue-conscious German market being one of Darjeeling's main sales channels), and also opportunity, because the pest prevalence in such high-altitude producing regions is less severe than at lower elevations. Organic tea at lower altitudes is more of a challenge, and the accepted wisdom in the tea industry has long been that organic conversion is possible only with a crop loss of 40%–50%, a deficit that is seldom recovered in the tea price. However, the success of projects in parts of Assam show great potential in this method. The sciences of soil health and integrated pest management are becoming much better understood, and as technical experts apply this to organic tea production there is direct evidence that organic conversion can be achieved without the sharp drop in yields seen in earlier attempts.

Although there is a very small volume of certified organic tea produced relative to the whole, there

Accelerated composting at Jalinga in North India.

are nonetheless large variations in the level of agrochemical use depending upon circumstance and origin. Most African producers, for example, have very few pests to worry about and pesticide use is correspondingly slight. There are also pockets of smallholder production where pesticide use is either too expensive or just plain impractical. The more traditional artisanal corners of Myanmar, Laos and Vietnam are not organic certified but there has never been a big culture of intensive cultivation and the associated chemical use. In those areas where tea is plucked from trees, the use of pesticides is impractical in any case, as the equipment to do such a job effectively in such terrain does not exist.

BIODYNAMISM AND PERMACULTURE

A small volume of biodynamic tea is produced in Darjeeling on the Makaibari estate and in South India by POABS. The practice of biodynamism evolved in the 1920s through the work of Austrian educator and activist Rudolf Steiner. Biodynamism is more than just an alternative system of farming (such as organic cultivation); it encompasses a whole set of beliefs that extend into the realm of cosmic rhythms. The aim of biodynamic agriculture is to try to consider the farm as a self-contained organism. In the day-to-day running of the estate this can be seen in the creation of fertilisers and natural methods of disease or pest control that respect all aspects of the local environment, rather than the priority of the cash crop (tea) at the expense of all else. The theory suggests that

Preparation 500, a biodynamic process involving the burial of cow horns filled with manure over the winter months

soil health and fertility can be built through respecting varied and complementary uses of the land, with a rejection of imported inputs that would not ordinarily be a part of the local ecosystem.

Makaibari also takes this further through its adoption of the principles of permaculture, a philosophy that tries to adopt an integrated approach to the planet, the people occupying it, and the reinvestment of surplus back into the system. Taken together, Makaibari believes that these philosophies give it a means of production that boasts the impact of having enhanced the local community and environment, thereby better ensuring the long-term survival of the estate and the local community upon which it depends.

CO2

Even though large-scale tea production has long made widespread use of timber and fossil fuels to heat dryers and boilers for withering, the largest CO_2 impact in the chain from bush to cup is usually due to the consumer boiling their water for the final brew, so we should be careful about excessive focus on the producer in this. Tea producers are long-term thinkers, as is anyone farming a crop with no remunerative income for at least four years and a fifty-year plus life cycle. Such a mindset is actually very compatible with those in the sustainability industry, who are equally interested in ensuring the long-term viability of tea.

Numerous producers have looked to reduce their impact through greater efficiency in extracting the maximum calorific value from their fuel wood, or even better, through using the by-products of other locally cultivated crops to replace or supplement their fuel source. In Indonesia this may be oil palm husks, whilst in Malawi it is macadamia nut shells. Fuel use in factories and the stoves of those who work in the area is being minimised through better insulation and use of cleaner fuels such as briquettes.

These arguments are equally significant for smaller-scale local artisans in East Asia, where consultants armed with spreadsheets seldom venture. Improvements tend to be more difficult to identify, and the finances for investment are more difficult to come by. Nonetheless, new factory machinery targeted at the artisan, particularly those family businesses producing pan-fired green tea, is also becoming more effective.

A cattle-lending project in Bangladesh providing dairy products to participants and manure for the organic garden.

In the field there is a developing awareness of the potential for tea as a carbon sink, with the sequestration potential of the more vigorous lower-country teas especially encouraging. Such themes are close to home for many in the industry, which stands to suffer more than most through climate change. The standard-bearer in environmental consciousness is the organic estate of Jalinga in Cachar, which has become certified as the first CO_2-neutral tea producer. As at Makaibari, learnings here offer a number of pointers for the future, especially as regards the success of mixed farming and the role that on-site livestock can play in both a worker livelihood and a compost-generating capacity. Encouraging results have been achieved in the accelerated generation of rich compost with a low CO_2 and ammonia emission. The success of such projects raises questions about how genuinely sustainable an organic estate, which has trucked in organic composting ingredients over a long distance, and with a heavy carbon footprint, can claim to be.

There is lots of progress for tea to make, but the learning and development of recent years has been encouraging, with multiple successes that can be applied more widely across producing communities. As consumers, our best course of action is to identify brands or producers with whose approaches we identify, and to reward them for their progress. It is easy to discover what they are up to as the best are never shy about their successes, and the less corporate amongst them will even share their experience of the occasional failure in the interest of moving the cause forward.

*Indigenous forest in a
Malawian tea estate.*

Part 2

DRINKING TEA

TASTING TEA

The sample room.

ELL-TRAINED TASTERS CAN identify good, indifferent and defective teas, assess the market value and determine a suitable home in their blends within seconds. Tasting is an essential step in selecting a good tea before any money changes hands.

Tea – because it is the leaf of an evergreen shrub rather than its fruit – will always demand more tasting. By way of comparison, coffee or wine involves one large annual harvest that can be assessed for quality and homogenised with relative ease. This creates relatively little variation for a large volume of product. Yet there are potentially thousands of little parcels of tea issuing forth over the course of the same period, whether the producer is a Zhejiang artisan specialising in Long Jing, or a vast Assam tea factory.

Images of Edwardian-era tasting rooms testify that the tools of tasting have changed little over the course of the last century. The mechanics of brewing a fixed weight of tea for a fixed period provide for little in the way of process refinement, and indeed there is even an ISO standard for the brewing of tea for tasting.

It is important to make the distinction between tasting tea, and brewing it for enjoyment. The method and duration of the brew are likely to result in a stronger-tasting tea than most habitual tea-drinkers would be comfortable with. Tasting is about the process of selection. This is not to say that the procedure cannot be enjoyed – hours spent tasting batches of tea are always relished – but that by definition the point of the process is objectivising the comparison of teas.

TASTING PROCEDURE

WEIGHT

The quantity of tea is usually a little more than the standard recommended dose: 2g per 100ml is normal,[1] which equates to about double the normal consumer dose. The additional grammage registers itself as a more intense delivery of the key taste attributes, just as faults also show up more evidently. This is deposited into a white porcelain or earthenware pot.

WATER

Some multinationals stipulate consistency of water for all of their global offices. Water is deionised or distilled at vast expense in order to achieve the purest, most consistent base for the evaluation of a tea. For most this is overkill; the key focus should be on trying to ensure that the water used for tasting is as far as possible consistent with the water in which the teas will be consumed. This water is boiled to a rolling boil and then poured onto the leaf in the pot.

POT AND BOWL

Whether small or large (ISO stipulates the approved volume and weight),[2] it is important that they are clean and white. The cleanliness ensures no taints from previous brews – a Lapsang tasted prior to a delicate green tea could easily leave behind a smoky character, unfairly penalising the tea that occupies the same pot or bowl in the subsequent batch. The white colour of the bowl provides a bright, reflective background against which to better judge the colour of the liquor. Tea-drinkers are just as guided by their eyes as their palates and it is vital that the colour of a potential brew matches the expectations of the consumer.

BREW

The brew needs to be longer than most consumers would contemplate: six minutes. This lengthy wait permits the full delivery of all aspects of a tea's body, mouthfeel and flavour, yet without becoming stewed in taste. Because good teas are the sum of many parts, the act of tasting should help to discern how well-balanced these parts are in relation to one another, and therefore how appealing this particular tea will be to a tea-drinker.

When the six minutes have elapsed, the pot is tipped into the bowl and the liquor escapes. This will leave a bowlfull of liquid, and a pot containing the infusion that may then, according to the taster's wishes, be either left in the pot or deposited upon its upturned lid.

OPTIONAL EXTRAS

Some elements depend upon the taster's priorities. Blenders whose customers will all drink their tea with milk insist upon a controlled dose of milk being added to each bowl either before

---

THE ROLE OF THE SILVER SIXPENCE

Many tasters still religiously observe the seemingly curious weight of 2.8g of tea for each tasting pot. The 2.8 grams is a historical throwback to the weight of a silver sixpence (actually 2.83g) which was traditionally used by many as the counterweight on the scales of the taster weighing out his or her samples.

Tasting is ideally performed with a sparring partner who may discern different attributes or faults.

the pot is discharged into the bowl, or after having performed a preliminary slurp without milk.

HOW TO TASTE

THE INFUSION: AROMA AND APPEARANCE

Once the batch is set up, the first stage is to assess the aroma in the pot. This will now be empty, often with the infusion sitting upon its upturned lid. A sniff of the pot, or of the infusion atop it, is often an early guide to what awaits in the bowl. Our noses are considerably more sensitive than our taste buds, and defects such as smoke taint or burnt teas will show up clearly here. Any teas that are potentially unsound can now be discarded.

A further check can then be performed on the appearance of the infusion. For Assam teas in particular, coppery colours in the infusion are regarded as preferable to hues of brown or khaki. Bright infusions are suggestive of good keeping quality, an essential in seasonal teas that need to survive for at least a year.

TEA-TASTING: THE SLURP

For professional tea-tasters, the slurp and spit is an action that can be performed hundreds of times each day. Indeed, some tasters working for large auction trading houses may taste more than five million cups of tea during their lifetimes.

The ritual of drawing the tea into the mouth accompanied by a sufficient volume of air to activate all of the flavours has resulted in the slurp.

The slurp enables the tea to be evenly spread across all taste receptacles on the tongue in a fine, atomised mist. It is entirely possible to taste tea without slurping, but not necessarily possible to taste it well. Just taking a simple sip would not easily reveal the more glaring errors that a tea factory can perpetrate, such as burning the tea or tainting it with smoke, and it is precisely to weed out these teas that we taste.

Visits overseas can also reveal a variety of slurping techniques – the *Brazilian whistle*, for example, more often seen in the coffee trade, is notable as a variation on the ostensibly less refined sound of the slurp.

THE LIQUOR: APPEARANCE

The colour and brightness of tea occupies a surprising amount of tasters' time. Colour-blindness tests are a common feature of the job interview process, and the ability to differentiate red from brown and gold from grey is key in recognising quality attributes.

Are the teas bright and reflective with hues of gold and red, or dull with coffee-like hues of brown or grey? Some teas – East Africans in particular – will always look good, but it is often possible to differentiate between a batch of teas from the same origin by comparing the appearance of the liquor.

Green and oolong teas pose a different challenge. Here the oxidative action upon a tea after it has been produced can easily mean that what one sees in the tasting batch is not exactly how the tea will appear a couple of months later when the steamer transporting it has arrived at its destination.

THE LIQUOR: TASTE AND MOUTHFEEL

What we know as taste is actually an amalgam of a number of sensations, some of which (astringency and body) are best regarded as *mouthfeel* rather than taste as such. The optimum way to discover the taste of a tea is to slurp the tea in such a motion as to spray it in an atomised mist around the palate, a procedure that sounds worse than it is once it has been attempted a few times. This mist of liquid gives the olfactory bulb (the part of the brain responsible for sensing aroma) the best chance of an accurate reading of the aromatic qualities of the tea. Here temperature is also important, since tasted too hot a tea will scald the tongue and the day is lost; too cold and the tastes are improperly rendered and any faults are unclear.

FLAVOUR

The most immediate impacts will relate to flavour, and here tasters are looking for the key defining characteristics of a particular style. From Assams we expect malty notes, from seasonal Uvas pear drops, whilst at the other end of the scale Gyokuros from Japan should display a rich and sweet umami character. These flavours are all a matter of degree and the very best teas should boast a genuine persistence such that even when you have swallowed the liquor, the taste lingers long in the memory. This pungency or length of flavour will help to define the tea, and provide a balance with the physical sensations that are now manifesting themselves in the mouth.

BITTERNESS AND ASTRINGENCY

Bitterness is a much debated and misunderstood aspect of tea-tasting, often confused with astringency. Bitterness is a facet of taste. It tends to be sensed towards the back of the tongue, and although it is caffeine in tea that is largely (but not exclusively) responsible for the degree to which a tea can be said to be bitter, it is more often recognised because the delivery of other features of a particular tea – flavour, aroma or astringency – are out of balance with each other, either because the tea has been over-steeped or because it was a poor tea to start with.

Astringency shows as a drying sensation on the gums and sides of the tongue, and stems from the polyphenol content of the tea, specifically the theaflavins in black tea and catechins in green tea. All teas have some astringency, so it cannot be said to be either a positive or negative characteristic. What sets good teas apart is that they are astringent in balance with their pungency and aroma.

BODY

Body is the final piece in the organoleptic jigsaw. Is the tea possessed of an intense heaviness, or a lighter, thinner character? To really appreciate the extremes, a seasonal CTC Assam can be compared with an orthodox tea from elsewhere. Where the Assam will wrap itself around the mouth with a heavy and very conscious viscosity, the orthodox tea will occupy the same space with a lightness of touch that stands in very direct contrast.

There are a number of factors that contribute to body; most evident amongst them is the surface area of the leaf. This is linked to the leaf grade and whether the tea is orthodox or CTC, but origin, harvest period and processing style (the length of the steaming in sencha production, for example) can all have an impact.

Full-bodied teas are not by definition either good or bad – certain black tea-drinkers, especially those who add milk, will always require a little more body as a start point in order to balance the milk, but for those who drink their tea un-milked, full-bodied teas can be overwhelming.

THE LEAF

The final task is to examine the leaf. Some tea-drinking countries are so particular about leaf that the teas are scarcely tasted – low-grown Ceylons bound for the Middle East are often judged solely on leaf appearance. Whether we like it or not, for any loose tea, the leaf is usually the first thing we consider before buying. In the bazaar, a tea shop or via the internet it is often the only guide to potential quality.

The important areas to focus on are:

Evenness – are all the particles of roughly the same size? This guarantees consistency of brew.

Bloom – is there an appealing shine on the surface of the leaf? If there is, then this is a sign the leaf has been well manufactured, as the juices that coat the tiny hairs on the leaf surface (and then form a sheen when dried) have not been rubbed off by over-handling.

Tip – is there a scattering of golden or silver tips in the tea? These tips, which come from the bud of the plant, are at least a sign that a larger proportion of your tea has come from younger (and hence finer and potentially sweeter) leaf.

Fibre or stalk – this is almost the reverse of tip, although it is possible to confuse the two. Stalk shows as an orange fibre in black teas and as a white fibre in green teas. In general it tastes less good as it comes from the vein of the leaf or from the stem of the plant, endowing it with a lower caffeine and polyphenol content. Although tasters prefer less stalk, most would still prefer to find a stalky tea from a good origin than a clean tea from a less favoured producer. Not all stalk is bad; some teas consciously specialise in it – Kukicha, for example, is a Japanese tea made exclusively from stalks. Its celebrants revel in the lower caffeine and nutty quality that the twigs bring.

Examining the infusion's appearance and aroma.

BLENDING AND
FLAVOURING

WHY BLEND? THERE IS sufficient tea of excellent quality from individual estates to satisfy all of the world's ardent enthusiasts. Many tea devotees regard blending as superfluous. A dilution of quality. A rendering of mediocrity from something once exceptional. Yet a vast proportion of the world's consumption is of blended tea, often from multiple origins, and invariably much the better for it.

SINGLE ESTATE TEAS

The most simple and elemental way to enjoy a really fine tea is to provide it with the opportunity to shine and show its individual character unfettered by the influence of other teas. There is real joy in discovering the distinct brilliance of single estate teas, which in their own way fulfil the role of soloists to the orchestra that is a blend. By no means is every origin suited to being drunk alone. Many African teas are too coarse for most, whilst a number of consumers would find a good seasonal Assam tea to be overwhelmingly rich and strong.

But there are teas produced in such small volumes and with such elevated quality levels that they fall beneath the radar of larger tea companies and really beg to be appreciated just as they are. A small batch of first flush Darjeeling or an even more miniscule parcel of Pu Erh, lovingly crafted by a Chinese artisan from a single tree in Yunnan, cannot be of interest to any business with a national distribution network. It is precisely for this reason that the abundant variety available in the local tea merchant needs to be more fully explored. The great merit of the small tea shop or 'e-tailer' is the ability to offer teas of such stellar quality, and a day spent exploring small samples of numerous different sources of tea is rarely wasted.

BLENDS AND BRANDS

The fortunes of blends and brands are largely intertwined. Whether the brand in question is a local tea shop or a multinational, the raison d'être for buying it remains an assurance of consistency. The company in question has put its name to the product in order to provide a personal or corporate guarantee of quality.

BACKGROUND

The advent of tea blending in the Western world can be traced to the dawn of the tea age in the late 18th and early 19th centuries. The booming price of tea and seemingly limitless consumer demand, coupled with a loose regulatory hand, enticed unscrupulous individuals to debase their teas with all sorts of adulterants. Hawthorn, willow, elder, sloe and beech leaves were all reported as having been used,[1] either to bulk out the scarce supply of tea, or to replace it entirely. As less-savvy consumers keeled over, responsible merchants spied an opportunity to dispel consumer fears through offering teas with a personal guarantee of quality, often represented by a signature, identification mark, or 'brand'.

Through force of circumstance, early tea brands were necessarily local, developing teas that best suited their consumers and the water they brewed it with. As the more entrepreneurial merchants developed larger and more sophisticated marketing and logistical networks, the trade became dominated by fewer, larger companies. New consumers were enticed into the sophisticated world of tea and multiple offerings developed at different quality levels. Indian and Chinese teas were in the ascendancy. As both are largely the products of seasonal flushes, quality peaks and troughs created the need for stocks to be held in order to blend together different teas, thereby ensuring consistency of the house style.

BLENDING TODAY

The market today still largely requires consistency of product. Whether the product in question has all of the connotations of blending (English Breakfast), or is suggestive of a single origin lineage (Assam), it will usually have been created as a blend and should not be regarded as the poorer for it. By way of example, an Assam blend created in April or May will always have a higher proportion of better second flush teas in its recipe in order to ensure that the consumer does not lose out on quality in the months preceding the arrival of the new season's stock. Blending allows the individual qualities of diverse origins and seasons to build upon each other and shine. When performed well, it creates an end product that is greater than the sum of its parts.

The larger the brand, the more customers it needs to satisfy and, potentially, the greater its need to explore a number of origins or producers in order to guarantee consistency. This need not mean the watering down of quality, as the best brands will work with estates to reward the production of quality over quantity and recognise this financially. The most apparent evidence of this is in the price on the shelf, and a prime reason why it usually pays to pay up, whether in the supermarket or at the tea merchant's.

Notwithstanding the individual styles of the major blends offered by the larger houses, there are some globally known blends that merit explanation.

ENGLISH BREAKFAST

Seen all over the world, yet with no standard to define its assemblage, English Breakfast can mean something different wherever in the world it is drunk. Taken literally, it should accompany a full English breakfast and needs to be sufficiently robust to both provide a morning kick-start as well as stand up to the spicy flavours inherent in the meaty elements of the dish and its condiments. The better blends will usually maximise on rich, full-bodied Assams, with additional 'seasoning' coming from Ceylon for a mellow flavour and Africa for brightness.

English Breakfast will normally ape the style of the local preference if seen outside of the UK. Hence an English Breakfast blend created for French consumers will inevitably be designed for consumption without milk, and its relation to the British version is really only in name.

IRISH BREAKFAST

Irish Breakfast blends tend to feature an even greater Assam inclusion than the English style, lending a richer, maltier character. This is sometimes coupled with a Rwandan or Burundian element to create a brighter, brisker blend, although exceptions exist on both sides of the Irish Sea.

AFTERNOON TEA

This is an even more indistinct denomination than its morning counterpart. Afternoon blends tend to be lighter and more delicate in character. Orthodox teas are to the fore, their more nuanced style better matched to the lighter and softer flavours of the sandwiches and scones featured in the ceremonial interpretation of afternoon tea. High-grown teas such as Darjeeling and Ceylon are especially well suited, their heightened floral aromas providing a fine complement to the food without overwhelming it.

RUSSIAN CARAVAN

Whilst most Western European countries received their China tea via sea, early Russian supply was imported along the network of ancient trading routes known as the Silk Road. The journey usually took at least a year and required long camel caravans to travel across dangerous country through all weathers. During this time the cargo would have been in close proximity to countless night-time campfires, as well as the flanks of its camel. Such strong aromas so near to the tea lent it such a distinctive taste that Russian consumers came to favour the smoky character the route lent its cargo and regard it as usual in tea. This characteristic was further boosted by the local practice of burning pine or charcoal to heat the samovars. Since the demise of the camel caravan, many Russian Caravan blends now feature Lapsang Souchong, a factory-smoked tea, as a major inclusion.

FLAVOURING

One of tea's great merits is its capacity for flavouring. In contrast to coffee, which tends to overwhelm even the strongest of partners, the delicate subtleties of tea make a fine foil for a number of flavours.

SCENTED BLENDS

The flavouring of tea can take many forms. At its most basic, it plays upon tea's propensity to absorb foreign scents in the form of jasmine tea. The creation of jasmine tea, and its cousins osmanthus, lotus, rose and chrysanthemum, is as simple as blending in the source of the scent – the flower, ideally just as it is about to bloom – and then removing it. There is no ingredient as such beyond the aromatic transfer that occurs, and the purity of process is an appeal in itself.

Scenting is inevitably best when fine flowers meet equally fine tea – see the subtle distinction between Fujian jasmine and the Guangxi equivalent (p124). Unfortunately it can too often be used as a method of masking faulty teas or 'pimping up' those of indifferent quality.

OILS AND GRANULES

There are two basic methods in common use. For most loose-leaf blends of more elevated quality, the preferred method is to blend a base tea into an atomised mist of flavouring oil. The resultant blend will betray its flavour only through the intensity of its aroma and taste, but with minimal change in appearance. The alternative is to add flavour granules, which may be of similar formulation to an oil, save for a carrier upon which the flavour is loaded, typically a starch-derived substance such as maltodextrin. Granules come in all shapes and sizes, the most advanced being formed to mimic the shape of a tea leaf. They can be found with different degrees of porosity and longevity, but seldom deliver the same sensorial satisfaction as a recently compiled blend based upon oils.

The main reason for using granules is the enhanced level of protection that they have – materials responsible for flavouring are in general highly volatile at room temperature, especially certain fruit flavours such as raspberry or apple. Some are also prone to chemical change through reactions with atmospheric oxygen. This is at the heart of one of the fundamental challenges for tea flavourists. Whilst tea is a very good substrate for the absorption of flavourings, it offers very little protection to what has been absorbed. In reality a liquid-flavoured tea, unless foil-wrapped, has a matter of days before a large part of the aroma becomes lost through evaporation. Individual foil-enveloped bags or pouches have the best protection, and it is only these that can deliver high-impact, fresh, fruity profiles in real-world situations when liquid flavourings are employed.

Flavour granules in a black tea blend.

NATURAL OR ARTIFICIAL

Flavours are not only divided into oils and granules, but also, based upon their creation, into *natural* flavourings and flavourings.[2] A natural flavour must be derived from the named plant, but how this isolation of the flavour takes place will depend upon the plant in question. It could be by extraction, by distillation or through more complex biotechnological processes, such as the use of specially developed enzymes, but still under general 'kitchen conditions' and without the use of high-pressure, exotic catalysts or other hard chemistry.

Flavourings not classified as natural will be listed on the pack as *x flavouring*. These are the result of synthetic processes, so even if a flavouring has an identical chemical formula to its natural equivalent, if it has been obtained by a synthetic process it cannot claim to be natural.

The nature of flavouring is such that the variety of potential end products is almost limitless, but there is one blend in common usage around the world that requires explanation.

EARL GREY

For many drinkers Earl Grey *is* tea, so ubiquitous has its spread become. Some aren't aware that it is the product of a flavouring process no different to the ostensibly less noble lemon or strawberry-flavoured blends in common circulation. Earl Grey blends have become one of the great global must-haves in any selection, sometimes replacing plain black tea, to the frustration of enthusiasts. How often is a request for a cup of black tea in a continental café met with a cup of warm water and an Earl Grey teabag?

The name is believed to derive from a Chinese diplomatic gift of tea scented with bergamot oil. The ultimate recipient (he may not have been handed it directly, in the protocol of the time) was Charles Grey, who later, as the second Earl Grey, became Prime Minister in the 1830s. He in turn is believed to have passed on the formula to celebrated merchants Jacksons of Piccadilly, who duly christened the blend with the name of its patron.

The base of Chinese black tea combined with oil of bergamot proved to be a winning combination. The presence of bergamot, a citrus fruit now especially identified with southern Italy, brings a pleasing top note that marries well with like aromas in orthodox black teas.

Nowadays every tea business boasts an Earl Grey, with the only commonality being the use of bergamot, of which, any flavour house will explain, there are multiple interpretations – more aromatic, sweeter, juicier and more citric. As with a number of flavoured blends it is not unknown to see poor teas used as a base with the justification that the flavour is the primary partner in the relationship. It is not. The use of a poor base tea is inevitably a false economy, as it requires more flavour to paper over the tea's shortcomings.

Creating good Earl Grey is as much of an art as any blend. The base needs to be sufficiently strong in character to provide an adequate foil for the flavour, yet not so strong as to overwhelm it. Whilst orthodox China tea is the traditional base, good Ceylon high-growns can also be very effective, as both have different but complementary dimensions of citric notes in their armoury.

BREWING AND DRINKING TEA

Gong Fu tea preparation.

THE BREWING OF TEA is absolutely crucial to its enjoyment as a drink. There are myriad factors wholly within your control that have a major influence upon the potential quality of what is imbibed. Good brewing is important because it is entirely possible to make or break a perfectly decent tea depending upon how the activity is approached. The first thing to consider is the 'how'.

GŌNGFU, THE EAST ASIAN STYLE

In essence *gōngfu* is the formal Chinese method of brewing and serving tea – the Japanese version is known as *senchado*. Although commentators believe that *gōngfu* originated in Fujian it has since been adopted across East Asia and is applied with regional variations to take account of various local factors.

Gōngfu is a delight to observe, and the most evident reminder of the respect and reverence for tea in East Asian cultures. It is characterised by a succession of activities that aim to deliver a cup of the best possible tea in the most elegant fashion. On the face of it, *gōngfu* is a doctrinaire process that appears largely ceremonial, but deconstructed and with each element studied in detail it is evident that every activity is devised with the express purpose of maximising the potential quality of the brew.

A typical *gōngfu* tea set will include: a water-boiling apparatus such as an electric kettle or small stovetop kettle, a bamboo scoop or similar for dispensing tea, the tea itself, a small clay teapot or the ever-versatile *gaiwan* (a brewing bowl with a lid), a timer, a set of small cups to drink from: wide-brimmed for most black and green teas; tall and narrow for oolongs to better enable the aroma to be savoured after drinking, and a decanting pot known as a *chahai*. All this sits on a serving tray from which the inevitable excess water can be drained.

Gōngfu can be performed in a more or less rigid fashion, but the main stages are:

1. The teapot or *gaiwan* and bowls are washed with hot water.
2. A quantity of tea is deposited into the teapot with the bamboo scoop – this is typically around 1g for every 10ml (so 10g of tea for a 100ml teapot).
3. Hot water is poured onto the tea and the liquid then immediately discarded (the washing of the leaves).

> gōngfu 工夫: time (expended on some task); workmanship; skill gained through long effort and application of prolonged practice.[1]

4. Hot water is again poured onto the tea leaves until the pot is full, the lid is placed on and further hot water poured onto the closed pot.

5. The pot is brewed, around thirty seconds being normal depending on the tea (see p78).

6. The liquor is poured into the *chahai* in order to ensure an equalised quality of brew, and from there into each cup in a continuous process, alternating between them such that an entirely homogenous quality in each cup is assured. For oolongs, the liquid is poured into the long (aroma) cup onto which a stouter (drinking) cup is placed in the fashion of a lid.

7. The tea is drunk. In the case of the oolong it is poured into the drinking cup to permit the aroma of the tea to be savoured from the now-empty aroma cup.

8. The process is repeated from steps 4-7, usually with a progressively extended brew time, and can continue for as many brews as time or the quality of the tea permits, seven being about as many extractions as most teas can stand.

9. The equipment is thoroughly sterilised with boiling water and then cleaned and dried.

Although most tea in China is not consumed in this ceremonial fashion, the principle of multiple brews from fine-quality tea remains consistent. Any visitor to China will have been struck by the number of people wandering about clutching a clear glass tea vessel. This usually contains green tea of invariably fine quality, and can be refilled multiple times during the day from the numerous hot water bowsers that are dotted around offices, shops and restaurants.

Should you brew your tea *gōngfu*? The rule of thumb is that if the tea is of whole-leaf size, having been produced in an East Asian country where *gōngfu* brewing is practised, then the tea factory has probably optimised its product for this method.

An online search would suggest that *gōngfu* is the tea equivalent of golf as far as the amount of accessories is concerned, notwithstanding the widespread opportunity for offending someone through some unintended breach of etiquette. This is a shame – practitioners need not be intimidated, and the financial outlay can be modest.

With a teapot and a set of teacups it is possible to make a very close approximation without the investment. The key thing is the opportunity to savour the multiple brews and subtle changes in character as the process runs its course. The basic question to ask is this: why would you spend so much on a top-quality tea and only get to enjoy it once? With *gōngfu* it can be relished all afternoon.

WESTERN-STYLE

The joy of tea is that enthusiasts don't need to assemble a vast suite of expensive kit in order to make the best possible brew. If you start with good tea then you are already 90% of the way there. Of course there exist a few fundamentals. Ensure never to clean the teapot with detergent that is likely to taint the next brew. Store all teas away from moisture, strong smells and light, each of which can degrade the sensitive leaf. Make use of the sort of cup that will augment your enjoyment of the tea – think how much nicer wine tastes out of a thin-rimmed glass than a beaker. By far the principal factor in assuring the quality of what you are about to brew, though, is to make sure you have used the right water, and that you use it to infuse your tea at the optimum temperature.

WATER

In any cup of tea, more than 99% of what you actually consume is water, so it is potentially of profound impact upon the taste. The suitability of different types of water has long been debated by tea-drinkers. Even 1,200 years ago in *The Classic of Tea*, Lu Yu expressed a clear preference for spring water over river water, and each of these over well water.[2] Although water now comes from the mains for most, the basic premise that Lu Yu observed still holds true: well-oxygenated fresh water will always deliver a better cup of tea than water that has sat in some form of vessel for a period of time. This is because the amount of dissolved oxygen in water is thought to assist in the extraction of flavours from the tea leaf, and also because, much like tea, water absorbs foreign flavours and the longer it sits in your kettle, the more metallic it will taste.

The best water for tea-making is not heavy in minerals. It is two minerals in particular – calcium and magnesium – that have a prime influence on the taste: water with a high concentration of dissolved calcium and magnesium sulphates is known as *hard*. Tea made with hard water can have a metallic taste which tends to overwhelm the more subtle notes in tea, especially lighter teas such as Darjeelings, oolongs and spring crop green teas.

TEA PETS

Through the course of time, various tools have been devised in order to identify when the water in the kettle is hot enough for brewing. In the days before mercury thermometers, tea-makers had to rely on alternative methods for divining temperature.

Tea pets are hollow figurines of humans, animals or dragons, each with a small aperture. The tea pet is immersed in a bowl and filled to at least half its capacity with warm water. When the water for the ceremony is nearing readiness, its temperature is checked by pouring it onto the tea pet. If it is hot enough then through the principle of thermal expansion, the water inside the tea pet will spurt out.

Predictably, by far the most popular tea pet is known as *pee pee boy*. It is an inexact science as it does not reveal whether the water is *too* hot, but boundless fun nonetheless.

Related to this is *temporary hardness* coming from calcium and magnesium bicarbonate. This is destroyed by boiling and is responsible for the build-up of the limescale in kettles, and sometimes a scum on your tea. This does not mean by extension that *any* soft water is suitable. Very soft water, such as that treated with softeners, gives a flattish taste to the tea. The best solution if you have tried mains water and remain unhappy with the brew is to buy a water purifier. Bottled water can be a lottery unless you know what you are doing – generally highland waters are best and you should experiment, as some very widely distributed French brands are much less suitable even than tap water.

TEMPERATURE AND BREW TIME

The basic rule is that the tastes in tea come from a balance between amino acids and polyphenols. Amino acids, which bring sweetness, require a lower temperature (about 60°-70°), whilst polyphenols dissolve at around 80°. A delicate green tea such as a *Gyukuro* characterised by a very high amino acids content, is at its best when brewed in between these two temperatures. A more robust black tea is at its best when both amino acids and polyphenols (such as tannins) are dissolved, bringing the classic black tea attributes of astringency and flavour.

Temperature	How this looks in the kettle	Which tea	Western-style infusion time
95°-100°	Rolling boil, large bubbles	*Pu Erh, other dark teas, most black teas	3 to 6 minutes
90°-95°	Pea-sized bubbles rising in a stream	Darjeeling, good high-grown black orthodox, darker oolong	3 to 4 minutes
80°-90°	Rising lentil-sized bubbles	Jade oolongs, white tea, pan-fired green tea	2 to 3 minutes
70°-80°	Champagne bubbles sitting on bottom	Gyukuro, other good Sencha	1 to 2 minutes

*Because of its unique manufacture style, almost any litigation-conscious tea packer will suggest 100° for such teas. Whilst a well-manufactured Pu Erh does not require this temperature, a poorly made one does if only for food safety's sake.

MILK

IN A MUG

When making tea in a mug, adding milk first is out of the question. Teabags were not designed to lie in state in a cold milk bath pending the kettle's attainment of a rolling boil. This *Cleopatran* immersion only ensures that the boiling water will immediately become too cool when poured over the milk-soaked bag, as the resultant off-white liquor will betray. Brewing tea in a cup should always be done as a prelude to the addition of any milk in order to get the brew right, before adding milk to taste.

IN A TEAPOT

Opinion is divided over the original reason for the now well-rehearsed *Milk-in-First* or *MiF* debate. It seems likely that the main compulsion was the need to protect fine bone china from cracking due to thermal expansion resulting from the addition of hot water. We forget that for earlier European tea-drinkers, the fine china was stored in a cooler state than it is in our modern kitchens. It would have been brought upstairs by the maid from the less effectively heated service quarters, whereupon the milk would have provided a cushioning effect.

The main reason to add milk first now is the risk of the denaturation of the milk. If milk is poured into hot tea, individual drops separate from the bulk of the milk and come into contact with the high temperatures of the tea for enough time for significant denaturation or degradation to occur. This is much less likely to happen if hot water is added to the milk.

TEABAGS AND LOOSE TEA

We need to recognise that the 'modern' teabag blend is a style in its own right. Many tea-lovers are happy now to embrace both top-quality teabags and whole-leaf fine and rare teas, seeing them not as competing but complementary products, each catering to a different need.

THE CASE FOR TEABAGS

If convenience and speed is paramount, then teabags are difficult to argue against (although simple kit such as infusers make it possible to combine loose tea ceremony with teabag speed and convenience). But what is much more important than the bag or loose debate, is the quality of the tea used in the first place.

A search through the supermarket will reveal that the very best teabags cost at most 4p–5p each. Mid-range quality can be found at 2p per bag and bottom-end quality at less than 1/2p each (prices that have hardly changed in years). Much like wine, the fixed costs of a pack of tea are much the same whether the tea is at the economy or premium end of the scale, and we can therefore be pretty sure that any additional cost on the shelf is directly linked to the quality of the tea in the teabags. So a 4p bag is streets ahead of a 2p bag in quality terms.

At 4p each, the company blending the tea will have been able to afford the very best quality available from the offerings suitable for teabags; second flush Assams, high-grown seasonal Ceylons, sparkling Burundis, and ethical assurance can all be featured in a blend at 4p per bag. Under such circumstances, spending much less feels like the falsest of economies.

WHY BUY LOOSE?

Buying loose tea and the hardware to enjoy it properly at home opens up limitless possibilities for trying out the range from the local tea shop or online retailer. At the local tea shop you can usually buy much smaller 'taster' quantities of tea in the expectation that you are likely to return for more in the future. Loose tea opens up the possibility of finding a favourite estate, or experimenting with bespoke blends at home. You can allow your fancy unlimited licence to fly, free of the encumbrances of what the supermarket merchandiser has decided is good for you.

More importantly still, the larger leaf size of loose tea will inevitably deliver a smoother, less astringent quality to the brew. Both small and larger-leafed teas contain essential oils. It is these oils that are responsible for the delivery of flavour in all its forms, and they are present in greater volumes in larger-leafed teas, having had more of an opportunity to evaporate from the smaller-leafed teas present in teabags.

Having therefore started with a product that potentially contains more flavour, there is the brewing process to consider. Tea leaves need space to circulate in clear water whilst brewing. During this process they expand as they absorb water and infuse. Whereas in a teapot, the infusing leaf is free to flow where it wants, in a teabag there is a limited area for circulation and this means that the potential to extract the right colours and flavours from the tea leaf is compromised. Imagine trying to have a bath in a sleeping bag and you have some concept of the compromises involved in teabags. This adds to the temptation to aggressively stir, squeeze, prod and poke one's teabag when it is brewing to ensure that the brew is a good one. The problem here is that whilst this may encourage a darkening of the colour, it does not always mean that the right sort of flavours are being encouraged.

The solution is not to spurn either bags or loose tea, but to select which marries best with your lifestyle, the answer probably being both. Reserve a stock of top-quality teabags for rushed weekday mornings and the workplace, with a caddy on hand to relish the weekend ritual of enjoying fine loose tea.

LOOSE TEA OR WHOLE LEAF?

The act of buying loose tea rather than teabags does not automatically mean that what you receive is any better. The tea grading system is unregulated, snobbish, varies from country to country and is at best only a guideline and no substitute for scrutinising a sample of what you are buying before you pay your money. Many tea-drinkers erroneously suspect that because tea is not in a bag it must be 'whole leaf'. This is not true, and in fact there are a number of different grades in common use, with only the smallest two or three really being suited to teabags. Of the larger grades, only anything larger than a broken leaf can claim with honesty to be 'whole leaf', but do not rule out the rest as a result. If there is one key thing to remember it is that the quality of the raw material when it was plucked – first flush, second flush or rains, for example – and how it is handled in the factory is of greater importance than the size of the leaf itself.

The major Sri Lankan low-grown leaf grades.

Top row (from left): FBOPF, FBOPF ExSp, FBOP.
Middle row: BOP1, PEKOE1, PEKOE.
Bottom row: OP1, OP, OPA.

Only the OP grades can really claim to be 'whole leaf' but it does not necessarily make them better teas.

GLOBAL TEA
RITUALS

THE DEVELOPMENT OF diverse tea cultures has come about through multiple influences. Colonial links, water quality, local climate and force of fashion all count amongst the myriad stimuli that have created diversity and variation in tea-drinking styles across the globe. Each society's tea culture has been forged in the distant past, handed down through generations, and for many remains proudly guarded against foreign incursion. The British like a strong cup of tea with a liberal splash of milk; the Dutch a mild cup; the East Frisians add cream; on the subcontinent they cook their tea in milk; the Afghans like green tea but the Pakistanis black; the deep south of America drinks it iced; the Burmese eat it as a salad; the Tibetans mix it with butter…the list goes on. The only consistency is the bush that started it all: *Camellia sinensis*.

Some teas suit a particular consumption style and do not translate well into other cultures. The malty strength and richness of an Assam tea that may appeal above all others to the breakfasting British consumer will come across as unacceptably overwhelming and astringent to a Continental European used to drinking tea without milk. In reverse, a British consumer travelling abroad would find that adding milk to the tea they brew in the hotel restaurant results in an unappealing greyish colour with little flavour, whilst the Dutch on the neighbouring table rejoice in its subtle aroma and mellow flavour. It is no wonder we end up with the phrase *Not my cup of tea*.

So if different cultures have different tastes and habits it should come as no surprise that tea producers across the world cater to this. We should be careful about dismissing teas for what we regard as poor quality without an appreciation of which drinker they were designed for. The below is of course a generalisation and should be regarded as a guide, but it provides a picture of the world's major tea preparation and consumption rituals.

EAST ASIA

The East Asian tea-drinking tradition cannot be distilled into a single paragraph, so diverse are the cultures. If there are common threads, they are for a continued respect for the product and an appreciation of its value. Whilst tea is a common staple, it is also regarded as a luxury item. Large proportions of the household purse are reserved for its purchase, and to give tea as a gift is a mark of respect and appreciation.

Most tea is consumed loose, a ritual that can take place anywhere, whether at home, on the go, or in the workplace. Large numbers of people can be seen clasping clear glass or Pyrex tea flasks on their daily commute. Hot water taps abound to facilitate the brewing of tea, and tea-drinkers make the most of the multiple brews that can potentially be taken from a single dose of leaf.

East Asian cultures are the home of the tea ceremony. The best-known ceremonies are Japanese, but there are a number of local variations in China as well. Such rituals are extreme acts of hospitality and culture that bear witness to the reverence for tea and its preparation.

Typical teas: locally produced teas, depending upon taste.

The tapping of fingers by the recipient when being poured a cup of tea is a common sight in China, especially south of the Yangtze river. The fore and middle fingers (and ideally also the third finger) are curled and tapped upon the table in order to show respect and thanks for the hospitality.

It is said that the origins of this lie in a Qing dynasty emperor's attempts to circulate incognito within his lands to assess the state of the empire and its subjects. Deprived of his regal robes, yet with protocol demanding respect be shown the emperor, the convention of the tapping of three fingers evolved amongst his court, should he take turns with the pouring of the tea.

The two outer fingers are said to symbolise the kneeling of the subject, whilst the middle finger represents the bowing of the head. Respect could still be accorded the emperor, yet interested bystanders would never have known of their proximity to the 'Son of Heaven'.

HIMALAYAN BUTTER TEA

Tibet is the most famous of the butter tea-consuming cultures, but one also finds such tea drunk in Nepal, Bhutan and some other parts of western China.

Typical butter tea (or *Po cha*) should start with a brew of dark tea which is extracted via a lengthy period in boiling water in order to achieve an exceptionally strong liquor. A five or six-hour cooking time on the boil is considered to be normal for the most authentic traditional recipes. The concentrated brew at this stage is referred to as *Chaku*, which is then combined with salt, cream, yak's butter and more boiling water in a large churn called a *dongmo*, which functions as a blending device. The mixture is churned to the point where an emulsion of the water and butter has almost formed before being served.

The resultant mixture, which can have a bitter, cheesy character, is anathema to many Western tastes. But in a sometimes cold, high-altitude environment where maintaining a high calorific intake is vital, the use of locally available staples such as yak's butter and the dark tea seems an obvious combination.

Typical teas: Fu tea, Pu Erh, local Tibetan dark tea.

SUBCONTINENT

In India, Pakistan and Bangladesh, tea is brewed in a pan containing milk and water. As a rule, the tea is cooked in the pan rather than being infused within already heated liquid, as is common in many other parts of the world. The ratio of milk to water depends upon the region: the further north and west, the greater the inclusion of milk – Punjabi tea is the thickest and milkiest of all, whereas in West Bengal, home to Darjeeling, which is notoriously milk-shy, they occasionally do without milk entirely.

Variations on the recipe often include a combination of spices, the most popular being cardamom or ginger, as well as a healthy dose of sugar or similar sweetener. The proliferation of robust ingredients and the presence of milk mean that even the strongest CTC can be used; indeed, many orthodox teas struggle to stand up to the milk, sugar and spices.

This recipe has come to be known as chai in Western countries, although strictly speaking *chai* is just the Hindi word for tea, and need not feature an inclusion of spices. *Masala chai* would be a more accurate rendering for the spice-based drink.

Typical origins: Bangladesh, India or Kenya (for Pakistan).

EAST FRIESIA

East Friesia in northern Germany sits between the Dutch frontier and the river Weser as an island of tea-drinkers within a sea of coffee culture. Tea consumption is so widespread and fervent that, were the East Frisians a nation in their own right, they could make a credible claim to be the greatest tea consumers in the world.

East Frisian tea features three vital ingredients: a chunk of sugar called a *kluntje*, the brew, which ideally should be based around a full-bodied Assam tea, and the single cream particular to the area.

The *kluntje* is added to a small porcelain cup before the brew is poured over it, resulting in an audible crackling sound as it splits. The final ingredient is the cream, which is dribbled onto the liquor with a customised spoon resembling a mini ladle. As the cream rises to the top of the cup it is said to resemble the white clouds of the vast Frisian skies. Although the cup is equipped with a saucer and teaspoon, the spoon should not be used to stir the liquid, which instead should be consumed in three gulps: the cream first as a starter, its indulgent dairy notes lining the mouth, then the rich, powerful tea, finishing with the sweeter liquid around the *kluntje*.

Street chai being prepared in India.

The host will then immediately refill the cups as before, the process being repeated at least three times (less than three being regarded as impolite). When the guest is satisfied that they wish for no more, then they should place their as yet unused teaspoon into the cup, which acts as a signal to the host to cease dispensing any further hospitality.

Likely origins: Assam.

BRITISH ISLES, CANADA, AUSTRALIA AND NEW ZEALAND

The first teas to make their way to the aristocratic salons of the British Isles were Chinese green teas, undoubtedly consumed without milk. It is likely that tastes changed as the British opened up their own source of tea production in India. The stronger-tasting Assam and Ceylon black teas demanded a little milk to mellow down the power of these newcomers.

In the UK and Ireland black tea is now usually consumed with milk. For the overwhelming majority of tea-drinkers, tea is brewed from teabags, which at 3.125g typically contain about 50% more tea than their Continental peers, and are therefore able to deliver a sufficiently strong brew not to become overwhelmed by the milk. Through the addition of milk the clear liquor becomes opaque, its colour having a great impact on the perception of the consumer, whether they consciously acknowledge it or not. Shades of brown or grey are inevitably regarded as less attractive than golds or reds. The sorts of tea that perform well in such conditions are East Africans, which provide an attractive bright colour, and Assams, which give blends body and strength. These blends are usually designed to be consumed with milk, and for many they can taste excessively strong and astringent if drunk black.

Likely origins: India, East and Central Africa.

TEA OR CHAI?

The French, Dutch and German words for tea are *thé*, *thee* and *tee* respectively, whereas the Farsi, Arabic, Hindi, Turkish, Russian and Greek variants are *chai*, *shai*, *chai*, *cay*, *chay* and *tsai*. The origin derives from the trade route through which the earliest consignments of tea arrived.

The form *te/thé* comes from the Amoy (also known as Xiamen) word *t'e*, consignments of which were believed first to have been brought west by Dutch traders and then spread elsewhere in Western and Central Europe.

Variants of *ch'a* derive from both the Mandarin spoken in Northern China and the Cantonese spoken in the province of Guangdong as well as in Hong Kong and Macao.

The Eastern Europeans initially received their tea via the overland 'caravan route' originating in Mandarin-speaking parts of China, and hence immediately used variants of *ch'a*. Portugal is a notable linguistic exception to the rule that sea-traded goods use the Amoy variant. The Portuguese word *cha* derives from their establishment of a trading post in Macao in the 16th century.

A samovar.

CONTINENTAL EUROPE

A broad geographical descriptor for what is in fact a number of tea cultures. The common denominator is the consumption of tea without milk. This requires milder teas at a lower dosage, with more orthodox or green tea and fewer strong CTCs. It is likely that the early Continental consumers, often fed through Dutch or Portuguese traders, would have enjoyed more Indonesian or Chinese teas, neither of which require any milk. Such historical rituals endure well beyond the colonial links that established them, and will continue to exert their influence for some time yet. Some national habits have stubbornly resisted the brands' attempts at reformation, notably the regularity with which Dutch tea-drinkers re-use their teabags.

Typical origins: China, Sri Lanka, Indonesia.

RUSSIA AND MIDDLE EAST

The traditional ritual makes use either of a samovar (literally *self-boiler*) or two teapots, stacked one atop the other.

A samovar consists of a heat source cooking a tank of water, upon which sits a teapot containing a strong concentrate of tea which has undergone a lengthy brew time. The strong brew from the teapot is diluted with boiling water from the lower tank. It was formerly common to see such tea poured into a cup and then from the cup into a saucer to be drunk. In samovar preparation, the heat source was traditionally charcoal or wood, and this further explains the continuing Russian fondness for smoky teas.

In the teapot method more common in Turkey and neighbouring cultures, the smaller, upper pot contains the tea leaves and will be filled with boiling water from the bottom pot, which sits on a stove. The concentrate of tea is dispensed into small glasses to be topped up with hot water from the bottom pot. This will often be sweetened, but never milked.

Typical origins: in Russia, teas from India or Sri Lanka; in Turkey, domestic teas or Sri Lankan.

CHIFIR

An eye-wateringly strong tea preparation that is popularly linked to the Russian gulag and prison population. Large doses of black tea, up to five or six times the regular amount per person, are added to boiling water and infused for extended periods: fifteen to twenty minutes being regarded as normal. The caffeine-laden brew is often consumed with sweets in the mouth and a splash of milk, although neither of these do much to transform the nauseatingly bitter liquid. Some proponents describe a quasi-hypnotic state that can be achieved for those who have fought through the biliousness.

Although the USA is rapidly becoming known as a consumer of quality speciality teas, it can still be distinguished for its iced tea industry which continues to represent a substantial share of consumption, especially in the southern states.

Tea is brewed in the morning and placed in a refrigerator to chill. Paramount amongst the quality parameters is that the tea does not cloud when it chills, Argentine teas being especially well suited to this task. After a day in the fridge, the brew can be poured over ice, with a sprig of mint or a slice of lemon and sometimes a generous dose of sugar.

Typical origins: Argentina.

WEST AFRICA

The hot climate here is well suited to the consumption of *Attaya*, a brutally strong green tea, usually Chinese gunpowder, which is rendered drinkable with the addition of vast doses of sugar and sprigs of fresh mint.

In the preparation, a cupful of gunpowder is added to a kettle of boiling water, ideally sitting upon a charcoal stove. When it has boiled, a cupful of sugar is added and the kettle brought back to the boil. At this stage the glasses are prepared; a dose of the brew, by now a deep brown colour and scarcely recognisable as a green tea, is poured from one glass into another from such a height as to generate a thick foam. The liquid is added back into the pot, often alongside some fresh mint. When it has come back to the boil it is ready to serve. The astringency of the strong green tea is well balanced by the cooling freshness of the mint and the mellifluousness of the sugar.

CAFFEINE IN TEA: *COFFEE EXCITES, TEA STIMULATES*

Caffeine (sometimes referred to as *theine* when found in tea) is a substance present in dry tea in relatively high concentrations, indeed higher than in an equivalent weight of coffee. However, because the weight of coffee needed per cup is around four to five times that which is needed for tea, the in-cup caffeine for coffee is more than twice that for tea.

Caffeine acts as a stimulant such that its positive impacts on the body include increased alertness and reduced fatigue, however it can also make consumers jittery and irritable. It is the presence of certain antioxidants and the amino acid *L-theanine* in tea which creates a different impact to the caffeine in coffee. Curves that indicate the level of alertness of caffeine consumers usually show a short-term hit and steep drop in coffee consumers whilst tea consumers show a more gentle and sustained curve. It is believed that this is partly due to the L-theanine which has a relaxing effect counteracting some of the negative side-effects of caffeine without affecting the levels of alertness and partly because the caffeine is released slower as it forms complexes with the antioxidants.

Decaffeinated teas are widely available, the extraction of caffeine made possible via a range of processes. Most notable amongst them are the solvents methylene chloride and ethyl acetate or the use of CO_2 under high pressures. Whilst each manages to remove almost all bar a trace amount of the caffeine, it is methylene chloride that tends to result in the least compromise of quality.

It is believed that the ritual reached Moorish dealers in West Africa via ancient overland trading routes – variations of *Attaya* are served throughout West Africa and the area imports prodigious volumes of Chinese green tea. This ritual has been 'Westernised' as the alliteratively satisfying Moroccan Mint Tea, Morocco being the most visited of the *Attaya* countries.

Typical origins: China.

Attaya preparation in Morocco.

Part 3

PRODUCING COUNTRIES

CHINA

Tea's birthplace is now its global powerhouse, producing all conceivable types at every quality level. China has a tea for everyone.

BACKGROUND

HERE RESIDES SEEMINGLY infinite variety, encompassing more than a third of the world's tea crop, spread about a vast continent shaped by three different climate zones. A thousand different catalogued types, many named in different dialects, span all six production methods. *All the tea in China* is a well-coined phrase indeed.

Tea is regarded here both as a luxury product around which a revered culture has grown, just as it also fulfils the role of simple beverage. China's 1.4 billion people spend a vast proportion of their wage packet on the enjoyment of exceptionally fine tea in large quantities. Indeed, if we allow for the fact that the Chinese brewing method obtains multiple extractions from each portion of leaf, then the per-head consumption is at least twice that of the UK and Ireland, the Western world's bastions of the tea tradition.

TEA'S EMERGENCE IN CHINA

China is so much more than just 'significant' to the development of tea. It is highly probable that were it not for the Chinese, we would be yet to discover the delights of the beverage. In China, where history and legend often go hand-in-hand, finding an authoritative history of the development of *Camellia sinensis* (or Chinese Camellia) is usually a matter of sifting fable from fact.

THE LEGEND

The traditional stories like to suggest that in 2437 BC Emperor Shennong – also sometimes spelt Sheng Nun – discovered the drink by accident. Some tea leaves are said to have been deposited into his cauldron, either from an overhead tea tree or from the fuel wood he was using. The emperor is supposed to have tasted and enjoyed the liquor, and an industry was born. He was celebrated as a herbalist, and the legend has him responsible for a great leap forward in the understanding of medicinal plants. Indeed, it is believed that his final act as emperor was an attempt to discover whether a particular plant was poisonous (it was). However, he is also credited with so many other technological and social advancements, and from an era so long ahead of the transcribing of accurate histories, that we do best to enjoy the legend without seeking to press the credibility of the story.

CHA

The Chinese character for tea is 茶, and is composed of three parts. The composition is best explained by Solala Towler in Cha Dao: The Way of Tea.[1] The top one represents plants. The middle one represents a human or person. The bottom one means wood, or 'being rooted'. It has been argued that in the Chinese tradition, the true meaning of tea could be 'something that gives humans a sense of being rooted or balanced'. It is immediately apparent that for the Chinese, tea is more than just a beverage.

What appears certain is that around the 8th century AD tea became widely consumed within the royal court of the Tang dynasty, the growth in significance of the beverage being marked by the publication of Lu Yu's masterpiece *Cha Jing* (*The Book of Tea*). This book, still accepted 1,200 years later as the greatest work ever to have been inspired by tea, gave readers a comprehensive instruction in every aspect of tea culture. Its all-encompassing scope ranges from the provenance of the tea bush and the influence of geography and seasonality on quality, to the folklore of tea, via ceramics, tea-ware, hydrology, social factors and much else in-between. *Cha Jing* was to tea what *The Origin of Species* became to natural history, or *The Wealth of Nations* to economics. It is this seminal text that gave rise to a movement and defined rules and customs throughout the process from bush to cup, rules that in most cases are still just as valid today.

Tea consumption became more widespread following *Cha Jing* as the aristocracy and wealthier merchant classes began to consume tea with enthusiasm. Inevitably this passion for tea fed down the social orders to the point where anyone who could afford it would drink it.

Lu Yu commemorated in bronze.

COMMUNIST CHINA

The industry scarcely changed until the advent of Communist China. Post-civil war China was characterised both by Mao's need for hard currency,[2] and the perceived link between quality products and so-called 'enemies of the revolution'.[3] Exports were prioritised at the expense of local sales, and crucially quantity was stressed at the expense of quality, lest a producer should find himself denounced as a bourgeois counter-revolutionary on the basis of his superior teas. The impact of this was both to lower the reputation of Chinese tea internationally, and to lose many of the artisanal skills that the manufacture of the best tea requires.

MODERN CHINA

Happily, since the liberalisation of the economy, the industry has been free to revert to a quality focus, even if it has sometimes been difficult to shake off the shackles of its past. The reins of central control were initially loosened in 1978, resulting in the demise of the community tea farm and the creation of more smallholders. This morphed in the 1990s into more widespread liberalisation and private ownership of tea gardens.

The transformation of the Chinese economy in the past twenty years, and the disposable wealth that this has brought to the domestic consumer, has resulted in a corresponding revolution within the Chinese industry. Investments in factories and gardens have almost doubled the crop. In boosting the output of hitherto very exclusive teas, we are all now able to enjoy the very treasures that had formerly been out of reach for all bar the senior public officials. If there is an issue now, it is in finding people willing to work in a somewhat stigmatised agriculture sector, increasingly the poor relation when judged against the seductive lure of urban employment.

UNDERSTANDING CHINA'S TEAS

China is the most difficult of all tea-producing countries to comprehend. The first barrier is a linguistic one: the names of the teas often mean little when translated into Western languages, losing the nuance that makes them so evocative in their native tongue. Thus *Bai Hao Wang* is surely better left in Hanyu Pinyin than being translated to *The King of the White Downy*.

The second hurdle to grasping Chinese teas is the geographical distribution and organisation of the tea gardens. Whereas in tea-growing areas west of China one is able to point definitively to an area of tea bushes and establish which tea factory the leaf will be produced in, and therefore under what name it will be sold, matters of provenance are more ambiguous in the East.

Individual family-run plots of tea are a significant source of leaf, and it is often problematic to trace these back from the tea factory if one wants to establish who has produced what. It has long been the Chinese way to amalgamate teas of similar style. These are blended into numbered standards of homogenised quality. Hence, one can find a Long Jing 6015 priced well below 6018, but neither number gives any clue as to the merits or otherwise that hide behind it.

The third and arguably most significant challenge to overcome is cultural. The very best Chinese teas have always been drunk in China, the Chinese being much more prepared to pay good money for good tea. To properly appreciate them it is incumbent on Western consumers to learn a few rudiments of tea-brewing Chinese-style. Trying to shoehorn a first-class Mao Feng into most teabags is physically impossible, whilst cutting such a tea to achieve this end is tantamount to shredding 100RMB notes.

There is a significant distinction to draw between Western-facing tea producers such as the Kenyans or Sri Lankans, and the Chinese. When a Kenyan or high-elevation Sri Lankan tea factory make their tea, they know that a large proportion of it will end up in teabags in the West. Accordingly, the whole production process is designed around this end, and anyone who suggests that teabags are made of sweepings from the floor has clearly not visited such a tea factory. It is insupportable to claim that a large-leafed Kenyan CTC tea is appreciably superior to what is packed into a teabag. However, in China, the smaller-leafed grades are very definitely a by-product of the 'quality' large-leafed production where the real money is made. We should therefore not expect most China-derived green teabag blends containing smaller leaf particles to represent a peak quality product in the same way that black teabags can arguably justify such an assertion.

The ten 'famous teas' should appeal to the list-lover in anyone; a compilation of the ten best teas in China, reflecting the opinions of tea experts. This is the closest that China comes to Bordeaux-style 'first growth' classification in that the honour and recognition that come with making it onto the list are in many ways a licence to name one's price as a producer.

Where it differs from Bordeaux' classification is that fresh lists seem to emanate each year from numerous sources, and demotions are inevitably overlooked by those with an interest in a particular tea (see *Henan Maojian*). The best way of establishing a hierarchy is to take four or five such lists and count the recurrences.

A gift of *famous tea*, always elaborately and expensively packaged, represents recognition and appreciation of the highest sort for one's host such that you can always be assured of a warm welcome.

The ten famous teas (based upon recurrence):
1. Long Jing (Dragon Well)
2. Bi Lo Chun (Green Snail Spring)
3. Jun Shan Yin Zhen (Jun Shan Silver Needle)
4. Lu Shan Yun Wu (Lu Shan Cloud Mist)
5. Quimen (Keemun)
6. Huangshan Mao Feng (Huangshan Downy Peak)
7. Anxi TieGuan Yin (Iron Goddess of Mercy)
8. Pu Erh
9. Wuyi Da Hong Pao (Wuyi Big Red Robe)
10. Jasmine

CAVEAT EMPTOR

Just because China is home to some of the world's greatest teas and tea enthusiasts, it is not beyond also producing some less esteemed offerings. China plays host to many cottage industry producers, the best of whom are capable of producing wondrous teas with great consistency. The flip-side of such a large artisanal trade is that some teas are produced in conditions that would send a European food safety auditor scurrying.

As with any exclusive product, it is also important to beware the shark. Just as China remains a significant source for branded items of dubious provenance, there are unscrupulous producers out to capitalise on the lure of high-quality famous teas. This is no reason to avoid Chinese tea – in doing so you would miss out on some of the world's greatest teas. It is more a caveat emptor forewarning that Chinese provenance does not automatically confer a quality label; as with any tea, the proof is in the tasting. If it carries a famous tea label and is unfeasibly cheap then there is probably a good reason.

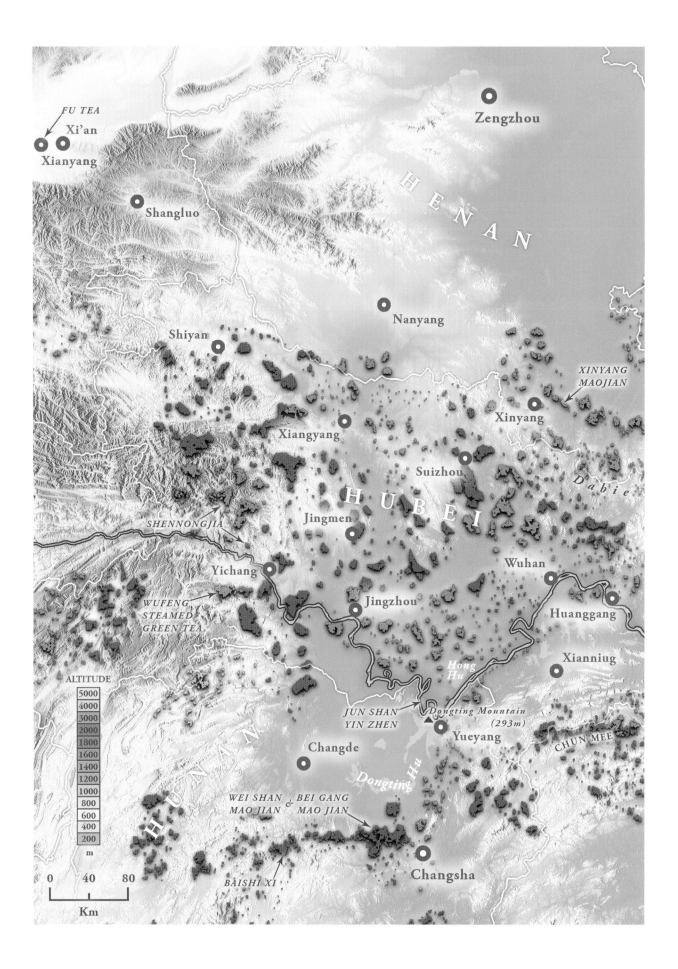

FU TEA
Xi'an
Xianyang

Shangluo

HENAN

Zengzhou

Nanyang

Shiyan

XINYANG
MAOJIAN

Xinyang

Xiangyang

Suizhou

Dabie

HUBEI

SHENNONGJIA

Jingmen

Wuhan

Yichang

WUFENG
STEAMED
GREEN TEA

Jingzhou

Huanggang

Xianniug

Hong
Hu

ALTITUDE

5000
4000
3000
2000
1800
1600
1400
1200
1000
800
600
400
200

m

JUN SHAN
YIN ZHEN

Dongting Mountain
(293m)

Yueyang

CHUN MEE

Changde

HUNAN

Dongting Hu

WEI SHAN   BEI GANG
MAO JIAN   &   MAO JIAN

0   40   80

Km

BAISHI XI

Changsha

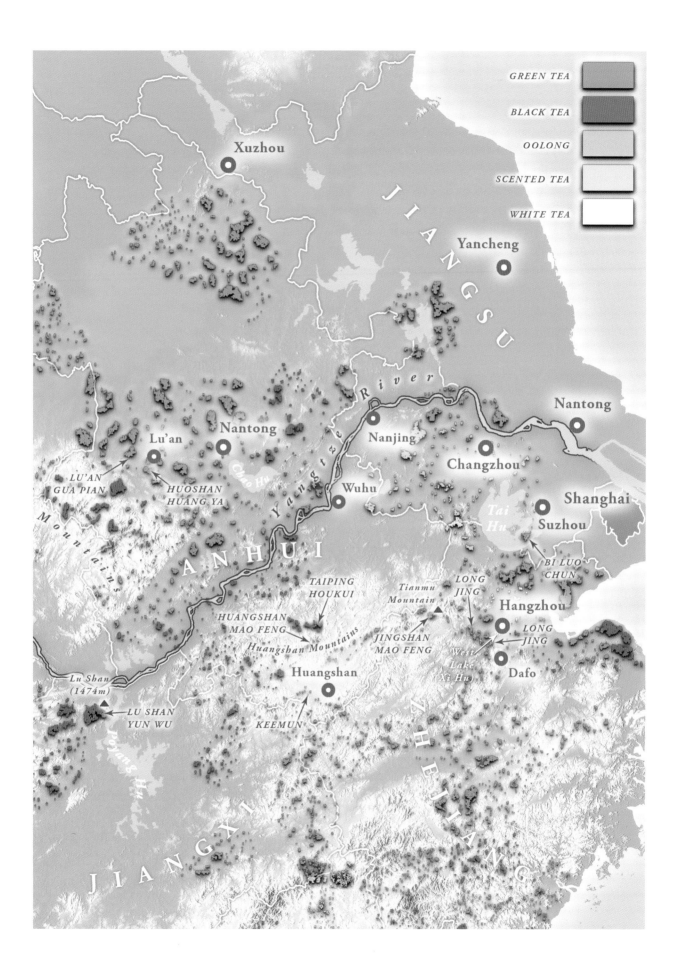

GREEN TEA

BLACK TEA

OOLONG

SCENTED TEA

WHITE TEA

Xuzhou

JIANGSU

Yancheng

Nantong

Lu'an

Nantong

Nanjing

Changzhou

Chao Hu

Shanghai

LU'AN
GUA PIAN

HUOSHAN
HUANG YA

Wuhu

Yangtze River

Suzhou

Tai Hu

ANHUI

BI LUO
CHUN

Mountains

TAIPING
HOUKUI

Tianmu Mountain

LONG
JING

Hangzhou

HUANGSHAN
MAO FENG

JINGSHAN
MAO FENG

LONG
JING

Huangshan Mountains

West Lake Xi Hu

Dafo

*Lu Shan
(1474m)*

Huangshan

ZHEJIANG

LU SHAN
YUN WU

KEEMUN

Poyang Hu

JIANGXI

PRUSSIAN BLUE AND GYPSUM

British taste for green tea seemed to know no bounds in the early part of the 19th century. Tea consumers were not only ill informed on aspects of quality, but also increasingly *ill*. They began to place value on the greenness of the leaf: the more vibrant and green the colour of the leaf, the more they paid. With this trend, adulteration soon became a concern.

Whilst a modern-day buyer is able to visit a factory without too much negotiation, early buyers needed to disguise themselves in order to gain access to an inland China (justifiably) fearful of losing its monopoly on the manufacture of tea.

On one of his early visits Robert Fortune discovered that the addition of Prussian blue and gypsum to the tea was resulting in the very bright green colour so beloved of the home market at that time. The producer was effectively poisoning his consumers, albeit with no malicious intent. The practice was soon stopped when it was revealed to consumers why the slightly eggy-tasting green tea was of such a lurid colour.

The colour of green tea leaf is indeed a measure of quality, with a deep jade colour being valued over shades of khaki and brown; however producers, are now achieving this through a natural focus on quality and nothing underhand.

JIANGSU

Jiangsu is a largely flat maritime province that sits towards the northern margin of remunerative tea cultivation in China. Although temperatures are by and large lower than those further south, the maritime influence assists in providing a moderating influence upon both winter and summer extremes. Although the province itself is comprised mainly of level agricultural and industrial land, it is its few hills that are of interest to tea-drinkers, specifically Dong Ting 'mountain' adjoining Lake Tai, which provides Jiangsu's greatest tea and its entry onto the list of China's famous teas.

BI LO CHUN/BI LUO CHUN/PI LO CHUN

Only 100 kilometres (60 miles) west of Shanghai's sprawling conurbation lies the relative tranquillity of Taihu (or Lake Tai). Taihu is a vast yet shallow expanse of water that is believed to be the result of a meteor strike; a theory that is supported by the semi-circle traced by its southern and western shores, and its modest 2-metre average depth. This shallow water is instrumental in Taihu's propensity to heat up and form mists, which drift onto the adjacent hills. This proximity of the lake and the hill on its south-eastern peninsula is the prime physical factor in creating one of China's great green teas.

Dong Ting is a name with rich potential for confusion in connection with fine teas. The Jiangsu Dong Ting mountain is not to be confused with Lake Dongting in Hunan province, or the Taiwanese Dong Ding from which we get oolong of the same name. In this case it comprises of east and west peaks separated by around 5 kilometres (3 miles) of open water, although 'peak' is a somewhat grandiose

Tea plucking amongst the fruit trees of Dong Ting.

Bi Luo Chun's distinctive leaf.

term for the 150-200-metre (500-650-feet) altitude on the upper slopes. Dong Ting West is an island in the lake, whilst Dong Ting East is an increasingly built-upon peninsula known for its fruit and tea cultivation. This human factor – the combination of fruit and tea, specifically the inter-planting of both crops – is the final link in the chain that makes the peninsula so unique and marks out authentic Bi Luo Chun.

Classic Bi Luo Chun is spring crop green tea with a classically distinctive silvered, tippy leaf. Its name goes some way towards illustrating the defining characteristics: *bi* means green, *luo* translates as snail, which is a reference to the whirling spiral shape of the leaf and its likeness to a snail's shell, whilst *chun* means spring and is suggestive of the cropping period – ideally before Qing Ming, which falls around 5th April.

The best leaf is finely plucked – usually one leaf and a bud in the peak quality season – and derived from bushes that grow alongside the fruit trees of the district. Apricot, peach, citrus and plum can all be found in the area, and during blossom time in particular they transmit a scent that augments the naturally floral characteristics of spring flush green tea. The aroma is the defining characteristic of the tea, all soft fruit and floral notes, whilst the small silver-flecked pearls of leaf on the best teas lend a visual delight that fuels the anticipation.

Bi Luo Chun can now be found in a number of provinces but Jiangsu's remains the best, the most fruity, supremely floral and most visually delightful, with the poorer imitations from further south often betraying themselves via a more golden tip or browner leaf.

ANHUI PROVINCE

Anhui province can boast excellence in the crafting of green, black and yellow teas, and as such it is arguably host to the greatest variety outside of Fujian. The hills of southern Anhui are the home of Keemun, perhaps the most famous of the black teas to hail from China.

Qimen county

KEEMUN

Qimen county – Europeanised to Keemun – was only interested in green tea manufacture until well into the 19th century. It is said that the area came into black tea when an enterprising civil servant fallen upon hard times decided to learn about the art of black tea-making. He took himself off to Fujian province to learn the trade and returned to establish a number of factories processing the local leaf into black tea. It emerged that the local strains of bush flourishing in the well-drained, sandy soil were well-suited to black tea-making, and the local *hong cha* went from strength to strength. What the enterprising official had discovered was the essence of terroir – the importance of the local.

Qimen county had made perfectly adequate green tea for centuries; the local conditions, however, are unique in their ability to allow black tea to reach levels of floral aroma only normally seen in oolong or some green teas and often likened to orchid or rose. It seems to be easy to write *Keemun* on the tin; it's rather more difficult to find a really *good* Keemun. Whereas the taste characteristics of, say, an Assam second flush tea are distinctive enough to ensure that even a poor version can convey a sense of what the quality product *should* taste like, the qualities of Keemun are so subtle, so ethereal that you really do need to know what to look for if you want to get a real sense of the aromatic floral burst that is fine Keemun.

The first question should be from which season the tea comes – take the freshest, most recent crop as a matter of course. You can then turn to the leaf; it should be very fine, thinner and wirier than an equivalent Assam owing to the use of the local China jat leaf, which is inherently smaller. The highest grade available outside of oligarch pricing is known as Haoya, further subdivided into superior

'A' and inferior 'B' qualities. Haoya A may contain lashings of golden tip and feature the most delicate and wiry leaf of all, but both are sublime teas.

Descending beneath the Haoya quality levels, the leaf becomes visibly coarser and more open, but there remains beautiful tea to be found from within the mainstream standard numbers. If you can persuade the retailer to make you a tasting sample then look for the aroma and a bright reddish liquor (without milk). It should be perfectly balanced, with the medium-bodied character never overwhelming the beautiful floral aroma (something that can happen on cheaper Keemuns).

HUANGSHAN MAO FENG

There is more to Anhui than just Keemun; Huangshan Mao Feng is perhaps most notable for its inclusion in the list of famous teas. Plucked as only one leaf and a bud, instead of the more conventional Chinese quality standard of two and a bud, the leaf is therefore younger, more delicate and potentially more aromatic than the standard Chinese Mao Feng. The preponderance of young leaf and bud endows the leaf with a silvery appearance thanks to the fine downy hairs or *mao*,

The mist-shrouded Huangshan Mountains.

especially on the end (*feng*) of the youngest terminal growth. This ensures that it has a beautiful silky feel, but its distinctive feature lies in the powerful magnolia aroma of a fine example of the style.

Huangshan Mao Feng

Huangshan is significant as a source. Whilst many other areas can produce fine Mao Feng teas, the rugged granite-topped Huangshan range can boast both a hard winter and those all-important mists, which often create fine teas. The beautifully rugged mountains do not offer many suitable tea-growing sites, so supply is limited.

TAIPING HOUKUI/MONKEY KING

Taiping Houkui is one of the most distinctive green teas that China produces. Its characteristic flattened shape, known as 'two knives and a pole', is unseen anywhere else in the tea world, whilst the sheer size of these leaves alone marks it out as something special. Anhui itself is important in this equation, as the tea should really come from the *Shi Da* variety of bush that is seldom if ever seen outside of Anhui. This long-leafed strain bears a large bud and small, downy hairs even on its second or third leaves, and as such should be more distinguishable from the occasional falsifications available on the market.

Authentic Taiping Houkui hails from the villages around Xinming in the

The distinctive flattened shape of Taiping Houkui.

Tea gardens near to Xingming. Leaf from here will be processed into Taiping Houkui.

Huangshan range of mountains, the very best batches usually being from the April crop. Pluckers aim to take only the two large leaves and their equally oversized bud. The leaf is hand-fried (see p30) in order to 'fix' or ensure that no oxidation is possible, before being placed onto large bamboo trays for roasting. The four-stage roasting process aims to stabilise the leaf whilst applying ever more pressure upon it in order to coax the distinctive knife-shape. The culmination of this is the placing of a cloth upon the leaf, coupled with strong manual pressure. This will ensure that the final appearance of a good Taiping Houkui should reveal miniscule indentations where the individual threads of this cloth remain visible. Lower grades can be machine processed, but one more often sees broken leaves entering the finished product the lower down the quality ladder one ventures.

It is not unknown for producers to store their teas alongside *Indocalamus* leaves pending packing. This bamboo variety itself is sometimes brewed into a tea, and I speculate whether the period of contact endows it with an additional tinge of seductive sweetness. The liquor yields an orchid-like flavour and aroma, coupled with an enduring smoothness. Taiping Houkui is a little more full-bodied than some green teas, perhaps due to the extraction coming from the larger surface area of its distinctive leaves.

LU'AN GUA PIAN/LU'AN MELON SEED

Taking their name from the town of Lu'an, the best teas actually hail from Qi Shan village in Jinzhai county on the Anhui side of the extensive Dabie mountain range. Here, the altitude of around 500 to 1,000 metres (1,640-3,300 feet) tends to suit the production of excellent spring crop green teas however they are processed, but Lu'an Gua Pian's appeal lies in two relatively unique aspects of its production process – the plucking standard and the processing methodology.

The plucking style is the first variation from the norm – ordinary for good spring crop tea would be one leaf and a bud, or perhaps two and a bud, but here the pluckers target two leaves and no bud. This is a difficult activity to get right in itself, as the leaves need to be plucked individually with the stalk remaining on the bush. These leaves are normally taken a little after the usual spring crop teas are plucked elsewhere in eastern China, and as a consequence they tend to have less subtlety and sweetness, but in return they can offer strength and aroma to compensate in spades.

The manufacture follows a standard green tea panning process which in a couple of stages aims to achieve a twist to the leaf such that the leaf curls over upon itself. The procedure is concluded with a charcoal heating stage that aims to stabilise the leaf but is fraught with danger; the heat source

Tea in the Dabie mountains.

needs to be absolutely smoke-free and the tea's exposure to it must be brief enough to retain volatile top notes, but long enough to stabilise the produce. To witness a craftsman perform this with the bamboo basket of tea atop the fire is a real pleasure, and success here is borne out of years of experience.

The finished tea only begins to resemble its melon seed namesake when it has been brewed and the individual leaves, shorn of any bud or stalk, start to unfurl into their characteristic oval shape. The teas are charming in a defiantly unsubtle fashion, with a delightful grassy intensity when compared to other spring teas.

ANHUI YELLOW TEAS: HUO SHAN HUANG YA, HUANG XIAO CHA AND HUANG DA CHA

Whilst Anhui is best known for its black and green teas, it also produces some excellent yellow teas in a variety of styles. Judged on appearance, Huo Shan Huang Ya is the pick of the bunch, boasting a longer, tippier leaf style, whilst Huang Xiao Cha is a touch smaller and more wiry and Huang Da Cha rather blacker in style. Whilst all possess the creamy smoothness and lack of grassiness typical of yellow teas, Huang Ya has a lightly nutty character and the lightest liquor of the three, with Xiao Cha often a little more intensely sweet and floral owing to its smaller leaf size. Huang Da Cha is a different beast altogether, and is sometimes more reminiscent of chocolate or coffee in the liquor than the mellow notes typically associated with yellow teas.

HANDCRAFTED FLOWERING OR DISPLAY TEAS

Although such teas are made all over China, they are especially particular to Anhui and Fujian around Fuan. This is where tea enters the realm of theatre, and where the visual qualities of the infusion begin to eclipse the organoleptic aspect. Handmade assemblages of tea leaves, often also incorporating elaborate flower blooms, represent better than anything else the Chinese attitude to tea. Here, tea is to be revered as a piece of craftsmanship rather than consumed as a humble agricultural product. A flowering tea is a work of art produced using exceptionally fine raw materials, and usually by groups of craftsmen and women with years of experience. These artisans are able to create painstakingly-constructed balls, stars, pearls and other improbable forms, each usually given an equally magnificent name suggestive of the 'show' that lies within the tea.

For a typical ball-shape, the tea-maker will start with a set of buds, some fine thread, and the flowers: often jasmine or globe amaranth, which features a round, red bloom. The buds themselves need to be of a sufficiently long length and large leaf in order to facilitate assembly, coupled with

Handcrafted flowering teas on sale in a local tea market.

a relative lack of astringency under the extended brewing needed for the tea to 'come alive' when infused. The local Huangshan strain satisfies on both counts.

Still attached to a long stalk but with all lower leaves removed, the buds will be arranged into a bundle around a central flower with the stalk-end grouped around the bloom. This bundle of stalk and bloom is secured with thread. The buds are then gathered up and around the bloom and wrapped in cloth in order to secure the distinctive shape. This is then dried and the cloth removed, leaving a ball shape with the flower at its core.

The brewing of the tea must take place in a glass teapot in order to most effectively witness the slow unfurling of the buds and the release of the bloom at its core. Depending upon the method of creation, this flower may unfurl to reveal any number of shapes in a process akin to performance. Taste is in many ways secondary: at least a three-minute brew is required in order to induce the bloom to reveal itself, which is far longer than any normal Chinese green tea would experience. The joy here is in the giving of gifts, the assembly of a collection, and the theatre of the brew as the flower is slowly revealed with grace and beauty. If you are after taste alone, then it is best to save your money and buy a conventionally processed tea because crafted teas are as much about the experience as the liquid imbibed at the end.

A handcrafted tea unfurls under brewing.

HUBEI PROVINCE

As you would expect of a province neighbouring Anhui, Hubei is capable of producing excellent teas which, if they do not have the brand equity of a fine Keemun or Huangshan Mao Feng, are no less worth drinking and arguably keener value because of it. In fact Hubei produces twice as much tea as its more showy neighbour, so there are plenty of gems to discover, especially in the western mountains which can boast some of China's few steamed green teas.

A tea garden in Hubei Province.

Hubei is suggestive of an area to the north of a lake (*hu*), the lake in question being Dongting, which sits just within Hunan province. Hubei's geography is defined by its rugged mountains in the west, through which the Yangtze river cuts a swathe, and its flatter central and southern plains. The Yangtze river's importance to the province is significant as the Three Gorges Dam Project now dominates the riverscape east of Yichang. Its western borderlands, from where some of the finer green teas hail, play host to a forest zone known as Shennongjia, so-named for the famous herbalist who is reputed to have discovered the tea bush.

HUBEI BLACK TEA

Early crop spring teas produced around Yichang are arguably the best black teas in Hubei. They have some of the qualities of Keemun (although can tend to lack the ethereal aroma and delicate liquor), but they also tend to come without the Keemun price tag, with an early crop Hubei tea easily a match for a rather later Keemun.

HUBEI PAN-FRIED GREEN TEA

A number of types are produced from the rugged, high-elevation areas in the west. These teas tend to carry a sappy, grassy aroma and clarity of liquor. With baking temperatures on the plains a constant feature of the Hubei summer, the better teas come from highest up the hill, with the greater preponderance of mists and cooler daytime temperatures.

HUBEI STEAMED GREEN TEA/LU ZHEN/EN SHI LU YU

Although there exist other Chinese tea producers who steam their tea (rather than roasting, the traditional Chinese 'kill green' technique), these tend to operate on a more industrial than artisanal scale. Hubei – especially the rugged, mountainous area around Wufeng – is unique in Chinese tea-making tradition in that it is one of the sole repositories of genuine artisanal steamed tea processing.

The steamed green teas from Hubei differ from their Japanese cousins in that they lack the needle-like leaf that a sencha can boast, replacing it instead with more of a twist. The finer plucked buds will form Lu Zhen, whilst the 'one-and-a-bud' pluck will go into En Shi Lu Yu, which has a more intense character. Floral aromas are more overt and liquors are less overtly vegetal and spinach-like than the Japanese versions.

SHAANXI PROVINCE

Shaanxi sits on the northern boundary for remunerative tea production, before temperatures become too low and rainfall insufficient. The province straddles the old Silk Road and for years was a valuable staging post for caravans who collected the local Fu Brick tea for trading in the west.

FU BRICK TEA

The name *Fu*, suggestive of the hottest period of the summer, is a clue to the production season for this unique tea. The main sources of the raw material have always been Hunan, Sichuan and Shaanxi itself. Fu tea fits into the dark tea family, with the production process similar in its early stages to the traditional Pu Erh. A 'kill green' roasting is performed in order to kill the enzymes and prevent oxidation, followed by a heaping process, all taking place at or close to the garden. Heaping, as with Sheng Pu Erh, can take a year, following which the tea will be sold to the dealers of Xiangyang who will sort and grade the leaf. The leaf is steamed for a period of about fifty seconds to remove unwanted bacteria and moisten the leaves. It is then loaded in a specially designed cabinet

Golden flecks of Jin Hua on Fu Tea leaf.

for three to four hours at about 75°C in order to ferment before being sprayed with a special mix and compressed into bricks. The compression process is a skill in itself, requiring the orientation of the wiry leaf to be transverse to the direction of pressure in order to achieve a tighter brick with less breakage during packing. The bricks are then stored in a special room at controlled humidity and temperatures for twelve to fifteen days, a process known as *Fahua*.

It is the mix that is sprayed onto the tea that is key to this process, and its recipe remains a closely guarded secret. It is probable that it contains the spores of *Eurotium cristatum*, a form of bacteria that grows on and within the brick during the *Fahua* in the form of minute golden spores that the Chinese call *Jin Hua*. The quality of a Fu Brick can be measured by the abundance of the golden flower, although this is linked to the distinction drawn between hand-compressed brick tea and that compressed by machine. The handmade tea tends to be compressed less densely than the machine-produced tea, making it easier for the golden flower to spread. As a consequence, the handmade product boasts more Jin Hua and a softer, more refined taste in the cup. The colour is a little deeper and the aroma a level sweeter.

Tests have shown *Eurotium cristatum* to be safe for consumption,[4] and it lends a unique rich smoothness to the tea. The health claims are numerous and encompass a large number of conditions. Whether consumed as a digestive (as many local Chinese do) or as a health or probiotic boost, it is as unique as anything in the world of tea.

GANSU

Gansu is a sizeable and generally rather arid province with only its southerly counties capable of successful tea cultivation. As with Shaanxi, it sits astride the old Silk Road trade routes and its modest tea fame is due to the processing of pressed teas for onward export to the north-western provinces and Mongolia. Although some tea is grown here, notably in the borderlands with Sichuan around Longnan city, this is more of local interest and seldom seen elsewhere in China for the good reason that other provinces produce better. Much of the tea ostensibly 'produced' in Gansu has started its life outside the province as a conventional black tea before being further elaborated in the dark-tea style.

Xinjang Maojian

HENAN

XINJANG MAOJIAN

Hailing from the handsome Dabie mountains area south east of Xinjang, Maojian is a pan-fired, very fine-plucked green tea. It is usually grown at altitudes between 500 and 800 metres (1,600-2,600 feet), benefiting from classic mountain mists. As it is situated relatively far north there is a distinctive seasonality and comparatively short growing season, with the best crop usually coming around the middle of April during the spring period. Snow is an occasional factor over the winters, and this distinct seasonality and winter dormancy is a further positive in creating an appealing spring tea.

Ideally, Maojian would comprise only the buds, their downy hairs (*Mao*) giving the tea its name. The leaf is usually a characteristic needle shape, although this can curl with time. While relatively full in body for a green tea, the liquor tends to have an appealing sweetish, floral character when processed from well-made leaf. The provenance of the leaf is crucial as Maojian has been a victim of its own success. Less noble corners of the province at lower elevations have been pressed into cultivation in order to keep pace with demand. This lower-altitude tea has not endured the full stress of the winter snows and this more benign environment can dilute the floral character. Many attribute this to Maojian's recent demotion from the ten famous teas of China. This need not put you off because well-made Maojian, especially fresh-crop spring tea, can be a delight, its honest thwack of sweet notes well-balanced by an attractive floral aroma.

ZHEJIANG PROVINCE

Zhejiang, if not the geographical home of tea, has at least become something of a spiritual home. It was to the Jing Shan area of Zhejiang that Lu Yu retreated to study and write his classic *Cha Jing*, and it has a credible claim to have originated the tea ceremony during the Song Dynasty (then in the form of a tea banquet). Vast volumes of green tea emanate from the province, much of it of outstanding quality, and when we think of China's famous teas it is invariably Zhejiang's candidate Long Jing ('Dragon Well') tea that is top of the list.

LONG JING/LUNG CHING/DRAGON WELL

Although Bi Luo Chun connoisseurs may dispute it, Long Jing represents perhaps the ultimate incarnation of pan-fired green tea quality, and in its finest form (spring crop, fine-plucked, hand-roasted, from either the Long Jing #43 or Jiu Keng group cultivars) it is arguably the best way to appreciate roasted green tea.

As with almost all great Chinese green teas it is spring, before the Qing Ming festival, that traditionally produces the best Long Jing. Although even this can be problematic, as the traditional Long Jing cultivars tend to flush a little later than modern imposters, so an educated tasting of options is worthwhile before buying.

Long Jing can emanate from a number of Zhejiang's tea-producing counties. In order to qualify as a Long Jing it must be produced in the traditional hand-panned style and hail from within a 168-square kilometre (65-square mile) National Designated Protected Zone permitted to grow and label its tea as such. West Lake (Xihu) is the most famous of the producing areas, but excellent teas also come from around Dafo in Xinchang county, located about 50 kilometres (30 miles) south east of Xihu. The annual crop of genuine Long Jing is estimated to be between 500 to 1,000 tonnes, a crop that is dwarfed by the amount of tea carrying a Long Jing label when sold.

To visit Long Jing country is easier than that of almost any other great tea. The area around Hangzhou is especially well-geared for the tourist. In season, artisans sit outside their plots offering teas they have produced themselves, and giving demonstrations of the fine technique needed in order to turn

The Dragon Well Spring. A long stick is on hand to stir the spring which is then supposed to display interesting reflections.

finely-plucked green leaf into an iconic tea (see p30). This is an artisanal product at its best, and the skill with which the leaf is manually manipulated around the searingly hot, wok-shaped roasting pans is something to behold.

Ten different hand motions are required in order to create the ultimate Long Jing. These movements are learnt over years of apprenticeship and rehearsed thousands of times each day as the craftsman takes lightly withered leaf and steadily refines it to the characteristic flattened sword shape of Long Jing. Alternately killing the enzymes through pressing the leaf into the sides of the wok, then collecting and scattering the now-hot leaf from a height, ensures the leaf never overheats, which would put it in danger of losing its sweetness.

The aroma that emanates during the roasting process is a seductive, sappy scent, sadly lost to the world the moment the tea is roasted, yet a reward for those who have made the journey. The leaf is left with distinctive darker roasting spots on the surface, evidence of hand processing and something to be celebrated as indicative of handmade quality.

The first thing to do when sizing up a potential purchase of

Picking at Jingshan.

Long Jing (although this may be problematic in a tea shop) is to breathe on the leaf and then savour the aroma that is released. An intense, sappy note should result, and is an indication of a fine tea, recently produced. The older the tea, the more golden the leaf becomes and the softer its aroma, neither being any good for quality. It is advisable to look at two or three samples if you can to find something that is properly characteristic of the style, the very best teas commanding a price of $200 a kilo and upwards, although very fine tea can still be had for a tenth of that.

True connoisseurs suggest that only by infusing the Long Jing leaf with water from the nearby Tiger Spring (Hu Pao) can one achieve the supreme expression of Long Jing taste. The best early pre-Qing Ming teas have a sweetish chestnut character, mild in power but with a pleasant length of flavour. As the season progresses, the teas can tend to lose some of the sappy aromas but gain in intensity.

JING SHAN MAO FENG

Mao Feng is produced in a number of regions, but Jing Shan's is worth highlighting for its cultural significance as much as its endemic quality. Lying west of Hangzhou en route to Zhejiang's north-western border with Anhui is a hilly, forested area of misty peaks and verdant valleys. Here in the tea-growing counties around Tianmu mountain sits some of Zhejiang's best tea land. The microclimates generated by the mountain help to ensure mild temperatures, the local mists help to diffuse the sunlight and further moderate the heat, whilst the yellow and red forest soils are abundantly fertile.

The local varietal was extensively planted out by Buddhist monks affiliated to the local Jing Shan temple (Jing Shan mountain itself is the north-east peak of Tianmu). It has the high concentration of downy hairs on its youngest leaves necessary for fine Mao Feng, and the husbandry of the bushes was for long a feature of the monks' daily ritual. The Mao Feng is beautifully clean and aromatic, with the classic attributes of a sappy floral fragrance and soft fruit notes.

This local tea would have been the highlight of Buddhist monastic hospitality, and helped in spreading both the ceremonial aspects of tea which gave rise to the tea ceremonies we know today, as well as the fame of Jing Shan in particular. It was here in the temple that the local monks schooled a Japanese visitor named Eisai. He took this knowledge of tea cultivation, processing and ceremony, as well as some seeds, with him to Japan and was largely responsible for introducing tea to Japan's theocracy and aristocracy.

GUNPOWDER/ZHU CHA

Gunpowder. Never was a tea named more evocatively. Gunpowder tea at its best tends to hail from Zhejiang, although fine versions are also produced in a number of provinces. The principle behind the style is that a reduced surface area should protect more of the leaf from its nemeses – light, oxygen and moisture. Hence, if a producer can twist the leaf into a fine, shotty pellet, then the theory runs that such a tea should retain its quality for longer, or 'keep better' in the parlance of the industry.

The start point for gunpowder is a classic pan-fired green tea process as seen all over China, but what makes the process unique is the adaptation of the rolling stage to achieve a shotty twist to the leaf. Whilst this is usually performed by a device known as a balling machine, even such machines require skilled operators to strike the right balance between the twist and over-handling the leaf, and more importantly require feeding with the best leaf in order to provide the shottiest tea. Good teas are judged by the size of the pellet as well as by its polish: a well-made tea having a light sheen that should be the result of extensive pressing and polishing, and not as a consequence of a liberal application of starch, which can be a risk.

The very best is still done by hand. Gunpowder in its highest form – sometimes called *pinhead* gunpowder – goes through an intricate and highly skilled hand-twisting, drying and polishing process. The size of the pearls is generally a good representation of their quality; small pearls not only have less surface area, they also tend to come from smaller and hence younger, more tender and more tasty leaf. The best gunpowder should have a light amber colour and a delicately toasty character; lower grades can have a less pleasant tobacco note to them. Gunpowder's finest application is arguably its marriage with fresh mint in the *Attaya* ceremony of West Africa (see p91).

GUNPOWDER

The nervous young interpreter assisting the delegation of Chinese provincial tea exporters managed to make contact from Casablanca airport. They would not be meeting us as planned. Their plane to London had long since departed, and their crucial parcel of trade samples had been impounded. Would we excuse their late arrival and be assured that there was nothing untoward in their detention, just a misunderstanding?

The problem? A large proportion of their trade samples were listed as *Gunpowder*, which had raised alarm bells amongst the security and customs staff upon their departure from Morocco. An afternoon of interrogation and the opening and brewing of the samples was needed before those in authority could be persuaded that the gunpowder in question was Zhejiang green tea destined for the *Attaya* drinkers of West Africa, where it would be blended with fresh mint and a generous dose of sugar.

JIANGXI

LU SHAN YUN WU

Lu Shan Yun Wu is classic mountain green tea hailing from the precipitous Lu range that sits in the northern part of the province. They are not especially high (the highest peak is 1,474 metres (4,834 feet)), but what the Lu mountains lack in outright height, they make up for with spectacular views of the vast Po Yang lake on the few days each year when they are not bedecked in mountain mists. *Yun Wu* itself is a reference to the clouds and mists that are responsible for the favourable growing conditions.

The best Lu Shan Yun Wu tea tends to have been plucked as one leaf and a bud, or sometimes just the bud. Many will claim that the bud alone should form the authentic product, but much more

The mists of Lu Shan.

important than this is the period of harvest. Pre-Qing Ming leaf provides the most authentic chestnut character, intermingled with notes of spinach and seaweed. The dry leaf itself should have a sweetish aroma; the later in the season it is processed, the less intense the fragrance.

Lu Shan Yun Wu is one of China's famous teas, and as such sees an intense demand, particularly during the immediate post-spring flush season. The Lu Shan hills are not an especially vast cultivation area so, where possible, the provenance and period of plucking should be verified.

CHUN MEE

A tea that can be largely summed up in its name: *Chun* representing a number of significant tea attributes – either *spring* (see Bi Luo Chun) or *precious*, whilst *Mee* unambiguously means *eyebrow*, and is indicative of the distinctive curl of the leaf. Chun Mee is a generic pan-fired green-tea style that one finds in a number of provinces. Jiangxi is its natural home, although Zhejiang could also stake a convincing claim itself.

The leaf bears some resemblance to low-grade gunpowder in its twist and greenish-grey sheen, such that one could be forgiven for imagining that Chun Mee is 'unsuccessfully produced' gunpowder. In fact the two styles are different in production methodology, with less effort in the Chun Mee production process expended upon forming the shotty pellet form, a distinction that actually reduces leaf handling; usually a positive, although keeping quality is impacted as a consequence.

Classic Chun Mee is relatively astringent; its critics suggest that it lacks the refined sweetness and aroma of the top quality famous teas, but as it carries a much lower valuation, the comparison is in

Lu Shan Yun Wu

any case inappropriate. Whilst some lower-end teas can show a rubbery-smoky character if produced without due care and attention, the clue is in the price and the ideal choice would be a spring tea. Such teas require little infusion and can still show themselves well after a number of brews.

WEI SHAN MAO JIAN AND BEI GANG MAO JIAN

These teas, emanating from separate villages, are amongst the smaller-leafed yellow teas emanating from Hunan province. Wei Shan Mao Jian from Ningxiang county are baked with more secondary aromas, sometimes even a touch of smokiness. Bei Gang Mao Jian from Yueyang is cleaner, with some sweetness. Both have classic yellow tea pale-orange liquors.

HUNAN

Hunan province is one of the most happening places in China's tea industry, full of innovative, quality-minded tea businesses. The area under tea is expanding rapidly and crop has more than doubled within a decade. The stock in trade here is honest but fine-quality green and black teas, frequently from the abundant organic producers. What marks Hunan out in particular, though, are the old-school artisans crafting that most subtle of teas: the yellow tea.

JUN SHAN YIN ZHEN/JUN SHAN SILVER NEEDLE

The most elevated of Hunan (and China's) yellow teas, Jun Shan Yin Zhen is produced in accordance with a time-honoured tradition and strictly-speaking only from Jun Shan island, a tiny triangle of land in lake Dongting. Seven to ten days before the Qing Ming festival, teams of skilled pluckers will be sent out to find only the buds of the tea bush. The many

Terraces around Ningxiang.

Qian Liang tea seasoning outdoors.

thousands of buds needed for a viable lot of tea require massive plucking resources, and the inputs are such that prices are out of reach for most.

Most of these buds will be processed in the yellow tea tradition – there is also a small volume processed as green tea, but this is less unique. Emphasis is placed on minimal disruption, hence no kneading or rolling. Best made in a glass (or a glass teapot), it is a joy to witness the buds as they dance around the vessel before steadily standing to attention for the drinker. Inevitably this gives a lighter character, but with a seductive, sweet aroma and orange-tinged liquor, with a surprisingly rich length of flavour for a tea that is exclusively processed from the bud.

Binding Qian Liang.

These are dark, compressed teas, typically hailing from Anhua county towards the centre of Hunan. What makes Hunanese dark tea special is a tendency to burn the abundant local pine wood as a heat source towards the start of the process, which endows the finished product with a distinct strength of smoky flavour. Bai Shi Xi is a traditional-style brick tea, although processed more like a Shaanxi Fu tea than a Pu Erh, and with that smoky character balancing the earthiness.

Qian Liang is a shape apart, more like a long pole or tree trunk than a tea, and deriving its name from its weight. *Qian* means a thousand whilst *liang* is a unit of weight equivalent to 50 grams. Until weights and measures were reconstituted in 1959, the old liang weighed 37g, so while a traditionally authentic Qian Liang should weigh 37 kilogrammes, the style is much more important than the weight.

It is traditional for this tea to be processed first with a *sha qing* step to deactivate the enzymes, before it follows a dark-tea style ageing that concludes with the leaf being compressed into a traditional log shape for maturation and transit. These logs, wrapped in bamboo and readied for dispatch, are familiar sights in parts of the county. The log should be matured for a number of years before it can really be regarded as *à point*, whereupon it is cut or sawn into disc or cube shapes before sale.

The character is a classic earthy-nutty dark-tea style; the liquors should have a tawny brown colour. Anything darker would suggest overly accelerated manufacture or improper storage.

GUIZHOU

Guizhou is a classic Chinese tea-cultivating province of rugged limestone hills and fertile valleys. It is a crossroads province, marking the point where Han Chinese start to give way to greater local ethnicities, and there is a rich local minority culture here as a result.

Ample rainfall and lack of competition with other forms of land use have ensured that Guizhou's tea areas have expanded rapidly over the last decade.

Local dress in Guizhou.

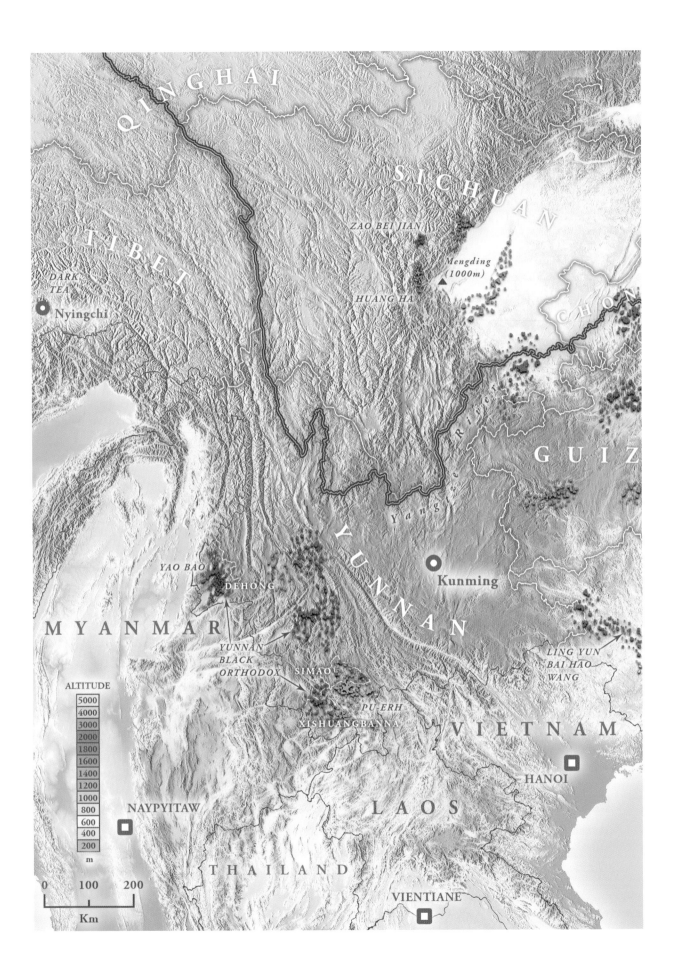

QINGHAI

SICHUAN

TIBET

ZAO BEI JIAN

Mengding
(1000m) ▲

HUANG HA

C H O N

*DARK
TEA*

◎ Nyingchi

Yangtse River

G U I Z

Y U N N A N

◎
Kunming

YAO BAO

DEHONG

M Y A N M A R

*YUNNAN
BLACK
ORTHODOX*

*LING YUN
BAI HAO
WANG*

ALTITUDE

| 5000 |
| 4000 |
| 3000 |
| 2000 |
| 1800 |
| 1600 |
| 1400 |
| 1200 |
| 1000 |
| 800 |
| 600 |
| 400 |
| 200 |

m

SIMAO

PU-ERH

XISHUANGBANNA

V I E T N A M

◻
HANOI

NAYPYITAW

◻

L A O S

0   100   200

Km

T H A I L A N D

VIENTIANE
◻

JUN
SHAN
YIN
ZHEN

LUSHAN
YUN WU

*Lu Shan
(1474m)*

BEI GANG
MAO JIAN

*Dongting
Hu*

*Poyang
Hu*

Changsha

WUYISHAN

BAI HAO
YINZHEN
& BAI MU
TAN

MEIJIANG
CUIPAN

BAI SHI XI
& QUIAN
LIANG

WEI SHAN
MAO JIAN

LAPSANG
SOUCHONG
& DA HONG
PAO

FUDING

DUYIAN MAOJIAN
OR YUGOU

Ningde

FUZHOU

Fuzhou

Quinnan

JIN XUAN
TIEGUANYIN
& OTHER
OOLONGS

ANXI

JASMINE

Quanzhou

JASMINE

Guangzhou

Nanning

GULAO

Hong
Kong

South China

Sea

GREEN
TEA

HAINAN

	GREEN TEA
	BLACK TEA
	OOLONG
	PU-ERH
	SCENTED TEA
	WHITE TEA

Having expanded by an estimated 300% over the past decade, Guizhou's tea scene is undergoing a boom. Its traditional mainstay has been green tea, but the planting of cultivars suitable for black tea is now accelerating growth here as well.

DUYUN MAOJIAN GREEN TEA/YUGOU

Maojian is Guizhou's best-known tea, with the premier produce usually emanating from Duyun county, which sits towards the south of the province. The basic style is much like its Hunan namesake – one leaf and a bud yielding that classic downy leaf. The Duyun advocates claim a characteristic yellow tinge to the liquors, with local partisanship insisting their version is both sweeter and more aromatic than Xingjang's version. Occasionally one sees the tea labelled as Yugou (meaning *fish hook*), a fine descriptor of the shape and make of the distinctive leaf.

MEIJIANG CUIPAN

This is arguably the most distinctive of Guizhou's remaining teas. It hails from the county of Meitan in the north of the province, which is the most significant of the Guizhou tea counties. These tea areas close to the river Mei are unusual for China and more akin to the great Indian and African estates. Large expanses of contiguous tea help to define the contours, here planted in rows rather than as a plucking table.

The leaf is plucked and then left to shade-dry for up to five hours. This period, whilst not as extreme as the oolong solar withering process, nonetheless helps to engender a little oxidation and injects an enhanced strength, fullness in body, and deeper colour to the leaf.

FUJIAN

Fujian province is not only China's largest producing province, boasting a vast annual crop not far short of that of Sri Lanka, it is also the home of some of China's greatest teas – the teas we are most

The Meitan tea gardens.

likely to see outside of China. Perhaps because it is a maritime province with a long trading history, Fujian has always looked out more than some of its neighbours. Perhaps it is because its climate and plant material are so suited to white tea and oolong, popular export types. Or perhaps the large Fujianese diaspora has unconsciously promoted it native produce. Either way, Fujian makes some beautiful teas and is a must-visit province, especially in spring.

To understand what it is that makes Fujian special you need to travel to the counties around Fuding and look hard at some of its tea bushes, and particularly at the youngest leaves and buds. There, in springtime in particular, you will see the *Da Bai* variety at its most characteristic: young leaves and buds bedecked in fine, downy hairs, giving the bush a beautifully smooth handle and bestowing the tea that it produces with a price tag to rival anything else in the world. It is this bush: *Da Bai* or *Big White*, and those distinctive tiny hairs, that give the tea a silvery white appearance and help to secure a place for the resultant 'white' tea within the list of China's famous teas.

BAI HAO YINZHEN, SILVER NEEDLE, PAI MU TAN (OR BAI MU DAN), SHOU MEI, SOW MEE AND OTHER WHITE TEAS

White tea is a product that sells itself. It has such an iconic name, story and visual appearance that you cannot help but be conscious of its sense of uniqueness. Its provenance is usually from the *Da Bai* (or Big White) bush variety, which, when examined closely, is every bit as downy as its name would suggest. The silky-smooth needles of the top-grade Bai Hao Yinzhen don't even look like a

Different qualities of white tea on sale in a Fujian tea market.

tea, the downy coating being more reminiscent of willow catkins. The aromas shed by the dry leaf are themselves an enticement; so intense and seductive in their pungency that you are immediately conscious that some serious work has gone into its creation.

The brew is delicate in the extreme: pale yellow, mild, light-bodied, but certainly not toasty or vegetal in the direction of a green tea. Aromas are subtle and the leaf is quicker than any other type of tea in betraying any influences it may have had in the factory, whether from smoke or over-firing. The taste is mild – how could it be other, given the minimal intervention in the factory?

Stepping down a grade brings Pai Mu Tan, a mixture of bud and uppermost two leaves, but with the characteristic hairs still adorning the leaf. Pai Mu Tan has a little more astringency and concentration of flavour than the Bai Hao, but still with most of the mildness and aroma of a good white tea. It is always priced more attractively than Bai Hao Yinzhen, but some regard it as the better tea, its greater intensity outweighing the visual attractiveness of the otherwise mild silver tips.

The lowest grade of white tea is Sow Mee or Shou Mei, usually both coarser in leaf quality and produced later in the season than its more noble brothers, both factors helping to create teas that are darker in colour, fuller in body and stronger in flavour than finer white teas. It is often seen as a base for white teabags, as well as for flavouring.

Plucking underway in Fujian. These bushes near to Fuding can produce the finest white tea.

FUJIANESE JASMINE

Although most jasmine tea is now made in Guangxi province, it is Fuzhou city in Fujian that was historically regarded as the source of the best jasmine-scented teas. Some merchants continue to insist that the teas are scented there, and regard the Fujianese jasmine blossoms as more elegant in scent than their Guangxi rivals, although using superior Fujian green tea as a base may also play its part.

FUJIANESE OOLONG

It is no accident that the two greatest oolong-producing areas in the world are Fujian and Taiwan. They face each other across the South China Sea, and a number of Fujianese émigrés and exiles have subsequently powered Taiwan's tea industry. Fujian can produce oolongs that are the equal of almost anything in Taiwan, particularly lightly oxidised teas. Dong Tings, Pouchongs and Jin Xuan teas are produced in abundance, most especially in areas around Anxi, which is the home to another of China's great teas.

TIEGUANYIN/TI KUAN YIN/IRON GODDESS OF MERCY

Tieguanyin derives its name from Guanyin, the Goddess of Mercy who, in one of the legends surrounding the tea, is held to have directed a local farmer towards a tea shoot that, when planted out, yielded teas of unparalleled flavour. Tieguanyin is the original of the great oolong teas. Produced in both a floral jade style and a more baked style, it does everything expected of a great oolong endorsed by a goddess.

Anxi county can most credibly lay claim to be the home of Tieguanyin. Almost on the coast, but with a more rugged interior, it provides a fine, mild maritime climate ideal for oolong manufacture. The teas are produced along similar lines to their Taiwanese cousins; no surprise as it is predominantly Fujianese exiles who have made the Taiwanese industry what it is.

Be careful what you buy and have in mind that whilst a jade oolong can be suffused with floral orchid and blossom notes, the baking process also practised on Tieguanyin can give an entirely different, more toasty note to the finished product. The toasty oolongs are no less pleasant (and are arguably the more traditional style), but they are less immediately accessible, meaning one should attempt the jade oolong first and then progress to the more toasty styles.

WU YI SHAN DA HONG PAO/BIG RED ROBE/WU YI ROCK TEA

The Wu Yi mountains of Northern Fujian are home to a couple of China's greatest teas. Whilst Lapsang Souchong may be better known outside of China, it is Da Hong Pao that claims the domestic honours, where its extreme rarity, elevated customer base and astronomic pricing have created China's most coveted tea. Da Hong Pao in its truly authentic and genuine form can come from only three ancient tea bushes that sit squeezed onto the vertiginous Jiu Long cliff face.

These bushes were propagated a number of years ago and it is now possible to buy a Da Hong Pao from identical plant material, if not identical terroir. The original is out of reach for all bar the most elevated of foreign statesmen. Less vertiginous corners of the Wu Yi mountains have been planted out with Da Hong Pao plant material, the output now being substantial enough to place such teas within the reach of most mortals.

The processing is typical for more fully oxidised oolong manufacture, which leaves the leaf more blackish than green in colour. The characteristic taste is sometimes known as 'minerally', but suffused with layers of chocolate and caramel with a richness seldom seen in such teas. Many put the mineral character down to the rocks themselves, but as most publicly available tea hails from a more benign environment it seems more likely that the strain of bush itself is responsible.

LAPSANG SOUCHONG/ZENGSHAN XIAOZHONG/TARRY SOUCHONG

The Lapsang legend dates back to the Taipei Rebellion in the mid-19th century. Rebel forces were billeted amongst the tea-growers of a village called Xingchun[6] at a critical time of year for the tea crop. The rebels had been camping in the local tea factory, thereby interfering with the delicate process of tea manufacture. With the critical date looming by when the tea needed to be dispatched to market, and with sacks of yet-to-be-manufactured green leaf in danger of spoiling, the peasants speeded up the drying process with the use of pinewood fires. Finding the tarry, smoke-laced tea remarkably palatable, they found an enthusiastic market in the form of European traders, especially the Dutch.

Today the home of Lapsang remains those same Wu Yi mountains, which form Fujian's north-western border with Jiangxi province. Spectacular gorges and towering volcanic domes define a landscape that plays host to an annual throng of tourists with a love of the outdoors. Those same tourists are unlikely to leave without at some stage finding themselves exposed to the distinctive smoky speciality.

The hills of northern Fujian.

Top-quality Lapsang, the bohea grade for example, is a class apart from the cheaper interpretations of the style. The best Lapsang tea is withered in lofts that have been gently heated by pinewood fires. The wood, from which the bark has been stripped, burns to emit a delightfully aromatic smoke. The tea is then packed into baskets for a maturing phase that aims to develop some of the stronger aromas within the tea. Following this maturing stage, which can last a number of hours, it would typically be roasted again and laid out on mats for up to twelve hours within a smoking shed to be exposed to the smoke from green pinewood fires. The duration of exposure and volume of smoke (dictated by its height within the shed) regulate the relative tarriness of the tea when tasted. A final roasting is sufficient to stabilise the tea and seal in the distinctive character.

Lower grades of Lapsang will skip the more complex processing and maturing phases and start off with a conventional orthodox black tea as the base. Real Lapsang lovers find that such teas lack some of the complexity of the traditional method, and it is these teas that will make their way into the cheaper blends. Increasingly, modern Lapsangs are being overexposed in the smoking sheds, thereby losing the subtlety of the earlier interpretations of the style.

Lapsang is about the balance between the inherent character and body of the tea, and the influence of the pine smoke which helps it to marry very well with a number of foods, smoked salmon being an especially successful foil. More doesn't have to be better – a well-balanced Lapsang is a joy: the steamy brew carrying the fuggy notes of a bothy peat fire, whilst the liquor merits comparisons with Islay whisky: smoky, iodine, laced with character and distinctiveness.

GUANGXI PROVINCE

Guangxi is one of China's most striking provinces. Northern Guangxi's characteristic thimble-shaped karst limestone mountains form a spectacular backdrop to many tea gardens, and the more southerly location ensures a luxuriant flora surrounding the tea, with a preponderance of rice paddies where soil, terrain and water supply permit.

JASMINE TEA

Guangxi's primary claim to fame is as the home of jasmine tea, another of the ten famous teas of China. Indeed, for many reluctant tea-drinkers, its status as the tea of choice in many Chinese restaurants ensures that jasmine is the only tea they will ever drink.

The interesting thing about Guangxi is that it is not especially renowned as a green tea-producing province. It lies further south, and therefore relative to its more illustrious northerly neighbours, Fujian, Anhui and Zhejiang, it enjoys a longer season and with less extremes of temperature: good for crop, but less positive for quality as it is precisely these bush-threatening extremes that stress the plant to the point that it is producing potentially great leaf. What Guangxi can do well, though, is grow flowers, and it is this strength that makes it unrivalled as a jasmine producer of scale and substance.

Tea's great defining character (just ask any coffee experts) is that it is built on subtlety, nuances of flavour, variety and variations of aroma, but it is also this feature that proves its downfall when it is so sensitive and willing to assume other, stronger flavours such as the spices, smoke, fruit or herbs that are sometimes stored or shipped alongside. Here in Guangxi, however, this is the making of the tea.

Guangxi's tea terraces are the produce of centuries of labour.

The jasmine harvest (that typically takes place during May) is a scene of frenzied activity as it is during the brief window, measured in hours, before the jasmine blooms that the buds must be picked in order that they flower whilst in contact with the green tea that will be more intensely scented as a result. A period overnight amongst the sweet aromas of the jasmine blossoms transforms the local

Overnight scenting with jasmine, near Nanning in Guangxi.

perfectly serviceable but relatively ordinary tea into a majestic swoosh of sweet floral aroma. The harshness of the green tea is gone, but the astringency remains, now complemented by the sweet, floral aromas of the jasmine.

The blooms are sieved out the next morning (proper jasmine tea should look just like any other green tea, with no evidence of the flowers that have lent their scent to the tea). The addition of the blooms can smooth out even the harshest of green teas, and Guangxi has a few, and it is for this reason that Guangxi green tea and its flowers are so perfectly matched.

If you have eaten in Guangxi then you will appreciate the way the oily local cuisine can be brilliantly cut through by the jasmine tea in a fashion that few other teas can quite manage. Chinese restaurateurs around the world have noted this, and it is for this reason that we see jasmine tea almost universally served.

Guangxi has so much more to offer than just jasmine. The preponderance of other flower types, most notably chrysanthemum and the later-blooming osmanthus, represent a whopping opportunity for the tea producer. Both sweeter and more dominant flavours than jasmine, they are less obviously a complement to the camellia family (that itself has a jasmine-like aroma), yet they have their place. The intense syrupiness of both makes them fine after-dinner or pudding teas, and even served earlier they can be successful when combined with a sufficiently oily dish.

In Guangxi, jasmine is the winner though – even James Bond is claimed as a convert, which seems improbable for a character who was known more for his love of stronger beverages, but perhaps this is jasmine's great strength. I have always thought that oolong was the last hope of tea sceptics, but perhaps jasmine is the key: so sweet and accessible, so good with food, and difficult to dislike.

BAI HAO WANG/WHITE DOWNY

Guangxi is not just about scented teas, though; there are some fine white and green teas produced here as well. The county of Ling Yun, close to the Vietnamese border, is especially known for its white downy teas. They are typically produced in springtime when the buds and younger leaves are bedecked in the fine white down also seen in Fujian. White downy or Bai Hao Wang is a classic silver needle-type tea with mild liquor and a beautiful soft handle to the leaf. Varying quality gradations exist, some authentic, others triumphs of marketing over substance, and there remains some contention as to whether it should be classified as green or white, but a good one is a worthwhile purchase as it will typically command a lower premium than Fujianese white tea, but can be almost indistinguishable in style.

GUANGDONG PROVINCE

Guangdong is hot, often misty and not especially mountainous. This low-grown humid environment does not give rise to many memorable teas, whether black or green. Most lack subtlety and are often more workmanlike than their higher-grown rivals from elsewhere. One tea that is worth exploration though is Gulao.

GULAO/KOOLOO

Meaning *very old*, Gulao is the town around which tea of the same name is grown and produced in a flat area of land bordered by more mountainous topography. Here the rich soils yield relatively full-bodied and unexceptional green tea of modest quality; this tea, however, is then roasted in a large drum at around 300°C.[7] Local custom decrees ten revolutions of said roasting drum, although I have tasted Gulaos that taste as if they have been left in over the weekend. This process makes for a brownish-red colour, and imparts a distinctive toasted character.

In past times this baked note is said to have been most effective at masking the brackish taste of billabong water in Australia, and hence it continues to be a small but vital inclusion in authentic Billy Tea blends. Kooloos come with many different levels of roast and can vary widely in taste – if sampling one for the first time I would endorse something towards the milder end of the scale, as anything more toasty can be a little too hardcore for the Western palate.

HAINAN

Hainan has little in the way of tea-making reputation, being blessed with a climate orientated more around the tourist than the tea-maker. Hainan *Dao* (*dao* meaning 'island') has become a holidaymaker's playground since large-scale investment was made in its resorts. Benefiting from a less severe prevalence of pests due to the formidable barrier of the sea, and well suited to spice and fruit cultivation, the enterprising Hainanese have nonetheless found space for tea in the hills towards the interior of the island. However, Hainan's tourist blessing is also its tea-makers' curse. Hot summers ensure that the teas produced here lack some of the subtlety and finesse of the fine green teas produced on mainland China. The faster growth and more intense sunlight, with none of the mists sometimes seen in China's mountainous interior, lead to robust and sturdy teas of a more workmanlike character. Spring is still the time of year to buy, and as with almost any Chinese producer there are skilled producers making some very fine teas, but these almost always struggle to compete with the more rounded versions produced away from Hainan's shores.

SICHUAN

Sichuan has a resonance as a province that some of its neighbours lack. The fine, spicy cuisine has made a name for itself way outside China's borders, its mountains, canyons and giant pandas have

A Hainanese smallholder.

drawn tourists from far and wide, whilst global productions of Bertolt Brecht's *The Good Person of Szechwan* publicise the province to the more culturally inclined.

Sichuan's geography is defined by a fertile eastern plain and a more mountainous area in the west. It is these misty western mountains that provide the province's finest teas.

HUANG YA OR YELLOW BUD

Probably Sichuan's best-known tea, and for good reason. Mengding is effectively the first mountain one encounters upon entering the Sichuanese mountains from the plains. Good Mengding leaf typically tends to be drawn from the mid-elevations up to around 1,000 metres (3,280 feet) where mists (or *meng*) gather to provide optimal conditions. The mountains (there are actually five distinct peaks to Mengding) yield their best teas in the early spring, and it is the finely plucked buds that are so renowned. These will be processed in the yellow tea tradition into a sweetish tea that at its best has a cut-grass aroma to balance the sweetness.

ZAO BEI JIAN

Zao Bei Jian is a congou-style black tea that is arguably black tea's Pai Mu Dan to Golden Monkey's Bai Hao Yinzhen. It can come from across the producing areas of western Sichuan, including Mengding. Plucking is usually two leaves and a bud, which is fine enough to guarantee a modicum of tip but also

Beautifully manicured tea gardens in Sichuan.

Sichuan mists viewed from the mountains.

ensure a little extra intensity brought by the additional leaf. Well-processed Zao Bei Jian should have a sprinkling of golden tip and a fine twist to the black tea. The character of the liquor is malty, occasionally with a chocolatey note.

PANDA TEA

Marketing gimmick or genuine advancement in tea cultivation? The most recent arrival onto the Sichuanese tea scene is panda tea, which takes its name from the origin of the dung used to fertilise the tea bushes.

The theory behind the initiative is that in only absorbing 30% of its food intake, the panda's inherently poor digestive system endows it with especially nutritious poo, although this is open to challenge as bamboo is hardly the most fertile of start points.

The tea is processed either as a green tea or as a black tea and sold at appropriately exclusive prices.

YUNNAN

Yunnan is where China meets India, not just in blunt geographical terms, but also in the genetics and style of its teas. It feels different here; the heady altitude of Kunming notwithstanding, it is the mountains that divide Yunnan (*–nan* meaning 'south') from Sichuan and thence the rest of China that create a sense of otherness, and the clouds (or *Yu*) that sit atop the peaks that give it its name. James Hilton's mythical paradise of Shangri-La is believed to have been based upon a Yunnanese valley, and visits to the more remote parts of the province confirm that there remain the charmingly untouched idylls that Hilton would still recognise.

The bushes here are predominantly of the broad-leafed *assamica* type, which is native to the jungle borderlands between India, Myanmar and China. CTC, seldom seen elsewhere in China, is common here, and despite the much higher altitude, the style is towards thick-liquoring black teas more in the Assam fashion than anything else in China.

Yunnan can boast a unique tea heritage, and there is no better way of uncovering this than a visit to the tea quarter of Kunming. Formerly rather more architecturally charming than the modern low-rise development of tea merchants that remains today, the beauty is nevertheless on the inside. The local style is immediately evident in the store layout; beautifully wrapped and stacked cakes of tea adorn the shelves, and great baskets of intricately handmade variations on the local Pu Erh tea compete for attention.

PU ERH

Pu Erh is one of China's real tea curiosities, and recently subject to more column inches in the West than the other nine of the famous teas put together. Legend suggests that in a long-removed dynasty, the Beijing-based emperor had ordered a consignment of tea from the other end of his empire in Yunnan. The tea was duly produced and loaded onto a caravan bound for Beijing. The journey, around 1,700 miles (2,700 kilometres), crosses cool mountains and hot tropical plains. The teas, strapped to the flanks of horse and camel, were exposed to vast temperature variations and the daily process of warming and cooling as the pack animals laboured along the route. Upon arrival those charged with the custody of the cargo noted that the tea had changed over the course of the journey. Formerly perfectly acceptable and full-bodied green tea, it had ripened to develop secondary flavours and notes of what the Chinese now call *Chen Xiang*, best translated as *old fragrance*. The emperor took great pleasure in the resultant tea, in particular its properties as a digestive, and a legend was born.

Today the process for most of the Pu Erh sold continues along more industrial lines, but no less splendid is the tea. The cultivation areas regarded as best for the supply of top-quality Pu Erh are around the so-called six great tea mountains in the prefecture of Xishuangbanna in southern Yunnan, bordering both Myanmar and Laos (although, in practice, tracing where green leaf has come from is nigh on impossible). Lancang county in Simao district, for example, just north of Xishuangbanna, produces excellent Pu Erh tea despite its ostensibly less noble terroir.

> ### THE HUMP: LINKING ASSAM AND YUNNAN
>
> Kunming, the capital of Yunnan province, was one of the most significant cities in the story of the Asian theatre of operations during WW2.
>
> When Burma was overrun by the Japanese in 1942, efforts to supply the Chinese armies switched to an incredibly dangerous 800-kilometre (500-mile) airlift over the Eastern Himalayas, known to pilots as 'the Hump'.
>
> Airfields on or close to tea gardens in Assam at Dinjan, Chabua, Mohanbari, Jorhat, Dibrugarh and Sookerating kept up a constant supply of equipment to Kunming.

It is now accepted that there are two methods of processing Pu Erh tea: the more traditional *Sheng* method and the modern, accelerated *Shou* method. *Sheng* will always offer the best chance of a good tea, but it is also vastly more laborious to produce and considerably longer in the realisation of financial reward owing to the need for an extensive ageing period.

Shou is more financially accessible, but there are good and bad producers of *Shou* tea and those doing it well can achieve wonderful woody-earthy aromas, with pungent notes of truffle on the better teas. Too often one encounters teas with a fishy character. The poorest teas at the budget end of the market recall a wet dog emerging from a fenland drain having rolled in a long-decayed pike.

Sheng Pu Erh is notable for the complexity it acquires over the course of its ageing process. It is because of this that Pu Erh has become phenomenally collectable. Packaged into easily stored cakes

Xishuangbanna, site of the six great tea mountains.

with a wrapping that (theoretically) displays the vintage and the producer, it is the classed-growth Bordeaux of the tea world. Eye-watering bubbles have developed – initially in 2007 and then again in 2014 – as keen collectors and merchants have bought and sold the product to fund school fees and private wealth, just as wine merchants do with Bordeaux. To do this successfully you really have to know what you are doing, have bought well, and have phenomenal faith in your view of the market, as with any bubble there are substantially more speculators who have lost money than have made it.

It is best to find a small parcel and explore your compatibility with the product. Start with appreciating the packaging. Pu Erh is still largely a sector undiscovered by the brand consultant, and it is a joy to see that naïve early Communist-era packaging is still predominant. Imagine proposing *The China National Native Animal By-products Import and Export Corporation* as a viable branding option to a local retailer. First force yourself to open it at the back (many Pu Erh enthusiasts spend almost as much time admiring Pu Erh cakes as wall or shelf adornments as they do in the consumption). Then use a sharp knife to carefully chisel away a small volume of tea. Brew the tea *gōngfu*-style and remember that if you have been brought up with Western tastes and the mindset that good tea is brisk and bright, with good length of flavour coupled with a clean finish, then the chances are you will hate Pu Erh unless you can remain a little open-minded. The best Pu Erhs will feature a honeyed fruitiness, whilst those produced in a more accelerated fashion will feature earthy farmyard notes to the fore, sometimes accompanied by smoky, tarry characters.

*Yunnan is where China meets its southern neighbours. Here the topography
and teas start to bear resemblances to Myanmar, Laos and Vietnam.*

Pu Erh consumption even in mainland China has only really accelerated in the last fifteen years. Formerly consumed only in Hong Kong and South East Asia, Pu Erh has now found a place both in the Chinese diet, but also in the glossier Western press in recent years thanks to a number of celebrities who have endorsed it as a slimming tea. Certainly those versed in the Chinese medical tradition have long insisted that it reduces blood fat, and it is very often served after meals in restaurants in Hong Kong. I would sound a cautionary tone, however, that my two most corpulent Chinese friends are both Pu Erh dealers, and as such the usual rules about following a balanced diet apply.

YUNNAN BLACK ORTHODOX

As well as being home to decent CTC, Yunnan also produces some fine-quality orthodox black tea. A little like Assam, yet much higher-grown and hence with a more aromatic style, the teas are tippy, medium-bodied and with a fragrance that those with long memories have likened to the aroma of old-style artisanal Harris Tweed. It makes for a fine afternoon tea and is not bad as a base for spices and flavours such as vanilla and cinnamon. However, that aroma is as divisive as a jar of Marmite®, especially for tea-drinkers used to Assam teas and therefore expecting a malty character, but instead being overwhelmed with a rush of top-note aromas. Try it with an open mind.

GOLDEN MONKEY

A high-grade premium black tea counterpart to Bai Hao Yinzhen, Golden Monkey is arguably the finest expression of Chinese black tea manufacture, at least in terms of leaf appearance. It can be found either in Fujian or Yunnan provinces; the comparison with Bai Hao Yinzhen is no accident as both are products of the downy-leafed Da Bai bush.

The plucking for the very best teas will collect one leaf and a bud at the very coarsest, with many quality-focused producers electing to focus purely on the bud. It follows a traditional black tea manufacture process in very small and exclusive batches. Although usually very gently rolled by machine with immense care, it is not uncommon to see hand-rolling being employed, especially for the early crop.

One and a bud is no real compromise and can give a little more welcome intensity compared to the golden buds. The infusion will realise a pungent floral note, sometimes likened to roses, and the taste, whilst mild and generally lacking in astringency, tends to have a chocolatey character.

YAO BAO/WILD WHITE TEA

Yao Bao is the best example of the delightful variety that the world of tea has to offer. Growing only around the corner from the valleys that produce Pu Erh comes its antithesis: Yao Bao. Yao Bao doesn't even really look like tea. The unopened buds of a wild tea strain called Ye Sheng found in Dehong on the Yunnanese border with Myanmar, Yao Bao white tea is typically produced in March as the bush starts to flush in the intense sunlight characteristic of these hills. Looking more like the infant bud of a beech tree than anything from the tea world, these are genuinely unique teas. It doesn't stop at the appearance either; the taste is a singular pine and citrus combination that develops as you progress through multiple brews. As exclusive (and fearsomely expensive) as you should expect of a rare wild white tea.

TIBET AUTONOMOUS REGION

Tibet is little known as a tea producer, and indeed it hardly reaches the bar for inclusion as such. The extreme terrain tends to limit the availability of suitable land, whilst the 3,000-metre (9,800-feet) altitude, cold winters and relative lack of rainfall all combine to render the terrain marginal at best. There are some tea producers here, though, who are able to take advantage of the local taste for compressed dark tea, as well as small volumes of green tea for the local and tourist markets. The best-known gardens are located around Nyingchi, which functions as a regional base for exploring the spectacular Tibetan mountainscapes.

Nyingchi may only be around 250 kilometres (400 miles) north of Assam's tea heartland in

Dibrugarh, but the teas are a world away in style. The growing season is exceedingly short and permits only one flush of significance, which tends to supply both the local tourist trade with green tea, as well as some small-scale dark tea production for Tibetan-style preparation. The green tea is almost unseen outside of China, but the few samples seen of a pan-fried variant suggest that the altitude and stress of the extended dormancy period has endowed it with intense aromas and fine length of flavour.

Tibet's tea production is limited. These are smallholdings close to Nyingchi.

CHINA
at a glance

Plants
Camellia Sinensis var. sinensis, some assamica in Yunnan, Sichuan and Guangxi Numerous regional cultivars and varietals Long Jing #43 Tie Guan Yin Zhu Ye-(Keemun Quality)

Terroir
Variety of soils from red clays in Yunnan and Anhui, yellow loams in Fujian to brown alluvial soils in Zhejiang

Quality Season
Early spring crop

Harvesting
Manual, shear and machine. Yield 794 kg made tea per hectare

Processing
70% green tea, 15% black tea, balance oolong, dark tea, white tea and yellow tea

Drinking
Ideally all good Chinese teas should be consumed gōngfu-style

TAIWAN

A wealth of quality oolong emerges from the island that has become synonymous with the style.

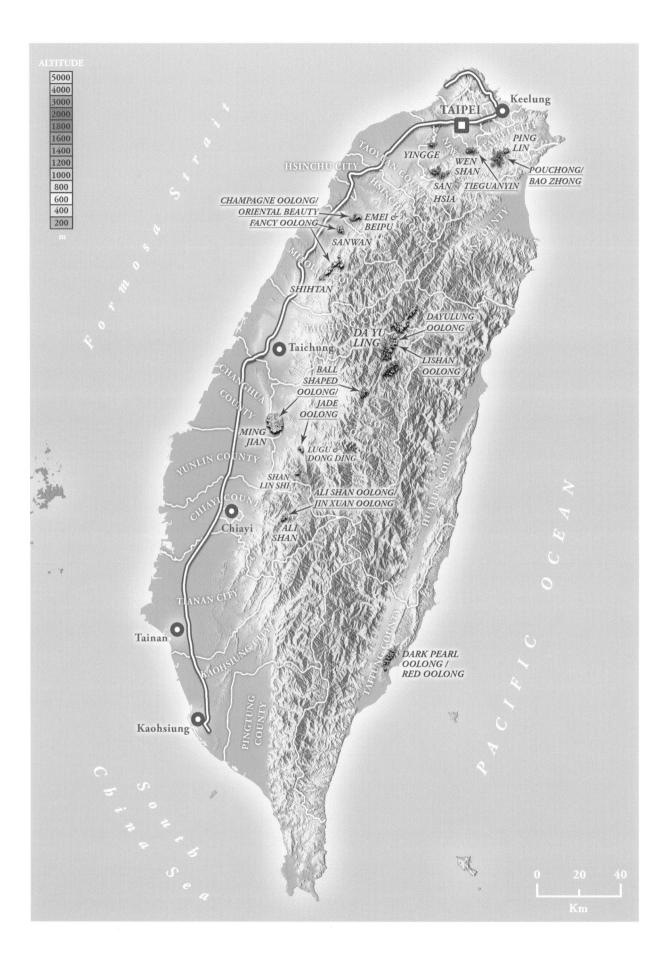

ALTITUDE

5000
4000
3000
2000
1800
1600
1400
1200
1000
800
600
400
200
m

Formosa Strait

South China Sea

PACIFIC OCEAN

TAIPEI

Keelung

HSINCHU CITY

TAOYUAN COUNTY

YINGGE

WEN SHAN

SAN HSIA

TIEGUANYIN

PING LIN

POUCHONG/ BAO ZHONG

CHAMPAGNE OOLONG/ ORIENTAL BEAUTY FANCY OOLONG

EMEI & BEIPU

SANWAN

SHIHTAN

MIAOLI COUNTY

Taichung

TAICHUNG

DA YU LING

DAYULUNG OOLONG

LISHAN OOLONG

BALL SHAPED OOLONG/ JADE OOLONG

CHANGHUA COUNTY

MING JIAN

LUGU & DONG DING

YUNLIN COUNTY

SHAN LIN SHI

ALI SHAN OOLONG/ JIN XUAN OOLONG

CHIAYI COUNTY

Chiayi

ALI SHAN

HUALIEN COUNTY

TAINAN CITY

Tainan

KAOHSIUNG CITY

DARK PEARL OOLONG / RED OOLONG

TAITUNG COUNTY

PINGTUNG COUNTY

Kaohsiung

0   20   40

Km

PORTUGUESE SAILORS FIRST LOGGED the mountainous island as *Ilha Formosa* or 'beautiful island' as they sailed by in 1544. If natural history has blessed the land with abundant charms, then political history has been less beneficent. The jaw-droppingly scenic island lying twixt the East and South China seas has become accustomed to finding itself at the centre of disputes between more powerful neighbours coveting its enviable location.

BACKGROUND

Tea has been cultivated on the island for centuries. Its geographical location just across the Taiwan straits from mainland China has ensured that it has inherited many cultural and commercial influences from the coastal provinces of the mainland just over 160 kilometres (100 miles) away. The 17th century saw the first appearance of tea, brought over from Fujian with which Taiwan shares so much of its natural history. Cultivated in the north of the island in what is now New Taipei City, the nascent tea industry soon found the conditions ideal for the production of the same style of oolong tea hitherto only produced across the water in Fujian. From 1895, the Japanese occupation saw a further expansion as the counties south and west of Taipei were encouraged to plant tea bushes. The third stage of development occurred post-1980 with legislation permitting individuals to establish factories, and the consequent expansion of the industry eastwards into the interior.

CLIMATE

Taiwan enjoys a maritime climate free from the excesses of heat and cold of some of the Chinese provinces further west (although terrifyingly prone to the typhoons that stalk the East Asian seaboards). The benign maritime weather pattern coupled with the mountainous terrain ensures that whilst there is reliability of rainfall and temperature, there is sufficient variety of aspect and terrain to assure widespread diversity of produce.

THE OOLONG FACTOR

Formosan tea is almost exclusively oolong (also often spelt as *Wulong*). Oolong tea is a world apart from the black teas consumed in the households of the West. The skill and batch-by-batch attention in the factory that is required to craft a good oolong is so far beyond that needed to make good black tea that a comparison can scarcely be made. Flavour, aroma and price mark oolongs out as a breed apart when set alongside their black and green cousins. Although the Fujianese can justifiably lay claim to being the spiritual home of oolong tea manufacture, it is the Taiwanese who have made it their own. Taiwan makes more than 50% of the world's oolong and consumes almost all of what it produces. Good oolong tea can encompass a staggering cornucopia of aromas. One tea can be an aromatic bombshell of lilies and sweet peas, whilst another seems more tropical fruits and peaches. The baked oolongs can taste smooth and caramel-laced, whilst champagne oolong is a Darjeeling-like hit of smoothness, sweetness and zesty fruit. Taiwan has them all, although its limited landmass ensures that they will never be available in great abundance.

OOLONG: THE BASICS

It helps to understand the processes before jumping headfirst into the oolong pool. Oolongs (as with many East Asian products) find themselves saddled with numerous names, all either meaning exactly the same thing but allowing for linguistic or dialect variation, or providing for subtle variations in the final product. Trying to learn all of the subdivisions is more likely to end in confusion than any greater understanding of the product. There are four principal scales along which any oolong sits so far as its manufacture style goes.

OXIDATION

First, and particular to oolong, is the degree of oxidation, which is best expressed as a percentage from lightly oxidised (generally around 10%-15%) to well oxidised at around 70%. The more lightly oxidised teas are generally speaking jade oolongs, whilst more fully oxidised teas are more often champagne oolongs.

BAKING

Second is the degree of baking that the tea has undergone after manufacture. Some teas, such as the jade and champagne oolongs, are manufactured and sold as they are; some however are baked in ovens over an extended period, which allows powerful secondary flavours to develop. These teas can be grouped as amber oolongs on account of their deeper colour in-cup.

LEAF

Open-leafed teas that are lightly oxidised tend not to be called oolong at all, instead being grouped as Pouchongs, whilst those formed into balls tend to fall into the more general oolong subdivision, being either jade or amber.

ELEVATION

There are also various elevations to choose from, whether high mountain oolongs cultivated above 1,000 metres (3,280 feet), such as Li Shan and Ali Shan, and less elevated oolongs such as Tung Ting, grown between 500 and 1,000 metres in height.

CHAMPAGNE OOLONG/ORIENTAL BEAUTY/FANCY OOLONG/BAI HAO OOLONG/PONG HONG/WHITE TIP OOLONG/DONG FANG MEI REN

Champagne oolong represents the pinnacle of what Taiwan has to offer. Produced in the western counties of Hsinchu, Taoyuan and Miaoli in the areas where planting was fostered during the Japanese occupation from 1895–1945, Oriental Beauty is a white-tipped, open-leafed, highly oxidised oolong. Popularised in the West initially through the efforts of British entrepreneur John Dodd, it has a silky sweetness overlaid with a seductive orchid aroma that has to be tasted to be believed.

The producing areas of Miaoli.

The quality season for these teas is during the first half of June, when rising temperatures initiate a flush of tender new growth on the bushes, simultaneously creating ideal conditions for the hatching of the pest population. *Jacobiasca formosana* is a tropical insect also known as the green leafhopper. It looks rather like a small grasshopper, and it flourishes on the sap of the tea bush. As they hatch in their millions, the jassids suck the phloem sap (the plant's sweetish sap) from the leaves and stems, inducing the bush to mobilise forces to defend itself through the generation of compounds known as monoterpene diols and hotrienols.[1] These compounds help to ensure that the orchid-like tastes are developed whilst the removal of sap concentrates the flavours within the leaf.

Oriental Beauty is generally oxidised to around 70%, sufficient to ensure that most of the lighter floral notes have gone, but leaving behind some body and structure. This is Taiwan's answer to early second flush Darjeeling, with a delightful orchid character to rival Darjeeling's muscatel, but with Darjeeling's astringency replaced with a floral, honey-laced sweetness.

Many markets favour the addition of brandy (or the champagne that gives the tea one of its many monikers), insisting that the two flavours complement each other well, but this falls very much into the personal preference camp and brandy in particular can soon overwhelm all but the most robust tea.

POUCHONG/BAO ZHONG/BLUE TEA

Pouchong is ostensibly the least processed tea within the oolong family. A twisted but relatively open leaf, the tea has not undergone formation into balls like the bulk of the oolong family. Pouchongs hail

*Here tea is being plucked in New Taipei City.
It will be processed into a Pouchong.*

primarily from the planting areas of New Taipei City in the first areas to have been planted with tea. Those Pouchongs that have undergone the mildest oxidation (up to about 10%-15% oxidised) have the most overt floral aromas. These teas are intensely feminine, with their scents of lily and sweet pea. Light-bodied and pale in-cup, the teas are all about perfume; special cups are used for tastings that allow the taster to 'nose' the empty vessel and more fully experience the vivid floral fragrance. Because of their relatively open leaf and the fact that their pleasure lies in the volatile flowery bouquet, they are best drunk whilst still in the freshness of their youth and not kept long enough for the aromas to depart, leaving the teas devoid of their raison d'être.

BALL-TYPE OOLONGS

Around 80% of the tea produced in Taiwan fits into the decidedly uninspiring-sounding category of the ball-type oolongs. Let not the innocuous title deceive you: ball oolong is a work of art and an expertly fashioned product almost unparalleled in the world of tea. Watching a skilled team of artisans create ball-type oolong is to witness teamwork and craftsmanship at its finely-tuned best. Although oolong tea is technically a middle ground between green tea and black tea, this is a wholly inadequate representation of the final product's unique characteristics, which draw from some of the finest aspects of the black and green tea fields, building upon them to create something distinctly exceptional.

TEAMWORK AND ARTISANAL SKILL

The key to creating these magnificent teas is a singular manufacture stage which involves the continuous wrapping, shaping and unwrapping of tea in large, medicine ball-sized cloth packages. Cloth-ball shaping, when performed over a number of cycles, gradually crimps the leaf from an open twist into a dense, tightly formed, shotty ball-shaped pellet of tea. The process is astonishingly time-consuming, yet mesmerising to observe as the cloth balls are formed, shaped, unwrapped, heated and then re-formed in a perfectly timed cycle of operations (see p35). Younger and more tender growth on the bush tends to form tighter and smaller balls when processed in the factory (and has a higher concentration of the key chemical constituents that provide the pleasant taste of tea), and not only that, but the tighter the final particle, the better its ability to keep out oxygen and moisture, the twin enemies of tea quality. Buyers therefore look for small-sized, dense and well-formed, shotty balls, relatively free from pieces of stalk. The more such boxes that are ticked, the higher the tea will be valued on the market. Ball oolongs themselves can be crudely subdivided into those that have been left unbaked post-production and those that undergo a secondary baking process.

The spiritual home of the ball oolongs is in the agricultural county of Nantou in the uplands towards the centre of the island. Jade oolong and Tung Ting oolong are both ball-type oolongs.

JADE OOLONG/GREEN OOLONG

The unbaked ball-type teas are grouped as jade oolongs, reflecting the deep greenish hue of the uninfused leaf. Unbaked oolong is all about aroma; the well-fashioned jade oolong is a seductress, all beguiling floral sweetness and feminine charm. The winter and spring seasons are the time to find the best quality, when the mists which shroud the steep-sided hills of Nantou county seem at their most reluctant to disperse, temperatures are at their lowest, growth slows and aroma is at its most potent.

DONG DING/TUNG TING OOLONG

Of the unbaked teas it is Dong Ding that is the most renowned. Legend has it that a Taiwanese returning from Fujian brought with him twelve tea bushes, which he planted around Chi-ling

Tea gardens cling to the slopes of Nantou County.

lake by Dong Ding mountain (the Taiwanese Dong Ding, not to be confused with the Chinese lake of the same name). It is these bushes which are reputed to have provided the plant material for the many gardens that now crowd this area at an elevation of 700 to 800 metres (2,300-2,600 feet). Local experts are especially aware of the importance of the local conditions to the potential tea quality. Morning and late afternoon mists combined with shelter in the form of areca palm and giant bamboo make for the optimum combination of windbreaks and dappled shade. Thirty per cent oxidation gives it a level more complexity than the least oxidised lily-scented teas, yet it still manages to combine a powerful orchid aroma with a smooth, sweet apricot-laced liquor.

HIGH-GROWN TAIWANESE TEAS/GAO SHAN

One may find Taiwanese teas labelled by leaf type (ball oolong), oxidation level (jade oolong) or planting districts (Li or Ali Shan), and it is entirely possible for a tea to fall into all three categories, making the process even more complex. The below two high-elevation areas are worthy of note because they are frequently used in Taiwanese nomenclature.

LI SHAN/DA YU LING

Da Yu Ling and Li Shan should have a light flavour with pungent notes of sweet, sappy aroma. Da Yu Ling is from the higher altitude eastern area of Li Shan, and should be grown above 2,500 metres (8,200 feet), making it the highest-grown of the oolongs available. Li Shan and Da Yu Ling command the greatest price premiums of any Taiwanese oolong. Some experts recognise a fruitier character on Li Shan and a more vegetal note on Da Yu Ling, but this can vary from producer to producer.

ALI SHAN

Further south in Chiayi county is Ali Shan. Ali Shan sits between 1,100 and 2,500 metres and can boast a larger plant area than Li Shan. Teas still demonstrate the same higher-elevation notes but usually in less marked fashion, and with a substantially reduced price tag. The Jin Xuan clone is often seen in Ali Shan (see below).

JIN XUAN AND MILK OOLONG

Note the title to this section: Jin Xuan *and* Milk Oolong – they are not one and the same. Jin Xuan (sometimes also Jin-Shuen or golden lily, and less romantically known to many farmers

High-grown tea in Taiwan's central mountains.

as #27) is a broad-leafed cultivar, specially developed for its appealing, creamy aroma, and although mainly grown at high elevations it is versatile enough to flourish almost anywhere. Jin Xuan performs best in the higher-elevation areas, especially around Ali mountain (Ali Shan). It needs altitude as it is at its best after very cold nights, which maximise notes of floral freshness. When grown well and manufactured carefully, especially with diligence to the firing process, Jin Xuan can yield a joyfully accessible creamy aroma redolent of the flowering lilies that its name hints at. It is attractive, subtle, not exceptionally strong, and becomes progressively milder the more it is brewed. Where the whole category becomes tricky and the waters muddied is when those producers who flavour their Jin Xuan with liquid aroma 'forget' to declare that it has been flavoured. To be absolutely clear, if it tastes unfeasibly milky for an unfeasibly cheap price, then it is certainly flavoured.

Milk oolong is a product that is so sweet and soft, so creamy and accessible that it scarcely seems possible for it to have been the product of a natural process. There are those in the trade who will insist that the sweet-creamy character that the milk oolongs display is naturally derived but they would be wrong: this is certainly a case of 'if it seems too good to be true, then it probably is'. However, you should not assume that just because it has been flavoured you should avoid it; it is just that you should be aware that you are drinking something that is not the exclusive sum product of the bush and the tea-maker. This book does not dwell upon flavoured teas as the potential for flavours is so vast that you can make a tea taste of anything you like; we are interested in how the origin and the local artisanal skills in place give us the tastes we enjoy from the world of tea.

With milk oolongs there is a grey area between expression of character and the addition of flavour that is sometimes capitalised upon by unscrupulous traders. Milk oolong is an extension of the flavour profile of Jin Xuan, a caricature, if you like, and it can be tricky to identify exactly where the good quality Jin Xuan finishes and the flavoured product starts. The best way to identify is to smell the dry leaf before you infuse the tea. If it has a sweet strawberry-candyfloss aroma then it will certainly have been flavoured.

It is for this reason that I write Jin Xuan *and* milk oolong, because most producers labelling their tea as milk oolong have flavoured it, and if they are reputable then they should tell you so. For me the joy is in the unflavoured, naturally occurring floral note of the Jin Xuan, and if you can find a good producer here then stick with them as it is one of the most accessible, alluring teas that the world can produce.

My standard line to those who cannot abide the taste of tea is that they should at least try a Jin Xuan oolong. If they still don't like tea then there is no hope for them.

AMBER OOLONG/RED OOLONG/DARK PEARL OOLONG/BAKED OOLONG

Although there are subtle variations in all of the above styles I group them together as they are stylistically at the opposite end of the scale from the lighter, more floral oolongs.

Developed by Dr Wu Shen-Shuen in Taitung, Dark Pearl oolong starts its life much as an ordinary jade oolong with the same succession of compressions into cloth balls. However, when most jade oolongs would be dried and stored, red oolong's defining characteristic is to be allowed to oxidise at high temperatures within its cloth ball. The best hails from Taitung county on the south-

eastern coast, and boasts beguiling deep caramel-singed fragrance, entirely contrasting with the lighter oolongs, but no less enjoyable.

In the post-manufacture stage it is possible to influence the style of the tea through prolonged baking in ovens that gives the tea a distinctive sweetish, burnt caramel character, a reaction known as the Maillard reaction. The baking process can be tailored to fit whatever the market wants, but typically will be a series of bakings taking place over a number of days. The most immediate effect is the killing of the primary floral aromas, which are replaced by enhanced length, body and a pervading smoothness. These teas are often kept for years, being served on special occasions having been 'cellared' for

A batch of tea that has undergone extended baking. The white substance that is released is almost pure caffeine, one reason why baked teas are so popular as digestives.

forty years or more. There is no trace of bitterness, just a smooth, clean flavour suffused with the toasted notes that betray its processing. The Taiwanese swear by these teas as excellent digestives, and given that the baking removes some of the caffeine they make for especially apposite after-dinner options.

TIEGUANYIN

Produced in the northern areas around New Taipei City, which with their maritime influence are rather similar in terroir to the Fujianese Tieguanyin districts. As with the Anxi product, Taiwanese Tieguanyins can be either greenish in style or tend towards a toastier, fuller-bodied style, with the majority of Taiwanese teas following the toasty route.

AGED TEAS

These teas are well accepted in Taiwan, but still anathema to many of us in the West. The ageing of teas is practised on a number of types, some more successfully than others. The greatest successes inevitably come where the well-developed characteristics of the more oxidised teas are built upon by the complexity and mellowness of age.

The cellaring of such teas is best performed in a terracotta pot that permits the tea within to breathe, whilst still affording it a level of protection from the evils of light and excessive moisture. The goal is to permit the natural enzymes to work in breaking down the polyphenols within the leaf into smaller

Tea gardens in Ali Shan

molecules. This usually also entails the steady reduction in the caffeine level in the leaf, estimated to be up to a 70% reduction over a period of around ten years. This goes to explain why such teas also often find a place in the after-dinner slot. The smooth liquors underscored by the complexity of age marry well with the requirements of a digestif, and as if this weren't enough, then the reduced caffeine acts as a final persuader.

JAPAN
Producer par excellence of steamed green tea in all its forms

ALTITUDE

5000
4000
3000
2000
1800
1600
1400
1200
1000
800
600
400
200

m

SHIZUOKA

KAWANE

Tenryu River

Oi River

OKABE

TENRYU

SHIDA

MORI

SHIMADA

MAKINOHARA

CHUUEN

HAMAMATSU

0   5   10

Km

Mount Fuji
(3776m)

Fuji River

FUJI

FUJI

NUMAZU

NUMAZU

SHIMIZU

SHIZUOKA

S u r u g a

B a y

I z u   P e n i n s u l a

I N JAPAN, THE COSY WORLD of tea and its attendant traditions collide with the culture of fast-paced, cutting-edge technological progress. Nowhere is this paradox clearer than in the contrast between the protocol-laden aesthetics of the tea ceremony, where centuries of tradition have given us tea as high art, and the technological mastery that has produced the tea the hostess will gracefully serve.

BACKGROUND

Tea has been part of the Japanese culture since the 8th century when Emperor Shōmu first had tea served at a special Buddhist ceremony. There is little subsequent mention of tea until the 12th century when Eisai, a Buddhist priest active in China, first brought seeds back with him, probably from the Jingshan mountains near Hangzhou. As in other emerging tea cultures, it was the social elite who enjoyed the delights of the drink, although in Japan Buddhist monks were also fortunate enough to enjoy green tea as a feature of their ceremonies and Zen training. A steadily increasing area under production during the Edo era (1603–1868) and the invention of the sencha steaming method in 1738, which made good tea available at a more accessible price level, ensured that tea-drinking filtered down through the social orders.

TECHNOLOGY

It is in the arena of technology that the Japanese tea gardens stand out. One would hardly expect the Japanese gift for technological brilliance to have passed the tea industry by, and they do not disappoint. A shortage of willing labour and the high costs associated with any form of human intervention in Japan dictate a mechanical involvement in any task that can accommodate a machine. The most evident manifestation of this is in the gardens themselves. The challenge of tea cultivation in northerly climes is mastered via giant fans programmed to disturb the air on frost-prone nights. Switched on automatically when the temperature drops below a trigger point, they prevent the otherwise inevitable ravaging that 'frost burn' can wreak on a vulnerable tea garden by circulating the air and preventing the formation of ice crystals.

When it comes to the harvest, mechanical plucking is the way here. Curved trimming machines akin to giant hedge cutters are the choice for many. These are passed to and fro along the long lines of tea bushes, a steadily filling sack trailing behind as they go. The resultant crop is an art form in itself, topiary by default, with the geometrically shaped semi-circular bushes pleasingly tracing the contours of the landscape. Where finances permit and the tea bushes stand on flatter land, the machine operators can be dispensed with and the trimmers make their way on rails along the rows of bushes.

SHIZUOKA

The province of Shizuoka *is* tea in Japan. With 40% of Japan's tea heralding from the gardens that on a clear day offer a sublime view of Mount Fuji, Shizuoka province is rightfully proud of its tea heritage. Shizuoka lies just south west of Japan's sprawling capital, a medium-sized town with the older industry of tea now becoming eclipsed by its flourishing manufacturers and excellent university. Shizuoka is the spiritual home of sencha, the standard steamed method of tea manufacture in Japan.

YABUKITA

The Japanese have worked hard to identify the ideal strains of bush, with those high in amino acid content and generally low in tannin ideal for steamed green tea manufacture, and if there is a hero in this story it is the Yabukita bush.

The name derives from the area the breeder Mr Sugiyama chose for his field trials in the early 1950s, surrounded by bamboo bushes (*Yabu*) and at the northern edge of the field (*kita*). Yabukita fits the Japanese tea farmer's needs perfectly, and now represents around 80% of the total planting. It is adaptive to different climates and soil types, can produce fine quality, and provided it is harvested in a timely fashion, should make excellent tea.

The cultivar has a distinctive appearance, its young shoots pointed towards the heavens like fingers grasping for the sunlight, a characteristic that also makes it easier to mechanically pluck relative to some less vigorous varieties. A visit to almost any Japanese tea garden today will guarantee you a sight of the bush, but its real home is in Shizuoka, which is around 90% Yabukita.

SENCHA

As ever, quality is made in the field. The optimum sites for tea cultivation are those perched on the south-facing hillsides where there is sufficient sunlight and moisture for growth, but neither so much sun as to scorch and harden the leaf, nor so much rain as to bloat it and dilute the final product. Altitude equals aroma – at least in part. The higher up the slope one's tea bushes lie, the better the theoretical quality that accompanies the slower growth, but one runs the risk of a correspondingly increased danger of frost.

A typical year should yield a farmer four flushes – in April/May, June/July, August and September/October – each taking around two weeks to complete. The most prized of the senchas is made from *shincha* or 'new tea' in the first harvest of the year. Traditionalists regard the official start of the season to be around 2nd or 3rd May (the eighty-eighth day after Shunbun, the day that marks the beginning of spring and falls on 20th or 21st March). Although Japan is as respectful of its traditions and protocols as any nation, a planter who looks at his calendar more than his tea is not a wealthy one, and April plucking can be seen on lower, warmer slopes when the spring has been mild.

Immediately upon plucking, the tea is sent for processing, either at a local co-operative or by the farmer himself (see pp31-32). The farmer must have his tea manufactured as soon as possible, as every second's delay increases the chance of some fermentation taking place, and the consequent dilution of the desired greenish purity of the ideal sencha.

Sencha has an agreeable needle shape and a tactile polished quality brought about by the seemingly endless rolling processes in the factory. Just running your fingers through the beautifully

A quality-minded smallholder brushes his tea bushes to remove water and any spiderwebs prior to plucking.

smooth, flattened shard-shaped leaf is a pleasure in itself. Tasting good sencha tea and appreciating it as the Japanese do is tricky in Western environments. Delicately flavoured sencha teas (and others from the same family) really require soft water if they are to show their true colours. Japanese water is very soft and carries low levels of magnesium and manganese, making it ideal, whilst London, for example, is as poor a place as any in which to taste sencha tea unless a supply of suitable bottled soft water or a mechanical softener can be located. Not only the water, but the accompaniment has an impact. Many Japanese drink their teas with rice crackers, vegetable pickles or sweet chestnuts. Such pairings are effective at cutting through the otherwise umami-vegetal character of the tea, while the two flavours manage to support and complement each other successfully.

FUKAMUSHICHA/FUKAMUSHI SENCHA

The factory has a profound effect upon the quality of what is produced: the longer a tea is steamed, the paler the colour of the leaf but the more intense the colour in-cup. Such teas are sometimes referred to as Fukamushicha. Typically, long steaming breaks up the leaf and detracts from the aroma but delivers a deep green colour and sweetish taste in-cup, whilst shorter steaming has the opposite effect, with much improved aromas but paleish liquors owing to the harder leaves. Whilst aroma is important, sweetness is also much valued by the Japanese so ultimately most final products are a blend of different steaming times, and Fukamushicha has a key part to play in contributing sweetness.

JAPANESE TEA AUCTIONS

Much of Shizuoka's tea is sold locally in a tea auction that takes place at the crack of dawn. Sterile white lab coats are de rigueur for all, with the protagonists being differentiated by their headgear. Buyers sport blue caps, producers green and brokers clutching abacuses wear yellow.

Tasting and negotiation happen on the spot, and it is fascinating to observe how the broker's abacus plays a key role in the subtleties of discreet price discussions.

More akin to a fish market than a tea auction, the method absolutely fits the model of multiple small producers making many small batches of very high-value tea.

Tasters in Japan deploy specially made sieves to assess the aroma.

BANCHA AND HOUJICHA

Where lower-grade leaf is used (the result of poor plucking, or third and fourth harvest later-season tea), the final product is often not regarded as sufficiently fine to be grouped into the sencha category, instead being downgraded as Bancha. Typically this will be stalky, more mixed and certainly cheaper, although not dissimilar to sencha in taste and invariably a touch more amber in colour.

There is a further derivation on the Bancha theme – Houjicha, a brownish-leafed roasted variant that gives a deep sandy-brown colour and baked aroma much closer in style to the Chinese roasted green teas than to its Japanese cousins. The milder flavour that the roasting lends to the tea makes this a popular 'starter tea' for younger tea-drinkers, and one will often see children in Japan graduating from Houjicha to the more acquired taste of bancha and sencha.

Japanese auction negotiation, a buyer strikes a deal with a broker, the producer looks on. Note the abacus by the broker's right hand.

GENMAICHA

When Bancha is blended together with toasted rice in a rough 50% rice, 50% tea mixture, Genmaicha is the result (see image p162). The rich, toasty notes in the rice act as an elegant foil to the rounded vegetal notes in the Bancha. The overriding aroma is of puffed rice breakfast cereal, both in the processing factory where the rice undergoes a series of washing, steaming, drying, roasting and sorting stages, and in the cup when the tea is infused. Although it often looks as if popcorn has been added, this is actually the popped rice. The effect is purely visual, as it makes precious little difference to the already distinctive flavours of the tea and rice.

NORTH
KOREA

Sea

☐ SEOUL

SOUTH

KOREA

Daegu

Busan

BOSEONG

Kitakyushu

Fukuoka   FUKUOKA

JAEJU

SAGA

KUMAMOTO

MIYAZAKI

KAGOSHIMA

East China Sea

ALTITUDE

| 5000 |
| 4000 |
| 3000 |
| 2000 |
| 1800 |
| 1600 |
| 1400 |
| 1200 |
| 1000 |
| 800 |
| 600 |
| 400 |
| 200 |

m

of Japan

SAITAMA

TOKYO

Yokohama

KYOTO

J   A   P

Shizuoka

Nagoya

Kyoto

SHIZUOKA

Okayama

Hiroshima   Kobe   Osaka

NARA

MIE

TOKUSHIMA

N

PACIFIC OCEAN

0   50   100

Km

The Genmaicha production process.

GYOKURO AND KABUSECHA

Enjoying the warmer climate further south and west of Shizuoka, the prefectures of Aichi, Kyoto and Mie can boast of their production of Japan's finest teas. The additional warmth at this more southerly latitude allows the growers to shade their bushes prior to plucking, thereby reducing the photosynthesis activity. One of the effects of photosynthesis is in converting theanine into less tasty compounds, so it should follow that a reduction in photosynthesis should increase a tea's flavour.

The shading (or *Ooishita* method), which takes place normally for the week prior to plucking in the case of Kabusecha, or for three weeks in the case of Gyokuro, demonstrates intense commitment to the quality of the product. During the period of shading, lack of sunlight acts as a severe check on growth and the producer suffers drastically curtailed crops. In this struggle in the shade, the plant tends to develop longer, softer buds with reduced levels of catechins and elevated levels of chlorophyll and theanine amino acids. Hand-plucking will typically then ensure that only the finest shoots are selected before the tea is processed in the sencha style.

The consequent jade-hued leaf, low astringency and sweet flavour combined with an agreeably pungent samphire aromaaroma more than make up for the low yields. Gyokuro is unquestionably the finest of Japan's many excellent teas, and can compete on quality with anything in the world. Whether Kabusecha or Gyokuro, the mellow sweetness is divine, refined and smooth in Kabusecha, otherworldly in Gyokuro.

It is a terrible shame that Gyokuro is seldom seen outside of Japan, as it is invariably a favourite in any green tea blind tastings. The combination of a captivating fresh grass aroma with umami notes and sweetness speak of the artistry and skill of the producer, who can manipulate the conditions at the point of growth to build upon what nature has provided and turn it into something even more special through the *Ooishita* process.

If you are buying Gyokuro in a tea shop you can often see evidence of quality in the colour alone. A deep green augurs well for the final product, whilst a pallid lime green is unlikely to unleash a storm of buyers beating a path to the factory door. Ask to compare the Gyokuro with the standard sencha and the quality difference should be visible.

MATCHA

Arguably the best known of the teas to come out of Japan, matcha starts off in a similar fashion to Gyokuro. Typically, a four-week period under ever more intensive shade ensures that chlorophyll and amino acid levels are built up; this is necessary as it is these constituents of the leaf that are so important in balancing the intense caffeine hit associated with the actual ingestion of the tea leaf. The leaves are fine-plucked and then processed through a number of stages to a product called Tencha, which is in essence an unrolled Gyokuro. Tencha is then ground in small batches on granite mills into a fine powder – the consistency of talcum powder is held as a gold standard,[1] whilst the hue of green is a key factor in assessing the quality. If a bush has not been properly shaded then there is a risk that the resultant powder will be too pale, and the tea will appear insipid. The best matchas come from the Uji district within Kyoto prefecture, and are a deep, vibrant jade in colour. Anything that appears lightish green or tends towards brown in colour is either too old, poorly stored or has been milled from lower quality, unshaded raw material.

    It is matcha that is used in the Japanese tea ceremony. To prepare and enjoy matcha as a Japanese tea master would requires some basic kit, a strong wrist and an open-minded approach to the final product. The key tools are a bamboo whisk and a high-sided bowl. A small quantity of the powder (about half a teaspoon suffices for one) is added to hot (80°C) but not boiling water. If the water is

From left: recently processed matcha, one-month-old matcha, matcha milled from unshaded bushes, Turkish milled green tea.

too hot then the more bitter notes in the tea tend to dominate, notwithstanding the more pressing problem of burning one's tongue, given that immediate consumption is demanded. At 80°C the sweetness is maximised, whilst still being warm enough to enable some extraction to occur. The powder should be briskly whisked into a froth before being handed to a guest, who should consume the pea-green liquor with the head still intact, thereby allowing the froth to dissipate some of the strength of the liquor. The drink itself is an intense hit as, in contrast to all other types of tea, one is actually consuming the tea leaf itself rather than the resultant infusion of tea and water.[2] Experts estimate that the body's uptake of the nutrients in the tea is around 65% compared with the 35% expected during the consumption of 'ordinary' infusions.

Distilled to its basic form outside of the context of the formality of the ceremony, poor matcha is not an easy drink to consume, a sort of tea variant of the cappuccino, but with a bitter, drying taste and fierce kick. Good matcha, however, should involve a nutty taste softened by chlorophyllic sweetness.[3] The scientific background to the matcha success story is based upon the immediate caffeine lift that comes with the ingestion of the tea, but without the subsequent crash as the amino acid L-theanine mutes the effects of caffeine – or so goes the theory.

The ceremony would provide sweets such as crystallised fruits to be presented to guests, and this is crucial to remember if attempting anything similar with matcha at home. The sweets complement the matcha like blue cheese does Sauternes in a winning match where each plays to the strengths of the other. The richness of the sugar cuts through the dryness of the matcha, whilst the nutty astringency of the tea prevents the sweet from seeming too cloying.

If in doubt – and initial encounters with matcha can be hit-and-miss at best – a well-advised route into matcha is to try it as an addition to a fruit or dairy smoothie, or for foodies to explore one of the many recipes that feature matcha as a signature ingredient.

TEMOMI

Temomi is the pinnacle of tea processing, an artisanal skill that has been lost to most of the world, but which represents the most original method of tea manufacture that all modern machines aim to mimic: handmade tea. The process starts with the steamed leaf being placed onto a heated table called a *hoiro*.

The first manual process is called *haburui*, in which the leaf is picked up from the *hoiro* and shaken to remove the excess moisture introduced by steaming. This is followed by some light rolling as the leaf is gently manipulated around the *hoiro*. The movement is called *kaiten momi*, and when you see it performed in person it is clear that the sense of hand on leaf is absolutely crucial in determining how much pressure to apply: at first gentle in order to equalise leaf moisture and prevent the exterior of the leaf becoming too dry, and then firmer in order to squeeze out moisture from the centre of the leaf. At this stage, the leaf is a rather compacted ball that in a tea factory would be loosened through a ball-breaker. In the manual process it is broken up in the fingers, a procedure known as *tamahodoki*, before being cooled (*nakaage*).

The next part is the difference between a good machine-produced tea and a handcrafted tea: *momikiri*, the shaping of the leaf into the distinctive needle shape of good Japanese tea. Small quantities of leaf are squeezed in the hands, which perform a rubbing motion not dissimilar to that of warming one's hands on a cold day. This elongates the leaf, and is built upon with larger quantities of leaf in the *denguri momi* stage, which has leaf acting upon leaf to further contract and twist the material

Shaping leaf by hand, a skilled craft retained by a diminishing number of artisans.

into needles. Next comes *kokuri*, an immensely time-consuming process designed to ensure that the leaves all point in the same direction as piles of developing needles are pressed, divided and then further pressed. It is at this stage that the ever-diminishing volume, as moisture departs the leaf, starts to justify the $200 or $300 price tag attached to the tea. The process is concluded by spreading the leaves on the heated *hoiro* to dry until they reach a stable moisture level. A day of effort for very little tea, but evidence that craftsmanship and the ability to create really special teas by hand is not dead. Today, finding such tea in European shops is like locating a needle in a haystack (a lame but somewhat appropriate pun). It is worth every penny for those who can find it; even just a cup's worth represents the very best that a human hand can craft from the tea plant.

KYUSHU

The island of Kyushu is as far south as tea is grown in Japan. The sunlight is more intense; the growth is earlier in the season, invariably challenging the convention that the first harvest should not happen until eighty-eight days after Shunbun. Among a number of tea-growing regions in Kyushu, Kagoshima on the south-eastern tip of the island is the centre, representing about 30% of Japanese tea production. Although Kagoshima produces mainly sencha like Shizuoka, its greater diversity of varietals creates a little more variation in the final product.

TAMARYOKUCHA (KAMAIRICHA OR GURICHA)

Tamaryokucha is produced through either a steamed or a pan-fired process, and fashioned into comma-shaped leaves by omitting the final kneading process of sencha, which creates the characteristic needle shape. There are two kinds of Tamaryokucha: the pan-fired Kamairicha and the steamed Guricha. Tamaryokuchas are more intense than the more northerly teas of Honshu Island and less grassy in aroma, but possessing an honest strength of flavour. Although Kagoshima is the centre of Kyushu tea cultivation, arguably the best Tamaryokuchas emanate from Saga prefecture in Ureshino.

GURICHA

Guricha is a standard sencha, usually with a longer steaming time to reduce the astringency. These teas were developed to compete with Chinese gunpowder-type teas, and the comma-shaped balls immediately recall their Chinese cousins.

KAMAIRICHA

Kamairicha is the closest that Japan's tea comes to China in style terms. With the leaf initially fried on a hot pan to deactivate the enzymes and then mechanically shaped in a roller, it is very similar to the production in vast swathes of China, and often of remarkably good quality, with a generally better chance of avoiding the rubbery character often seen on lesser China-roasted green teas.

AWABANCHA

Made primarily in Tokushima prefecture on the east coast of Shikoku Island, Awabancha is a real curiosity. Produced late in the season when summer is well set in, it requires first the boiling of the Bancha leaf followed by its bacterial fermentation (ideally in a barrel) with lactic acid bacteria. Not unlike a Pu Erh, the resultant rather sour tea is definitely an acquired taste and for most, even in its homeland, it is an effort to acquire it.

THE FUTURE

The future of the Japanese tea industry is uncertain. Much of the ceaseless technological march forward that is central to the recent Japanese success story runs counter to the basic essence of loose tea as a product. In the name of progress, homogeneity is replacing diversity, convenience is replacing traditional methods regarded as outmoded, and ready-to-drink products sold through vending machines are threatening to eclipse the loose tea known and loved by millions since the days of the Shoguns. However, at the same time Japan is a land where politeness, deference and honour still hold sway, and never more so than at the ancient Japanese tea ceremony, which remains to counterbalance the relentless march of the modernists.

JAPAN
at a glance

Plants
Camellia Sinensis var. sinensis
Yabukita- quality/yield on sencha
Samidori- Matcha quality
Okumidori- Matcha quality
Benifuuki- Black tea quality

Terroir
Volcanic soils
50-600 metres

Seasonality
Best quality from early teas in April

Harvesting
Mainly machine, some peak quality teas are manually plucked. Yield 1866 kg made tea per hectare

Processing
Steamed green tea

Drinking
Ideal with crystallised fruit or other similar sweets

SOUTH KOREA

Quality-focused producer increasingly specialising in fine organic steamed green tea

See map on pp160-161

SOUTH KOREA IS A PRODUCER ON THE UP. Although it counts among the older generation of tea producers, having cultivated the *Camellia sinensis* bush for centuries (since around 900 AD in fact), the rest of the world is only now discovering what Koreans have known for years. It is an increasingly badly-kept secret that the quality teas produced in Korea can stand comparison with the best in Japan, and often at more modest price levels. Korea is an enigma. Although there is a long history of tea consumption, it is in more ways now a coffee culture, the younger generation of drinkers seemingly happier nursing a latte macchiato than a spring crop Woojeon. Yet much of the real cutting-edge development in out-of-home consumption is centred around tea bars and not coffee shops.

The nadir of the tea industry in Korea came in 2007 thanks mainly to the Korean Broadcasting System's exposure of a prevalence of agrochemical residues in Korean tea. Permitting continued production even in the face of an insect attack, pesticides are a reality of all agricultural industries, wherever they may be. Where parts of the Korean industry went wrong was in moving towards a culture of inappropriate use of the wrong agrochemicals, both in the wrong doses and accompanied by the wrong plucking intervals. So far, so bad…

In many ways the crisis unleashed by the KBS report was a blessing in disguise. It was a *Stunde Null* moment that provided an opportunity to start afresh with a blank sheet of paper. Although at the time the report seemed a crippling setback, and many long-standing businesses employing thousands of people suffered, it did at least allow those with a long-term interest in Korean tea to take a step back and assess what they needed to do to safeguard its future. Now the peak-quality teas emanating from Korea are being garlanded with awards on the international stage, and with an increasing prevalence in speciality tea shops.

Predictably, the solution to the crisis was a single-minded focus on organic tea, especially on the volcanic island of Jeju. Although 70% of Korea's crop emanates from the mainland, often from small gardens under the control of temples, it is Jeju tea that is most often seen in tea shops abroad. Volcanic soils, rich in organic matter and with a high gravel content, provide a perfect location for tea cultivation. The soils are rich in minerals and nutrients, whilst the gravel provides for excellent drainage.

WOOJEON AND SEJAK

Woojeon represents the best of the twisted-style teas emanating from the first flush crop, which appears during April. The production process is a mixture of Japanese-style steaming and Chinese-style roasting. The finest leaves are steamed, hot-rolled, dried and then again hot-rolled before a final session in the dryer. The leaf is stylish: beautifully twisted and deep green in colour. Possessing a fine savoury, nutty taste with a pleasant mellowness and length of flavour, these are really the best of the local style of tea manufacture.

Sejak is not dissimilar, but tends to be made from a marginally inferior leaf, paler green in colour and usually plucked towards the end of the first flush period in the first week of May, and hence attracts a lower price.

Tea gardens in Jeju.

JOONGJAK

Joongjak is the second flush version of Woojeon. The leaf is clearly inferior to the earlier teas, being more olive green in colour, but the liquors possess more body and colour than the Woojeon whilst being a little less mellow and sweet. These teas are produced towards the end of June.

DAEJAK

Daejaks are the autumnal versions produced during September. The leaf is more brownish, a little harder and as a consequence tends to be a touch more bitter and less refined than its earlier brothers. It is nevertheless about a quarter of the price of Woojeon and as such well worth considering, especially if you wish for a bit more strength in your tea. It is also an ideal base for flavouring, being more robust and able to stand up to most fruits without becoming lost in the eventual brew.

JEONCHA

Jeonchas are the Korean equivalent of the Japanese senchas. Produced during the first and second flush periods (the deeper green of the first flush version often leads its producer to label it *Jeoncha Plus*), they very closely resemble their more famous Japanese cousins. The very best Japanese steamed green teas incline towards a silkier handle to the leaf, more sweetness and freshness on the nose, and more greenness in-cup than the Jeonchas, although it is a brave taster who could claim to pick the odd one out in a blind tasting.

GARUCHA

The Garuchas are the matcha equivalents – a finely milled version of Jeoncha, they ape their Japanese counterparts, being at their very best during the first flush period. It is very difficult to tell a Japanese matcha apart from a Garucha, with the only clue sometimes being in the deeper green of the very best Japanese matchas; at all other price levels they are virtually indistinguishable.

OOLONG

Korean oolongs are occasionally seen, usually produced from leaf later in the season. These gravitate towards the more bakey styles and have an amber liquor and modest body. They are similar to some of the bakey Taiwanese types, although the leaf style is cruder and less shotty.

SOUTH
KOREA
at a glance

Plants
Camellia Sinensis var.
sinensis
In Jeju mainly Yabukita-
Japanese quality/yield
cultivar
Some locally-developed
yield/quality cultivars on
mainland

Terroir
Volcanic gravelly
soil in Jeju

Seasonality
Best quality from teas
produced in April

Harvesting
Machine. Yield
1242 kg made tea per
hectare

Processing
95% green tea,
mainly steamed
in Jeju,
usually roasted
in Boseong

Drinking
Consume in the fashion
of any good Japanese
green tea

Tea fields near Boseong on the mainland.

VIETNAM

Ancient producer now undergoing a resurgence.

Vietnam has as ancient a history in tea as almost any country bar China. A culture of tea-drinking dating back at least a thousand years and possessing a number of trees today reckoned to be at least that age, tea here is as old as the country itself, which only broke free from Imperial Chinese rule in 938 AD. Indeed, with a fluid border and common terroir, there was inevitably a lot of cross-fertilisation between the two tea communities well before Westerners became interested in the product. Boasting massive historical expertise, a monsoonal weather pattern, the mountainous terroir beloved of the tea bush, all underpinned by a local populace eager to consume its teas, it is no surprise that Vietnam is now the world's fastest-growing tea producer.

The years of conflict that beset the country as it emerged from Japanese wartime occupation into renewed French colonial rule, civil war and then north-south unity did little to encourage any sort of entrepreneurship, let alone the long-term investment needed to grow tea. The plantations and human expertise that survived, though, were able to form the kernel of a resurgent tea industry.

Investment now abounds. World Bank money has dragged Vietnam to the top of the Robusta coffee-producing table, and in tea terms it is steadily recovering ground lost to its neighbours during the '60s and '70s as the enterprising Vietnamese develop higher-yielding cultivars and find new markets for their output. For me Vietnam is Asia's Uganda, and the parallels between the two abound: not just the tragic, unenviable history and rescue via Robusta, but the enterprising way that they have gone about rehabilitating their tea industry and its subsequent rapid resurgence.

Vietnam is now very definitely one of the world's tea powerhouses. Its annual production grows faster than any other and there is more to come. Whilst it is arguable whether more of this sort of tea is altogether a good thing for the world's already over-supplied market, it is a situation that is here to stay. But whilst much of Vietnam is about large-scale corporate or state-run factories, there are still some truly charming artisanal communities making small batches of tea with a quality focus in remote parts quite untouched by foreign incursion.

NORTH VIETNAM

SHAN TEA/MOUNTAIN TEA

The tribal areas in the hilly borderlands with China are a sight in themselves, quite apart from their relevance in the tea context. The remote communities located north of a line between Dien Bien Phu and Ha Giang sit isolated at the end of tenuous mountain tracks and exist much as they have for centuries. The near-impenetrable forest is punctuated by the occasional clearing for market garden crops to provide cash and housing for a scattering of livestock.

The traditional tribal lifestyle, where boys as young as eleven or twelve are married off to girls four or five years older, has scarcely changed in centuries. Once married, the girls wear their hair up to display their new civil status, but their place in the household is more akin to that of an employee. Management of the smallholding combined with domestic duties and the physical constraints of their tender age make for a hard existence. Pigs and chickens saunter about households organised around a downstairs devoted to commercial use such as tea production and livestock, whilst the upstairs is reserved for the family. Such conditions are not conducive to sanitary food production, but these tribal

Basic tea processing equipment in a smallholding near to Dien Bien Phu.

valleys are a long way from the hygienic new world of stainless steel and certified food standards found in the estates of the Central Highlands.

The tea cultivated here is unfamiliar in appearance to anyone used to plantation agriculture. There are few tea bushes, whilst many of the moss-coated tea trees are thought to be of ancient and unique sub-varieties such as *Camellia sinensis pubilimba* which yields an especially white downy bud. The frequent rainfall and pervading mists lend a greasy danger to any arboreal escapade, and there is great skill in the pluckers' forays into the tea.

Inevitably given the size of the trees, which reach 3-4 metres (10-13 feet) in height with no opportunity to form a flat plucking table, there is no chance of a uniformly fine plucking standard being achieved. The leaves are often older and harder, although there still exists a spring flush at the beginning of May, yielding the best quality of the year and indeed even the occasional bud. The logistics of ascending a tree complete with agrochemical apparatus are so perilous that production is fully organic even if not certified as such.

The tea is crudely processed in the downstairs floor of the local small homesteads, often sun-withered for the lack of any other equipment, although frequently this process is dispensed with, and then hand-roasted before being twisted for a brief three-minute period on archaic rolling tables. Weather permitting, the tea is then sun-dried for a day to stabilise it. All this is highly risky given the intermingling of chickens and pigs with the tea, but if you're brave enough (and the use of boiling water to brew the leaf should put your mind at rest) then you can enjoy one of the world's truly unique teas.

This is the taste of tea as our long-since departed ancestors would have enjoyed it in the days before India and Ceylon entered the picture. Where plucking has been especially fine the leaf is flecked with the silver buds, referred to by the local Vietnamese as 'snow'. The risk of such cottage industry teas is that a slightly smoky character can pervade the leaf if the producer is not careful. The better-made teas, most especially the spring crop from tender leaf, are straw-yellow in-cup with a sappy flavour that offers elements of early-season Zhejiang character, but at a fraction of the price. These teas and the trees from which they come represent a valuable heritage for Vietnam.

Scattering lotus flowers in order to scent green tea.

CTC BLACK TEA

The rugged northern province of Phu Tho has benefited from substantial foreign investment in recent years and boasts Vietnam's most credible quality-orientated producers. The gardens of Ha Hoa, Phu Tho and Doan Hung produce CTC teas in the Indonesian style for the export market. Using both estate and smallholder leaf, the teas are bright and liquor well, although can suffer from over-firing in the dryers. These gardens, now Indian-run, show what is possible in Vietnam and where the future may lie for the entrepreneurial country.

LOTUS TEA

If Vietnam has a speciality, then it is scented lotus teas. Produced in the same fashion as a Guangxi jasmine, Vietnam has a long heritage of using its national flower in its green teas.

Mixed into batches of green tea, ideally in layers within chests and left overnight, the sweet, somewhat heady aroma of the lotus flower imparts a mellowness onto the green tea that can temper even the harshest of bases. The producer will either leave the flowers in the tea in order to seduce the consumer with the appearance, or sieve them out, leaving no evidence of the scenting process. Nice as it is to admire the blooms in the tea, I would always favour the sieved product, as the taste of the long-dead petals by the time they reach the teapot is much less appealing than the scent.

CENTRAL HIGHLANDS

Much as the hill stations of India and Ceylon have remained little outposts of Britain long after the departure of the last grizzled planter, so has the French influence remained on the hill station of Da Lat: its *boulangerie* purveys the best croissants east of Pondicherry, whilst the Art Deco hotels recall the spa towns of Savoie. Da Lat functions as an excellent base from which to explore the Central

A green tea factory in the tribal areas of northern Vietnam. Green leaf is being loaded into the roasting drum.

Highlands and its tea gardens. The tea here grows between 500 and around 1,500 metres (1,600-4,900 feet), and sits in well-drained, basalt-derived soils of moderate fertility. The latitude is significant here, as the more southerly location (almost directly comparable with Coonoor) permits a longer season than its Chinese competitors further north, and should in the future help those trying to make better quality cold-weather teas as the industry develops.

GREEN TEA

The local green teas typically end up being consumed locally, or sent to Taiwan and the North West Frontier districts of Pakistan. These teas are manufactured very much in the Chinese style: pan-fired and with a deep yellow liquor, they often carry a slightly smoky taint, but make a very acceptable basis for flavouring if you buy the smaller types, whilst the larger-leafed styles have more subtlety and smoothness without ever quite approaching the refinement of their Chinese competitors.

BLACK TEA

The primary Central Highlands style is a black-leafed orthodox tea with a slightly weedy character, occasionally balanced by the bakey note that is a consequence of trying to generate black leaf in the dryers. Within this rather damning description one finds better-liquoring but rather browner-leafed teas from the factories closer to Da Lat, where the additional altitude helps the liquors but not the leaf, whilst on the lower-altitude smallholdings the familiar bakey taste comes out, but is balanced by that attractive blackish leaf. Buyers of such teas are usually interested in a cheaper alternative to low country Ceylons or a base for flavouring their Earl Greys, so quality is very much a relative term here, although the excellent clarity that the teas exhibit when chilled has also made them a big success in the USA in recent times. The best quality comes during the spring flush, but this is usually blended into later flushes in order to create a homogenous standard, much in the Chinese style.

There is some CTC produced in the Central Highlands and it does tend to avoid the slightly bakey character of the orthodox, but its fundamental problem is that the world produces a lot of such teas, many of them rather better than the Vietnamese interpretation of the style.

Teas here are a mixture of smallholder and estate and it is the management of the smallholder tea that has created Vietnam's biggest reputational headache in recent years. It has proven difficult to manage the over- or ill-timed use of agrochemicals. This is a shame, as when the teas are well made, the larger-leafed types can provide a very suitable base for flavouring.

VIETNAM
at a glance

Plants
Camellia Sinensis
var. sinensis

Terroir
Acrosils-Ferralsols,
400-1,600 metres

Seasonality
Best quality is
produced in Spring

Harvesting
Manual. Yield
1405 kg made tea
per hectare

Processing
About 60% green
tea, and 40%
black tea, mainly
orthodox

Drinking
Best green teas can
be prepared
gongfu-style

Smallholders in the hills of north Vietnam.

LAOS

An exciting source of numerous fine speciality teas.

See map on p176

L AOS IS NOT KNOWN as a tea producer, yet it is prime tea country from the perspective of the taxonomy of the bush. Northern Laos hosts the bulk of its tea production, and people have been making tea here for hundreds of years. It sits right in the heart of tea tree country, and can boast some of the oldest trees in the world.

BACKGROUND

The majority of Laotian tea hails from Phongsali province, which is bordered to the east by Vietnam and to its north and west by China – indeed, Phongsali was a part of China until 1885, when it was annexed to French Indochina. The tea-making and tea husbandry here largely reflect the province's shared history with its now estranged Yunnanese neighbour. It is unsurprising that the teas produced often filter back into China which, with its increasingly affluent tea-drinking population, will happily pay large premiums for Laotian Pu Erh-style dark teas, whether Sheng or Shou. This can be a blessing and a curse as each Pu Erh boom provides a much-needed boost to rural communities whilst simultaneously removing potentially interesting green and black teas from the market.

Tea trees in Phongsali are all *assamica* varietals, tall with spindly boughs and often covered on the trunk and lower branches with a silvery lichen that gives a birch-like appearance to the tree. Useful leaf grows on the uppermost branches, meaning that any plucking foray needs to scale the tree in its entirety if any meaningful crop is to be yielded. The thin branches make every trip a risky one.

The steep hillsides and altitude of 1,400-1,600 metres (4,600-5,200 feet) have left us venerable trees with deep roots and sparse crops yielding tea of distinctive quality. There is no agrochemical use, with many teas also certified as such. The teas are about as distant from mass production as is possible, and this is the charm of the Laotian industry. There is widespread batch variation, but the jewels outweigh the duds and it is a region to support because it represents tea at its most artisanal, and the continuation of an unbroken, centuries-old tradition of tea that has largely died out in China.

PHONGSALI WHITE TEA

The highlight of the Phongsali oeuvre is its white tea, produced only in spring from old tea trees in a strikingly labour-intensive process that may see a day's plucking result in less than 300 grams of bud and first leaf. The four-hundred-year-old trees present a formidable plucking challenge and offer miniscule yields of unique quality. There is no processing – the leaf is left on mats to shade-dry for two days, carefully distributed so that no one leaf touches another. The sweet, rich, complex and enduring character of the white teas makes them a unique experience. The quality of these teas is a genuine testament to the current custodians of the ancient bushes that started their lives long before tea arrived on European shores. So limited is the production and great is the demand that it inevitably sells out well before the harvest has started.

PHONGSALI GREEN TEA

Roasted green teas are produced here in the Chinese fashion. The old trees and small batches can result in widespread variability in quality, with a smoky character occasionally in evidence coming from the wood smoke invading the wok. This is part of the charm of such teas, though, and the handsome, wiry leaf, captivating smoothness and intense aroma more than make up for it.

An old tea tree in Phongsali.

PHONGSALI DARK TEA

We are only just across the border from Yunnan and the dark-tea style is very similar, with both Sheng and Shou Pu Erh-type teas. The best exhibit sweetness and smoothness without earthiness. A local cigar-shaped variant is often seen at a lower quality level than the very best Sheng dark teas.

Plucking requires the aid of a bamboo pole.

PHONGSALI BLACK ORTHODOX TEA

This can be a lottery, but at its best is a slightly floral black tea with notes of malt and smoke. The teas have a gentle character which is regarded as having come from the very old bushes. The best black teas here are handmade and are often distinguished by their more wiry appearance and a higher preponderance of golden tip.

BOLAVEN GREEN TEA

In the south of Laos in Champasak province, good green tea is to be found on the Bolaven plateau, but here produced using *sinensis* varietal bushes, and with a plainer character. The bushes here are more manicured than in Phongsali, a level of care afforded by the rather less vertiginous growing conditions of the plateau. The green tea produced here never seems to scale the heights of the best of Phongsali, but nonetheless has similar characteristics.

LAOS
at a glance

Plants
Camellia Sinensis
var. assamica - often
as trees
Mainly local trees
Some var. sinensis
in Bolaven

Terroir
Red and
yellow clay,
14,000 metres

Seasonality
Best quality in
March for
white and green
tea, April for
sheng Pu Erh, May
for black tea

Harvesting
Manual
Yield estimated at
200 kg made tea
per hectare

Processing
Green, white,
black and
dark tea

Drinking
Phongsali teas
are best prepared
gongfu-style

THAILAND

See map on p176

MIANG

As well as being the local name for the native Assam bush subspecies, *Miang* also refers to a pickled tea popular in the north of Thailand. Related to the *Lahphet* found across the border in Myanmar, *Miang* is chewed for alertness and can be eaten sweetened, salted or flavoured with all sorts of condiments.

Local traders estimate that about a quarter of Thailand's tea bushes are employed in the production of leaf for this delicacy, and the trade is a complex web of processors, middlemen and dealmakers.

MULTUM IN PARVO. Thailand crams a lot of tea-consuming opportunities into its modest space. Thais are modest tea-drinkers, enthusiastic tea-eaters, and increasingly successful tea producers of black, green and notably fine oolongs in the Taiwanese style.

Although oolong is probably Thailand's best-known tea export, this part of the trade is relatively young, with the bulk of the growth having come in the latter half of the 20th century. Less well-known are Thailand's credentials as an 'old world' tea producer, given that its forested northern border with Myanmar forms part of the area regarded by many as a plausible indigenous home of *Camellia sinensis var. assamica*. Indeed, it is Chiang Mai province in the north, the finger of Thailand that juts into Myanmar and Laos, that continues to play host to the bulk of Thailand's tea-growers. Here the Thais make rustic black and green teas alongside some fantastic oolong very much in the Formosan style. Ranging from the greener, floral, lightly oxidised types to fuller-bodied later-season teas, Thailand can rival much of what is produced in Fujian or Taiwan.

The Thai bushes are predominantly *var. assamica*, referred to by the Thais as *Miang*. These bushes are descended from the

Pluckers dressed in traditional costume in Chiang Mai.

Much of Thailand's tea is of Taiwanese cultivars; these plants will produce fine jade oolong.

original wild *assamica* strains found in this area, and many of them are to be found growing wild within tracts of forest.

CHIANG MAI AND CHIANG RAI OOLONG/JIN SHIEN/DOI TONG/DOI MAE SALONG

We have the Kuomintang to thank for Thailand's oolong industry. Ousted from their homeland as a result of Mao Zedong's Communist revolution, two regiments of indomitable nationalists found themselves on the wrong side of China for evacuation to Taiwan and continued their fight from Myanmar. By the early 1960s, after years of CIA-funded struggle, they eventually found sanctuary in Chiang Rai and Chiang Mai, Thailand's northern provinces, from where they were co-opted by Thailand's military to fight its own domestic Communist insurgency. Only from around 1980 did they naturalise as Thais and become free to concentrate on more agrarian pursuits. The Thai government expressed a clear preference for tea and coffee cultivation over the opium that was at the time rather more lucrative, and these exiles have since pioneered the production of oolong tea in these mountainous borderlands. What they produce is of admirable quality.

Often known as 'Little Switzerland', the misty hills around Doi Tung and Doi Mae Salong provide outstanding conditions for the Chinese bush varietals that prosper at higher elevations. At altitudes of 1,200-1,400 metres (3,900-4,600 feet) it is Taiwanese cultivars such as Jin Xuan, Four Seasons Spring and the delicious but disease-prone Chin shin that flourish in a relationship demonstrating the enduring link between the Kuomintang exiles and their erstwhile brethren in Taiwan. Long-standing research assistance between Taiwanese experts and local growers has fostered both Thai supply as well as Taiwanese demand.

It is mainly the lighter oolongs that excel here, with the cool temperatures and rich soils ensuring that speed of growth is regulated and flavours are enhanced. Floral aromas and hints of mango dominate in the teas, making them prime alternatives to their better-known Fujianese and Taiwanese cousins. Later in the season one can find fuller-bodied amber oolongs, although these are generally less refined than the excellent early flush greenish versions.

GREEN TEA

Thai green tea is processed in the same northern hills as the oolong. Using both imported Taiwanese varietals and the more robust Assam bush, the styles vary. Some of the local Assam green teas can be heavier and more full-bodied, whilst the teas processed from imported varietals are usually more sappy and aromatic. As is often the case, the early season teas are best.

THAI BLACK TEA

The greatest concentration of black tea production is around the Mae Taeng district in Chiang Mai province. Here native *assamica* bushes are processed both as a robust CTC and a more mellow orthodox style. Neither are world class, but there is genuine care taken in the production process and the full-bodied teas are similar in style to a Cachar type, which is certainly no criticism and demonstrates the Thai potential for those who like to add milk to their cup.

THAILAND
at a glance

Plants
Camellia Sinensis
var. sinensis for
oolong, some native
var. assamica
Chin shin- oolong
quality cultivar

Terroir
Red clay,
300-1,000 metres

Seasonality
Best quality from
first harvests
in late-March and
April

Harvesting
Manual
Yield estimated at
300-400 kg made
tea per hectare

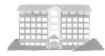

Processing
Mix of oolong,
green and
black tea

Drinking
Oolong is best
brewed gōngfu style

MYANMAR

Producer of unique green teas, artisanal orthodox black tea, and charming dark teas.

See map on p176

THANKS TO ITS YEARS spent in the political wilderness, Myanmar is one of the world's least known and visited countries, a situation that has also rendered its teas largely absent from our consciousness. But its Shan state hills sit amidst the forests that are regarded as the original homeland of the tea bush, and its climate is ideal for the plant.

BACKGROUND

Myanmar can boast one of the oldest tea industries in the world, but it has hardly moved beyond the small-scale cottage affair it was a century ago. Its annual crop of around 20,000 tonnes[1] sounds like a lot, but it comes from an area of tea land capable of producing more than twice as much with a little investment. Myanmar is the region's lowest yielding tea by some margin, although it does have its own extenuating circumstances in the form of *lahphet* – tea that has been pickled and is consumed as a food thereby escaping the statistics. But Myanmar is nonetheless a country of colossal potential and one that offers some exciting and unique teas.

The foremost producing region is the Shan state, which sits to the east of the country where it borders China, Laos and Thailand. Almost half of the total production emanates from the northern part of this area and around Bhamo, which lies just inside the Kachin state to the north. This is a rugged, mountainous territory boasting deep reddish-yellow clay soils and heavy monsoonal rainfall during the summer rains season, followed by a mild, dry winter. The altitude at which the tea is cultivated (1,200-1,800 metres/3,900-5,900 feet) is high enough to ensure both adequate rainfall and more bearable temperatures than on the parched plains further west, which are too dry for tea to flourish.

The season tends to start in April and run to October, with the best quality coming from the earlier production. Most farmers are de facto organic producers even if they do not have the certification to show it, a fact that goes some way towards explaining the very low yields (imported fertilisers having long been beyond reach since the country's isolation). There remains a genuine sense here that tea-making skills are valued assets to be passed from generation to generation, rather than borrowed from a consultant or sold to the highest bidder. This has left

LAHPHET

Myanmar is unique in that consumption of tea as a *food* is as significant to the culinary culture as its brewing as a *beverage*. Certainly other countries eat their tea at times, notably Thailand, Taiwan and China, but never with the relish of the Burmese. The delicacy *Lahphet* forms a key part of the national diet and accounts for around 20% of the national tea crop. Literally *pickled tea* which has then been steamed, it is served much like a vegetable or a salad all across the country. In its various forms it is both a food for the special occasion, a treatment in the local medical tradition, and a caffeine boost for the young, hard at work on their exam revision.

Myanmar as a unique repository of artisanal tea production, though as the country opens up it is difficult to imagine that this situation will endure for long.

Bhamo is only 20 kilometres (13 miles) from the Chinese frontier, which has long been sufficiently porous for small-scale trade and exchange of knowhow to flourish. On the Chinese side, the tea-growing areas of Yunnan can boast centuries of expertise in all facets of tea-making, whether black, green or dark, and it is no accident that Myanmar is also proficient in all three.

STEAMED GREEN TEA

Myanmar can boast a genuinely unique production methodology in its green tea tradition. The process requires leaf to be plucked and then steamed to deactivate the enzymes. This leaf is then left on drying mats to be sun-dried over an extended period that could be up to two days. The resultant darker leaf colour tricks many consumers into believing that the tea is a Pu Erh-style dark tea, but the liquor is unmistakeably that of a steamed green tea. The aromas are inimitable, with the clean sweetness that steaming can give to a tea allied to the animalic notes of more rustic production. The teas are well balanced, with a body and complexity that come from the sun-drying process. There is real character here, and the teas speak eloquently of their Shan homeland, with the influence of the roasting Burmese sun a prime factor in their character.

KOKANG STEAMED GREEN

Although much of the Kokang district sadly remains embroiled in insurgent warfare, it continues to produce the finest of all Shan state teas. Kokang lies alongside the border with Yunnan, and although it is a little lower in elevation it shares generally similar terroir. Although classified as green, the Kokang teas have a downy leaf appearance that recalls fine China white teas, with a refined aroma that is a little cleaner than the more mainstream green teas of Shan state.

Steamed green tea being sun-dried in Shan state.

ROASTED GREEN

Never was the difference between a steamed and a roasted green tea so plain as in Myanmar. The mountain roasted green tea offerings bear such a distinct baked character that they resemble the toasted rice used in Genmaicha. This has the effect of dominating any more subtle fruity or greenish notes, but leaving a tea of genuine character, albeit one that will polarise opinion amongst its drinkers.

ORTHODOX BLACK TEA

There are a large number of cottage industries producing orthodox tea in domestic settings for local sale. It is less common to see sufficient volumes available for export, but it is highly likely this side of the trade will grow. Current offerings are black-leafed and fully fired, with a caramel singe that has something of the Ceylon low country about it. Occasional examples have a smoky note, but this is rarer in the black teas than the greens.

KYAUKME CTC BLACK TEA

At lower elevations – around 700-800 metres (2,300-2,600 feet) – sit some of the smallholdings producing CTC black tea. Myanmar's black CTCs are clean, shotty-leafed paragons of well-processed tea. In a blind tasting they would give some North Indian teas a very good run for their money, being distinguished only by a fraction less body and astringency. This milder character makes them all the more adaptable to both those who like milk and those who drink their tea black.

MYANMAR
at a glance

Plants
Camellia Sinensis var. assamica

Terroir
Red-yellow clay, 700-1,800 metres

Seasonality
Best teas produced in late-March and April

Harvesting
Manual. Yield 225 kg made tea per hectare

Processing
Green, orthodox and black

Drinking
Great variety of black teas that can be consumed with or without milk.

Tea in Shan state.

INDONESIA

Once-great producer now on the wane, but with some fascinating speciality production remaining to tempt green and oolong tea enthusiasts.

NDONESIA'S GEOGRAPHY IS defined by its location on the notorious 'Ring of Fire'. Volcanoes, active, dormant and extinct, punctuate the long string of islands that extends from Banda Aceh in the north west, only 200 kilometres (120 miles) from the Indian territory of the Nicobars, to Papua almost 5,000 kilometres (3,000 miles) to the south east, and much more in the Australian orb of influence. That vast distance is significant as it is difficult to conceive of Indonesia as one entity; it is made up of five large islands and thousands of smaller islands speaking hundreds of different languages. Although tea in Indonesia is restricted to Sumatra and Java, the distances involved ensure considerable seasonal variation between the northern Sumatran offerings and those further south in Java. Predominantly planted out on the European model of large clearings (rather than small 'fields'), the seemingly limitless carpets of green that coat the lower reaches of these volcanic ranges ensure the tea plantations of Indonesia are amongst the most beautiful in the world.

BACKGROUND

We have the Dutch (as former colonial power) and vast quantities of local labour to thank for the magnificent tea estates of Java and Sumatra. A number of false starts preceded the first successful tea estates on a large scale in the mid to late 19th century. The well-drained volcanic soils were ideal for tea cultivation as soon as the Dutch had acquired the requisite expertise which was easy enough for a nation with such a grand trading history. At the time, with the British market focused upon its own production in India and Ceylon, the mild, aromatic teas that the Dutch East Indies produced were predominantly consumed in continental Europe where, because of Dutch trading relationships, the opportunity was greatest. This gave early continental consumers a taste for softer teas that do not require milk, a preference that endures to this day.

INDONESIAN TEA TODAY

Indonesian teas are now largely blending teas. The bulk of the production will end up either in Western teabag blends, processed into bottled iced tea and drunk domestically as the ever-popular jasmine-scented Teh Botol, or blended with more expensive Ceylons for the Russian market, and with Kenyans for the Pakistanis. Indonesian teas lend themselves especially well to blending as they are invariably neutral in character, available year-round, and represent good value when compared to their more expensive cousins further west. The CTCs are a passable imitation of the popular styles of tea produced in Kenya, whilst the orthodox is invariably a good value if workmanlike Sri Lankan alternative. That is not to say there aren't some real highlights produced from some parts of Java and in the quality season though.

The tea industry in Indonesia (as with other plantation industries such as rubber and palm oil) is oriented mainly around large state-owned estates, with a vast management and marketing bureaucracy attached. This is a model which has existed for years and does little to incentivise the creativity and innovation one often sees from ostensibly similar privately run estates in India, Sri Lanka or Kenya. What this means for the consumer is that we are unlikely to find many boutique-style white or oolong teas emanating from the public sector – this is best left to the smaller private factories, which do not have to fill out a form in triplicate in order to try something new. It does, however, guarantee that basic quality levels will be maintained in the publicly run sector.

Although estates are the present, the future of the industry in Indonesia, as with many producing countries, is likely to be the burgeoning smallholder sector. The West Javan ribbon between Bandung and Tasik Malay by way of Garut is host to thousands of smallholdings currently supplying Teh Botol or local consumers, but with the potential in the future for large export opportunities. It is these enterprising producers who hold the future of the industry in their hands, but for now we concentrate on the opportunities for the enthusiastic Westerner.

JAVA CTC

That Indonesia is not an origin 'brand' in the fashion of Ceylon or Formosa does not mean that some exceptionally fine teas are not also produced in Indonesia. Javanese estates in particular have the capability to make some world-class quality, most especially during the September to November quality season when high temperatures and low rainfall combine to ensure reduced crops and elevated quality. This is not immediately apparent in all Indonesian teas, but those with the happy task of tasting the teas appearing in the auction in that period will enthuse over the pointy, brisk freshness of teas from estates such as Wonosari. Wonosari is for nine months of the year a run-of-the-mill CTC tea that is dribbled into blends all over the world from Lahore to Liverpool. It is a CTC tea in the west-of-Rift Kenyan mould, and as such inoffensive but unexceptional. Show this garden some dry weather, though, and the quality is transformed into an assault of zingy freshness, briskness and aroma.

Elsewhere in Java, look out for Cibuni, a private Belgian-owned estate with a long-term quality focus, producing very bright African-style teas much favoured in Pakistan. Tasted blind, most would be hard-pressed to identify Indonesia as the origin, so bright and brisk are the teas.

JAVA ORTHODOX

The orthodox teas produced in Java can, during the quality season, ape some of their more illustrious Sri Lankan cousins. The high-grown tea districts to the south of Bandung at around 1,400 metres (4,600 feet) can produce teas with a suggestion of Uva-type medicated flavour that will recall the sports changing room for many. Purbawindu, Tanawattee, Cisaruni and Dayeuh Manggung in particular can at times taste more like an Uva Ceylon tea during September and October (and at less than half the price).

The tippy, beautifully twisted teas out of Javanese factories such as Malabar have much of the attractive appearance that the substantially pricier and more prized mid-country Ceylons have, with the added bonus of a higher concentration of silvery tip in the leaf. The more weathered and older red soils of Panglejar and Pangehotan create teas that are genuine alternatives to Ceylon low-growns, with similar malty notes and deep black leaf. Further south and east, the higher-grown and less humid Semugih and Kaligua have fresher, more flavoury top notes redolent of the Ceylon medium-grown types.

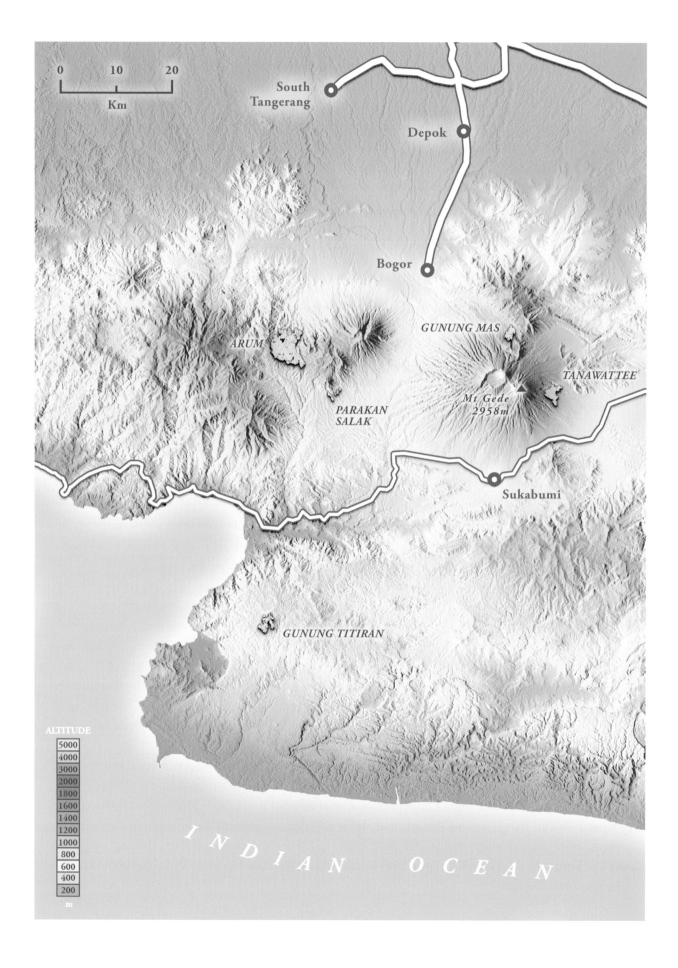

Pamanukan

Purwakarta

TAMBAKSARI

PANGLEJAR

CIATER / SUKAWANA

PANGHEOTAN

BANDUNG

SINUMBRA   SPERATA

WALINI   RANCABOLANG   KERTAMANAH

PASIR MALANG   MALABAR

SANTOSA   TALOON

Mt Papandayan
2665m   CISARUNI

JAVA GREEN, WHITE AND OOLONG

Around 10%-15% of the total Indonesian crop is processed into green tea. Usually roasted in the Chinese fashion and invariably consumed locally, it is a good value if often workmanlike alternative to Chinese green tea. Most notable amongst the exporters is Chakra, operating primarily out of West Java. The best known and first amongst the Chakra factories is Dewata or 'home of the gods', south of Bandung. Having suffered a tragic landslide in 2010 that claimed the lives of almost fifty people, they have diligently and steadfastly worked to get themselves back on their feet. Large investments in the estate and a new factory have much improved the formerly smoky quality of the offerings. Chakra now makes small quantities of beautiful sun-dried, classically floral oolong tea as well as delicate, silver-tipped white tea to go alongside their more everyday pan-fired green tea.

Gunung Titiran, producing fine green speciality teas west of Bandung around Sukabumi, can claim to be the most elevated in quality terms of the Indonesian producing fraternity. Fine green speciality types find their way to Japan and Taiwan, which are amongst the most discerning consuming markets in the tea industry. The delicately processed green tea, which in a good batch can ape some of the fruity notes of a Long Jing, is a match for anything produced in China and not an opportunity to be passed up.

SUMATRA ORTHODOX

The tea gardens in Sumatra are more dispersed than those in Java, and the act of visiting all of them tends to require some tolerance for long road journeys. Sumatra is less seasonal than Java due to its position closer to the Equator, and the quality is more consistent throughout the year but never reaches the peaks of Javanese production. The gardens of Bah Butong and Tobasari in the centre of the island

Mount Kenrici viewed from Kayo Aro estate

form the core of the Sumatran tea industry, but there are also further concentrations around Mount Kerinci further south, and in Gunung Dempo. It is these gardens that have long provided the lighter-bodied, more mellow counterweight to the brisker but coarser Kenyan teas used in many European blends. They show notes of nutmeg and cedar with a touch more body than their Javan counterparts, brought about by the 1,000-metre drop in altitude. The leafier teas from Bah Butong in particular have an abundance of tip and look very attractive when blended with more aristocratic offerings from Assam or Ceylon. In days gone by, the northern German tea-packers in particular appreciated the useful blending quality of these teas, and the Japanese occupation of Indonesia during the war meant that the Sumatran teas growing around Lake Toba were amongst the few teas that could find their way to occupied Europe.

Further south, through the few remaining patches of jungle inhabited by the occasional Sumatran tiger, lies Kayo Aro, a vast garden of now improving quality that sits at the base of the dormant Mount Kerinci. High-grown, with rich volcanic soils, it has many of the advantages that some of the other great East African gardens have, and as such it should produce fine bright-liquoring teas. Formerly let down by a factory that has suffered from underinvestment, especially in the boilers and dryers, it is

Cultivars earmarked for boutique oolong manufacture interplanted with bananas in Sumatra.

increasingly being whipped into shape to the point that its CTC teas are finding some favour with Western and Pakistani buyers.

SUMATRA OOLONG

In many ways the great thing about large, state-run conglomerates is that they create opportunities for those individualists who plough a more solitary furrow. The more standardised produce of the PTP stands in stark contrast with the artisanal specialities of the cottage industries producing tea. One such producer in Sumatra (ironically an ex-PTP executive) has taken it upon himself to develop a plantation dedicated to oolong tea production. This sort of bravery ought to be rewarded, and it is bravery indeed given how difficult it is to make good oolong tea. If there is a nation that appreciates fine oolong it is the Taiwanese, and it is no accident that the output from this particular estate goes predominantly to Taiwan.

Two varieties are cultivated: the floral Tapang that produces teas akin to the Four Seasons Spring Formosan variety, and the more austere Fuso, giving rise to liquors more suited to the baking process common in Taiwan. This is fine oolong tea at a fraction of the price of the more celebrated Taiwanese alternatives.

Tea gardens around Lake Toba in Sumatra

MALAYSIA

Beautiful planting areas producing teas of mainstream quality.

TEA IN MALAYSIA HAILS MAINLY from the gardens of the Cameron Highlands, where the footfall of Western tourists is heavier than in any other tea area across the globe. This has had the effect of enhancing the standing of Malay tea way beyond its actual quality level. Further east on Borneo, a sizeable organic tea garden produces similar teas. The small volumes of serviceable but unexceptional black tea produced are consumed almost exclusively domestically.

BACKGROUND

Tea has been cultivated in the Cameron Highlands from the late 1920s on land ostensibly similar to the great gardens of South India. Malaysian tea is now mainly mechanically harvested which is to be expected of one of the tea world's higher wage economies. Although a reasonable plucking standard is achieved, it does not compete with the quality of the green leaf in the better Ceylon or Nilgiri gardens, and this is one reason why the teas are a quality notch below.

The location very close to the Equator, with little clear seasonality, is a further factor that contributes to the run-of-the-mill quality. Really exceptional teas warrant some form of seasonality or stress in order to eke out their full potential, and the downfall of the Cameron Highlands is that the conditions are just too benign.

The attention in the factories is good, but there is less incentive to produce teas that mark out an origin as world-class. The domestic industry would happily take everything that is produced five times over, and such fortuitous circumstances make for a crop rather than quality-focused industry.

Tea in Malaysia looks set to remain as a small-scale sideshow. It entertains the tourists and produces reasonable volumes of acceptable quality. However, competition for land use from market gardens and an ever-increasing cost of labour will restrain any future development.

ORTHODOX BLACK TEA

The stock in trade of the Cameron Highlands is for bright, reddish teas with clear liquors, medium body, some briskness and length of flavour. The teas will take milk, but equally can work without it. Like many high-grown teas, leaf appearance

TEH TARIK

Translated as 'pulled tea', this Malaysian speciality involves a mixture of tea, sugar and condensed milk. The mixture is poured from one vessel to another in a theatrical motion that looks as if the tea is being pulled. The movement creates a foam on the tea, and more effectively mixes the tea and the milk. The process appears similar to the method used by some Indian chai vendors, although the condensed milk lends a thicker, sweeter taste.

is ordinary. The teas do not always transfer well when brought home by the visiting tourists but are well-suited to brewing in the local 'pulled tea'-style.

An organic tea garden is located on the island of Borneo, where, as with the Cameron Highlands, tourists are a significant factor in its support. It produces both a black tea, as well as a 'make-your-own' green tea for the tourist markets. Much of the output is flavoured with spices and sold locally. As with Cameron Highlands tea, it lends itself well to the local style.

Teh Tarik preparation

MALAYSIA
at a glance

Plants
Camellia Sinensis
var. assamica

Terroir
Sandy loam, 1,500
metres in Cameron
Highlands, 700
metres in Sabah

Seasonality
Best teas produced
during April

Harvesting
Mainly by machines.
Yield 696 kg made
tea per hectare

Processing
Black orthodox

Drinking
Tastes best
prepared in the local
style as *Teh Tarik*

INDIA

Diverse agroclimatic zones producing every conceivable type of tea, amongst them arguably the world's greatest black teas: Darjeeling and Assan.

INDIA IS A TEA LOVER'S PARADISE, with a host of variety within its sprawling borders. Teas from the majestic Himalayan slopes of Darjeeling in the north, the misty *ghats* of the Nilgiris in the south and the sultry flatlands of Assam in the east are all iconic claimants to a place on anyone's list of coveted favourites.

Tea plays a vital role in the daily life of India, elevating its status far beyond the cuppa we know in the West. The tea industry is India's second largest employer, and for millions of plantation workers and their dependants it is a means to a livelihood and a provider of rations, healthcare and education. For the union leaders, separatist movements and politicians it is a tool to be used in election campaigns and a carrot or stick to be wielded in periodic disputes with their neighbours to the west. For the poorer citizen, the daily cup of chai, heavily sweetened with sugar and perhaps taken on the street from a simple clay cup, may be a substitute for a 'square' meal.

The staggering variety and generous quantities on offer from the subcontinent mean that Indian tea is enjoyed all over the world from the bazaars of Tehran to the salons of Hamburg, notwithstanding the vast quantities that remain to meet the national demand. The simple fact that one in four cups of tea drunk around the world is Indian gives the subcontinent a leading role in the global development of the drink.

GEORGE ORWELL

George Orwell is one of history's best-known tea lovers, and was famously partial to Indian tea. The first of his eleven golden rules for a perfect cup of tea was most specific:

First of all, one should use Indian or Ceylonese tea. China tea has virtues which are not to be despised nowadays – it is economical, and one can drink it without milk – but there is not much stimulation in it. One does not feel wiser, braver or more optimistic after drinking it. Anyone who has used that comforting phrase 'a nice cup of tea' invariably means Indian tea. [1]

BACKGROUND

Kolkata, formerly Calcutta, is inevitably the start point. It forms the administrative and commercial epicentre of North Indian tea. Any Assam or Darjeeling plantation company worth its salt has its headquarters there, its auctions continue to account for a sizeable proportion of tea sales, and its port handles much of the export. But Kolkata is some way removed from the tea bushes that help to fuel its economy; for these we look primarily to Assam around 500 kilometres (300 miles) to the north.

The impetus to plant in Assam came from a period of escalating domestic politicking between the government and the British East India Company that had hitherto enjoyed a monopoly on trade with China. As the company restricted supply of the China teas in which it was dealing in order to maintain the increasingly artificial price, so it created the conditions for resentment amongst the burgeoning consumer market. By 1834 parliament had lost its patience[2]: the company's new charter would focus on administration of the lands it had conquered in India, rather than trade with China. From a position where an alternative source of supply was to be feared, the company was now highly incentivised to produce its own tea, and as much of it as possible.

The company was sure that the vast subcontinent would offer conditions suitable for growing tea somewhere within its borders, but lacked both plants to test this theory and knowhow in husbanding them. Inland China was off limits to foreigners, with the result that cloak-and-dagger attempts were made to steal Chinese plants – *Camellia sinensis var. sinensis* – and the coolies who knew how to husband them. An adventurer named Robert Fortune (see China, p102) succeeded in gaining access to Chinese tea-producing areas between 1848 and 1851, where he managed to secure both tea plants and the requisite expert Chinese farmers and tea-makers.

What the British had failed to appreciate was that the tea plant was also native to India. There is dispute about its precise origins but it seems likely that *Camellia sinensis* originated somewhere towards the head of the Irrawaddy river in what are now the borderlands between India, China and Myanmar. The *Camellia sinensis* subspecies native to North East India (*Camellia sinensis var. assamica*) was discovered in 1823 by Robert Bruce, but it was not until the 1830s that the plants he brought back from his jungle expeditions could be properly classified by his brother Charles in the Botanical Gardens of Calcutta. The consequences of the discovery were profound. The company (and Britain) had its own tea and need no longer be reliant upon the Chinese. There was not much of it yet, but the conditions under British control would permit its cultivation and that was a game-changer for all involved.

The efforts to steal the Chinese plants were not entirely in vain, however, as Darjeeling was planted up largely from *sinensis* and much of the world's tea is now a hybrid of the two varieties, albeit often exhibiting more of the characteristics of one or the other. As far as the industry in Assam was concerned, though, it was certainly the local plant rather than the stolen seeds that gave rise to the epic plantations of the valley.

Life as an early pioneer far to the north in Assam was a lonely existence. The planters sought to create gardens from the jungle and order from what they regarded as chaos, many of them having little training in how to go about it. They toiled with an almost equally alien labour force brought from the states of Bihar or Orissa to clear vast areas of rainforest using the most basic of equipment: manually wielded saws to fell the trees, masses of men to dig up the remaining stumps left behind, and trained elephants to remove the vegetation.

SHADE TREES

Camellia sinensis is native to areas of jungle and therefore at home where dappled shade can be found.

Almost wherever tea is planted in India it is accompanied by shade trees, spaced at regular intervals to provide some gentle shade but without overly restricting the sunlight. Too much sunlight can scorch the leaf and result in excessive transpiration during the hotter months, whilst too much shade can result in blister blight. The trees, whether *Grevillea robusta* (silver oak), acacia or dadap, have a beauty of their own and are part and parcel of the tea landscape in Assam and South India. Darjeeling does not require shade, as temperatures are more moderate.

Amgoorie Tea Estate, the birthplace of CTC.

This was hard, dangerous work in a severe environment. We chuckle at excesses of the health and safety police now, but in this era, well before the hard hat, the slightest injury could turn septic in hours, with the nearest medical intervention usually days away by horse and boat. The prospects were bleak: malarial mosquitos, leopards, tigers, elephants and snakes all took their toll on the planter and his native labour force. His clothes rotted in the extreme humidity, the primitive thatched bungalow providing scant protection against the elements, whilst his prospects of enticing a young bride to such a milieu were slim at best. It is unsurprising that of those who did survive to see the nascent plantations emerge into profit-making industries, many soon succumbed to the bottle in such a lonely environment. A sundowner on the veranda may conjure up romantic notions of the leisurely life of the Raj, but for the planter it was an all too brief opportunity to combine his daily dose of quinine with a brief escape from the brutal reality of establishing 'civilisation' from the darkness and disorder of tropical jungle.

So far from Kolkata, their rule was absolute. Until comparatively recently, the isolated environment of an Assam tea garden required the planter to be employer, paymaster, judge and jury, civil and mechanical engineer, botanist, village planner, forester and tea taster, much of this conducted in a foreign tongue. It is in this unforgiving, remote environment that the planters' labour has given rise to one of the world's most iconic teas: full-bodied, rich, strong, malty teas that must have been a real assault on the senses of a Victorian Britain accustomed to delicate China teas. For a long time the maids' question in London tea salons was 'China or India?' and once you have tasted an Assam tea, you can see why.

The vast meandering expanse of the Brahmaputra, here at Tezpur.

ASSAM

Assam is not an easy place to visit, wedged into India's distant north-eastern borderlands with the Himalayan range to the north and the more gentle hills of the Patkai range to the east and south. It is connected to the main subcontinent of India only via a jealously held and heavily patrolled 22-kilometre (14-mile) land corridor at Siliguri, known as the Chicken's Neck. It exists at the extremes of the subcontinent, geographically much closer to Rangoon in Myanmar and Kunming in China than it is to Delhi. The whole geography of the state is defined by the mighty Brahmaputra that weaves its way through the sultry flatlands, split during the drier months into ribbons of multiple streams. As the river flows past Dibrugarh it has around 1,300 kilometres (800 miles) to run to the Bay of Bengal, yet only 100 metres (330 feet) to drop. With no clearly defined channel and the prospect of titanic volumes of water to be drained from the melting Himalayan snows each spring and summer, it is no surprise that the river changes course at will, a situation not helped by occasional earthquakes that can impact upon the integrity of the riverbanks and the natural fall. Whole towns have been lost and it is estimated by local experts that around 2,000 square kilometres (770 square miles) of Assam's land has been lost to the river over the last eighty years, an area about the size of Nottinghamshire. Assam is born out of this river, and its teas are a direct result of the alluvial soils it deposits.

So much for the background to Assam's place in the tea world, but in order to determine which teas to select, there are three main considerations: Orthodox or CTC? Where to buy from? When to buy?

ALTITUDE

5000
4000
3000
2000
1800
1600
1400
1200
1000
800
600
400
200

m

H i m a l a y a s

BHUTAN

Manas

NONAIPARA
ORANGAJULI

ATTEREKHA

PANEERY

BORENGAJULI

PHULBARI

Chaulkboa

B r a h m a p u t r a

Guwahati
(56m)

I N D I A

*North
Cachar
Hills*

0   20   40

Km

BANGLADESH

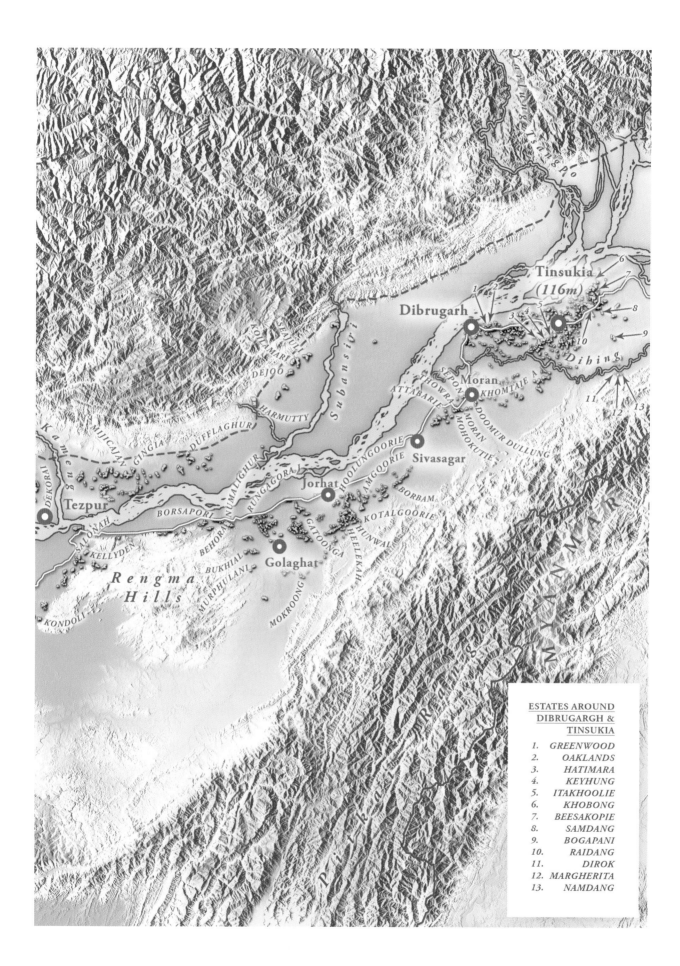

Tsangpo

Tinsukia
(116m)

Dibrugarh

Dihing

Moran

KHOMTAIE A

SEPON
MORAN
THOWRA
ATTABARIE
DOOMUR DULLUNG
MOHOKUTIE

Sivasagar

KOHIMARI
BEAULIE
DEJOO

HARMUTTY

Subansiri

Kameng

MIJICAJAN
GINGIA
DUFFLAGHUR

DEKORAI

Tezpur

Jorhat

HOOLUNGOORIE
RUNGAGORA
NUMALIGHUR

AMGOORIE

BORBAM

Sivasagar

KOTALGOORIE

BORSAPORI

BEHORA
BUKHIAL
MURPHULANI

GATOONGA
HEELEKAH
HUNWAL

SALONAH
KELLYDEN

Golaghat

Rengma
Hills

KONDOLI

MOKROONG

Rangit

MYANMAR

Patkai

ESTATES AROUND
DIBRUGARGH &
TINSUKIA

1.   GREENWOOD
2.   OAKLANDS
3.   HATIMARA
4.   KEYHUNG
5.   ITAKHOOLIE
6.   KHOBONG
7.   BEESAKOPIE
8.   SAMDANG
9.   BOGAPANI
10. RAIDANG
11. DIROK
12. MARGHERITA
13. NAMDANG

ORTHODOX OR CTC?

Assam produces tea using both manufacture methods; indeed, a large number of factories can interchange almost at will depending upon the demand of the major orthodox buyers in Iran. It is one of the greatest myths in tea today that orthodox is inherently good, whilst CTC is inherently poor. The truth is that the two are different styles, as comparable as Pinot Noir and Malbec, syphon coffee and espresso, IPA and *bière trappiste*, and they deserve to be recognised as such. CTC may be the latecomer, and it may in the meantime have gained the ascendancy over orthodox, but it should not be dismissed for its lack of refinement, its tannic brew and its one-dimensional nature.

For those who favour mellow teas, with layers of flavour, seductive, spicy aromas, the facility of consumption without milk and the tactile beauty of the tippy leaf, then the choice is clear. Orthodox has history on its side, and it can only triumph in any comparison between the leaf of a good example flecked with golden tips against CTC's more functional grape-nutty appearance.

However, for many, the rich strength of good Assam CTC is precisely its selling point: thick and full-bodied in the extreme, malty and boasting unrivalled length of flavour, this is a style of tea in its own right, and for a cold weekday morning I think there is nothing better. Indeed, CTC is an Assam innovation, developed on the Amgoorie Estate in the early 1930s with a view to enhanced colour and strength, and it has certainly worked.

CTCs demand a veritable dairy to mellow down the frontal assault of Rubenesque body and malt. The teas may be strong, but they are not crude and coarse like some lesser African teas can be; they boast sensuous richness and length of flavour that cannot be found anywhere else in the world, and work well with many foods. For those lucky enough to be drinking good Assam CTC at source, the local *Kaju Barfi* silver-coated sweets make a perfect foil to the richness and astringency of the tea.

Many tea-drinkers give up on Assam after finding the teas excessively full and strong. This is the point to experiment with adding more milk. Many prefer the lowest fat milk they can find, but for me a generous splash of Jersey cow full fat makes for a perfect marriage.

GARDEN TIME

Assam enjoys a location to the extreme east of the Indian subcontinent. As such it becomes light in Assam an hour earlier than it does 13° further west in Delhi (upon which the Indian Standard Time is orientated).

In order not to lose valuable daylight hours some gardens in Assam elect to follow 'Garden Time' or *Bagantime* which is usually an hour ahead of IST.

WHERE TO BUY FROM

The finest gardens in Assam can be found along a 160-kilometre (100-mile) stretch of the Brahmaputra's southern bank between Golaghat and Dibrugarh. Although not a vast area, it encompasses enough of the really fine properties with talented tea-makers to give a good chance of securing an excellent tea. The soils are rich alluviums and formed from the wash of old sandstone on the North Bank. Here can be seen the clearest expression of Assam character: rich, voluptuous, malty, strong teas. For CTC the so-called Quality Belt can be found in the Lower Assam districts between Golaghat and Sibsagar (Sivasagar). For orthodox, the best teas arguably hail from areas around Tinsukia between Dibrugarh

BUNGALOW TEA

It is always a good idea to accept an offer of bungalow tea, which represents the best of what a particular tea garden can produce. A select group of pluckers is dispatched during the quality season to select and harvest the very best leaf (often taking one leaf and a bud or just pure buds, rather than the customary 'two and a bud'). This most succulent and pure leaf is then processed in the factory by the senior staff under strict control. The resultant tea is what is taken home to the factory manager's bungalow and reserved for the visits of eminent personages.

and Tringri. Teas from these gardens are typically attractive in leaf, rich in liquor and with generous inclusion of golden tip. Outside of these areas the most reliably fine teas undoubtedly sit in an area known as the Moran Circle, where renowned gardens such as Doomur Dullung, Hajua, Mohokutie and Thowra strike a fine balance between the yield of Upper Assam and the quality of Lower Assam.

Whilst the Quality Belt gardens may have fame and some snob value on their side, they also tend to command the highest prices, with the price to value ratio not always being entirely appropriate to the outlay. There is a lot of Assam outside of this area, much of it also making very fine tea, especially the somewhat remote and isolated North Bank gardens where the circle of estates around Mangaldai usually manage to overcome large-scale incursions of elephants to make excellent tea.

A good Assam tea should be full-bodied, malty and rich in taste. The giveaway of poor quality Assams is usually in the infusion. Bright, coppery-coloured infusions are indicative of a good quality tea that will keep well, an essential facet of such a strongly seasonal origin. Dullish, brown infusions suggest that the tea will soon lose its quality.

WHEN TO BUY

In any strongly seasonal producing country, there is great potential for the quality of tea to vary across the year. Because the biochemical constituents of the leaf are primarily influenced by their environment, the decision about what point in the season to buy a tea carries some importance.

FIRST FLUSH

The Hindu Holi festival of colours, which usually falls between late February and mid-March, is regarded by many as the traditional start of the first flush. In practice a late Holi will not force the manager to be patient, and if the bushes are flushing then nothing should hold back the pluckers. At this point in Assam the average daily temperature starts to nudge above 20°C and rainfall steadily builds, both key factors in spurring the tea bush out of its dormancy.

The first flush teas that open the season may sound like good prospects if your only reference point is Darjeeling, but the Assam first flush can be raw and skinny. An early Darjeeling is a joy and the greenish taste that spring teas tend towards suits this style well, but early Assams are best left for those who have drunk too much tea over the winter and are nervously eyeing up a diminishing stock in the caddy.

Elephants continue to roam across Assam's tea gardens, especially on the north bank.

SECOND FLUSH

Following the first flush, the bushes in Assam normally enter a period of dormancy known as *bhanji*. Some tea will still be produced but usually more similar in style to the early teas. Not until May do rising temperatures coupled with daytime sun and heavy evening rains precipitate a new growth period of genuine class. The quality comes first in the Upper Assam gardens and takes around a week to spread down to the North Bank and Lower Assam districts. This period of rapid growth in May and June immediately preceding the monsoonal rains should provide both excellent growing conditions for the tea plant and relatively dry weather, ensuring that the leaf is in optimum condition when plucked and transported to the factory.

The second flush is Assam's raison d'être and can stake a convincing claim to be the world's greatest black tea. The defining characteristics are full-bodied teas that cream down well: a characteristic known as *croppy*. The better batches can have a tinned tomato soup character, a character that somehow works, with the taste being distinctly superior to the description. Don't overlook the attractive bright golden colour when a splash of milk is added, a quality not always seen in later Assams, which can often compare poorly with the brightness of East Africans.

Keep a keen eye out for some specific cultivars that tend to give a Raspberry Jam (RJ) character to the tea. The clone in question, Keyhung 1 or K1, can be found in a number of gardens in Assam, although sadly habitually mixed into the lot in modest enough concentration to dilute the character. Occasionally, though, you can be lucky enough to stumble across a real gem. The most likely gardens to show Raspberry Jam are Itakhooli, Oaklands, Khobong and Keyhung.

Any tea possessing a relatively high level of polyphenols is likely to cloud when it cools.[3] This clouding phenomenon is so strong in good Assam teas that when left for a few hours, the liquors appear to have been mixed with milk or cream. This is known as creaming down, and is a frequently seen method of determining overall Assam quality. It is precisely this property of tea that ensures that the teas suitable for strong black tea will be, by definition, poor quality for iced tea, where a cloudy liquor is regarded as undesirable.

Two Assam teas: the cup on the right is creaming down well.

Peak second flush tea is becoming increasingly difficult to find as the disruption wrought by climate change unsettles previously reliable seasonal patterns. In recent years, dry weather at the start of the season has had a significant impact on first flush growth. In turn this has led to extended bhanji periods and bush dormancy, ultimately impacting on the quality of the second flush.

RAINS

After the second flush come the rains teas. The north-east monsoon hits Assam in late June or early July, depositing vast amounts of water over the valley before moving on in September. This heralds the mass-production season in Assam. July, August and September are peak cropping months, with little respite for the factories or pluckers until the Puja holidays in October. Rains teas are still typically excellent quality if an early July tea can be found from a good garden, but the rule of thumb is *the earlier the better*. July is better than August and August is better than September, although there are always exceptions: 'tail-end Charlies' of excellent quality and a blast of Ovaltine® flavour quite belying their late-season manufacture date. By the time the Pujas arrive between the end of September and the beginning of November (the precise date being a factor of the lunar calendar), the quality is middling: duller, less brisk, and occasionally weedy. The Puja holidays have a secondary impact in that the four or five days of holiday disrupt the plucking rounds and ensure that everything that comes afterwards is suboptimal in leaf quality terms.

The more undulating landscapes of the Cachar Hills.

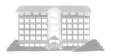

MARSHALL SONS & CO.

The Gainsborough manufacturer was at one stage a leading name in the production of tea-processing equipment. Visits to factories in far-flung corners of the world, especially India and Sri Lanka, still reveal decades-old Marshall orthodox rolling equipment and boilers running faultlessly, a testament to the legendary quality of the Lincolnshire firm and the talent of estate-based engineers who lovingly maintain them to this day. The Marshalls' site is now a shopping centre: an ignominious end for a once great engineering concern.

POST-PUJA

The period after the Pujas is still vital to the tea gardens, which will continue to pluck and manufacture until December. The later teas are thinner, softer, often with a walnut character and a little more wild and weedy in taste, few of them exhibiting the same full-bodied richness as the summer teas.

THE FUTURE

The future for Assam is an uncertain one. The state is incredibly vulnerable to flooding, which climate change seems to be making worse with each passing year, quite apart from the unsettling quality impact that climate change brings to the rhythm of the flushes. The blessing of the fertile alluvial soils that the Brahmaputra has laid down in its seasonal inundations is borne out of a curse that threatens the tea industry's very existence here. With some of the best properties being located close to the river, the fear is that as flooding increases, it is these prime gardens that we will lose first.

ESTATES OR SMALLHOLDINGS

The future brings also the question of tea-growing. Whilst the current situation in Assam sees the best teas made under estate and factory unitary control, the likelihood is that the model of a multitude of smallholders selling their green leaf into tea factories will more and more become the norm for the industry. This is both an opportunity and a threat. The opportunists will say that the lack of responsibility factories bear for those growing and plucking their tea gives them the ability to focus solely on processing it into the best possible product, just as we can see is possible in Kenya. The smallholders themselves become rural entrepreneurs, with the chance of an elevated standard of living and their destiny in their own hands. The naysayers will say that only bad will come of placing supply in different hands to marketing in a country prone to outbreaks of such pests as are entirely manageable under Indian pesticide residue legislation, but prohibited by the ever more discriminatory eyes of the EU legislators. Whatever the case, it does not alter the unmatchable growing conditions that Assam offers for producing premium tea.

CACHAR

Still part of the state of Assam, but with notably different teas, lies the district of Cachar. Defined by its mix of hills and plains, Cachar lies to the south of the mainstream tea-producing areas and borders Bangladesh on its western side. Cachar is an area both to watch and beware of. Although it is administratively Assam and therefore labellable as such, it is definitively not Assam in quality terms. It certainly has its merits, with elements of strength and brightness, but without the deep maltiness and body of pukka Assams. It is therefore a sort of Assam lite: light on taste and light on price. Buyer beware of the unfeasibly cheap Assam blend.

NORTH BENGAL   *(See map on pp240-241)*

North India is not all about Assam and Darjeeling. West of Assam in the state of West Bengal lie the districts of Dooars and Terai. Although they carry none of the blue-blooded heritage of Assam, in producing around a quarter of India's tea they cannot be discounted.

TERAI

West of the river Teesta and nestled in Darjeeling's foothills lies Terai. This is the tea-producing area that lies around the Chicken's Neck, the small corridor linking Assam and its neighbouring lands with the mainland of the subcontinent. Most of the CTC teas are pale in colour, relatively full-bodied (but nothing like Assams) and with a reddish, fibrous leaf appearance. However, we are on the way to Darjeeling here, so there are some quality speciality types produced in the rolling hills as one nears the Himalayas, Marionbarie being a distinct example falling much more into the Darjeeling style than typical Terai.

DOOARS

East of the Teesta and before the Bhutan foothills are the Dooars. Although politically part of the Jalpaiguri district, the teas from here are known as Dooars, the name deriving from the local language's word for 'door', the doors in this case being the passes into neighbouring Bhutan. This is an attractive region of hills and forests divided by rivers draining the Himalayan snows, and is a beautiful place to travel even if its teas do not enjoy the fame of its neighbours'. The teas show an attractive reddish colour and a neat, black leaf appearance, making them sought after in the local markets of areas such as Punjab.

TRIPURA

Tripura has a long heritage of tea cultivation, and has lately seen genuine enthusiasm for further planting by smallholders. The humid climate and more southerly location which extends the season a month longer than Assam's has given it a small head start in the competitiveness stakes. But the style of the teas lags behind, making the proposition marginal for those smallholders exclusively reliant upon tea. The teas are usually plain and lack body and strength.

DARJEELING

Only 500 kilometres to the west of Assam, but a world away in terms of the style of teas that it produces, lies Darjeeling. The combination of the Tibetan words *Dorje*, meaning 'thunderbolt' and *ling*, meaning 'place' or 'land' has given rise to the most evocative name in tea. Darjeeling is arguably the world's most iconic tea origin, a name redolent with quality, perhaps the ultimate expression of tea flavour and more misused and abused as a brand than any other.

Darjeeling is in the foothills of the Himalayas; indeed, for many years it was the launching point for expeditions towards Everest, and the view north towards the magnificent Himalayan range, dominated by the five snow-clad peaks of Mount Kangchenjunga, is the most spectacular in the world of tea. The proximity of the mountains to *Dorje-ling* can create spectacular thunderstorms as its Tibetan name suggests, and even snowfall is not uncommon during the winter months. It is the proximity of the Himalayas that makes Darjeeling what it is. Cold north winds emanating from the mountains blow southwards through Darjeeling's valleys, restricting temperatures. This phenomenon ensures that the average daily high in Darjeeling is a modest 18°C, whilst the Nilgiri Hills in South India at a similar altitude are at least ten degrees warmer without the influence of the mountains and the strong seasonality. Those sceptics who deny the impact of terroir on tea need to visit Darjeeling. This unique

The view towards Mount Kangchenjunga from the Darjeeling gardens is one of the tea world's great experiences.

area is made special by a number of factors, but it is its sense of place that is prime in creating the memorable teas that issue forth each spring.

Darjeeling is a region of hills divided by seven river valleys, of which the Teesta and its tributary the Rangeet are the most important. Tea dominates the sometimes precipitous valley sides where it is planted – between 600 and around 2,200 metres (1,970-7,200 feet). Where it has not been logged, this is often overlooked by indigenous forest above. The tea may all be Darjeeling in name, but this hides massive variations in quality. Where to look in Darjeeling for your teas? In one word, look up. What is all-important in Darjeeling is elevation. Elevation, as any Sri Lankan planter will tell you, is inextricably linked to temperature and hence speed of growth. Although it now boasts the world's first tea Certification Trade Mark (CTM), Darjeeling is an administrative region and not an appellation with grades of quality in the fashion of the French wine industry. This is important as it effectively means that the lowest elevation Darjeeling property, that may produce unexceptional tea, is sold under exactly the same quality denomination as the best high-elevation tea.

So altitude is key: quite simply, the lower the tea garden, the more ordinary its quality is likely to be. Of course there is a fine job to be performed by the factory manager and his staff in plucking the right quality of leaf and then manufacturing it with care and attention, which can haul a lower garden up the ladder. However, the better the garden in Darjeeling, the higher it is usually located up the mountain, and not only that, but the higher its factory is likely to be. A higher-altitude factory makes for cooler manufacture conditions, and in particular this enables a more successful first flush tea to be produced. In some origins, Assam for example, the low-grown conditions are instrumental

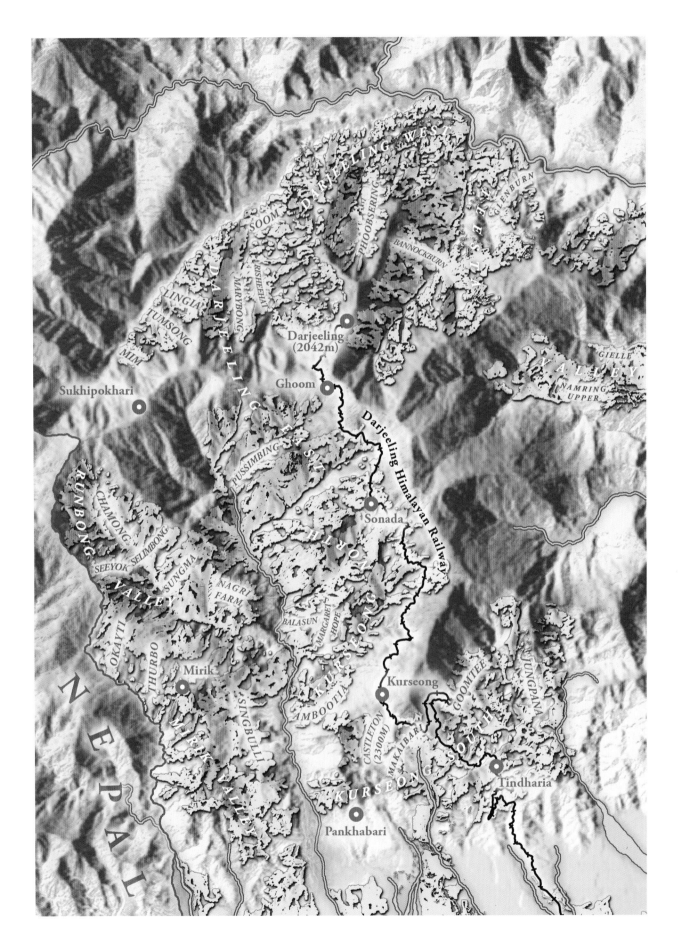

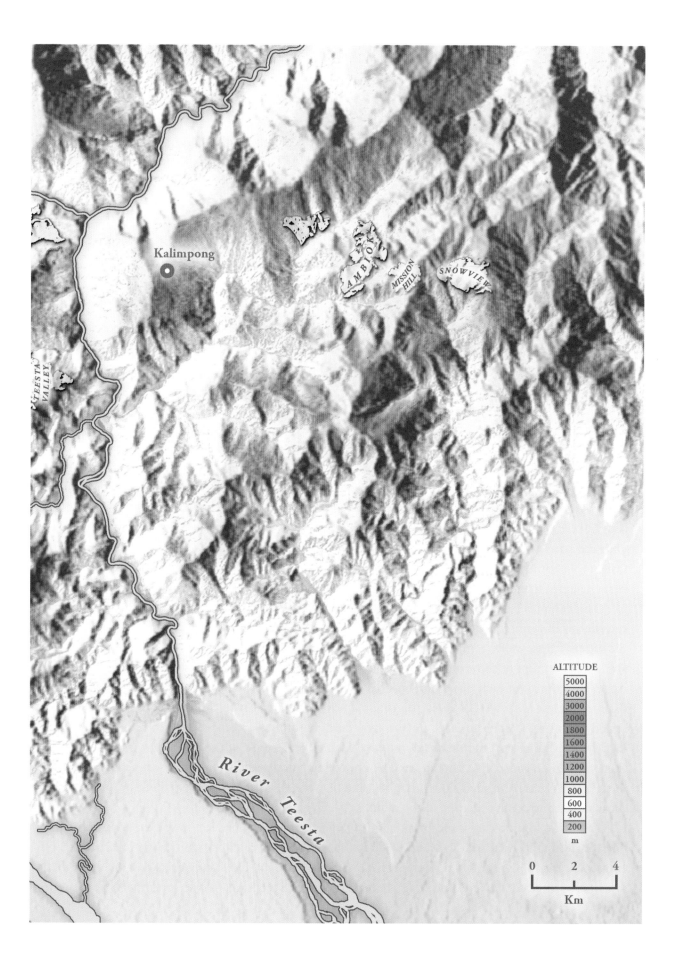

Kalimpong

TEESTA
VALLEY

AMBOK

MISSION
HILL

SNOWVIEW

River Teesta

ALTITUDE

5000
4000
3000
2000
1800
1600
1400
1200
1000
800
600
400
200

m

0   2   4

Km

Soom Tea Garden

in creating the rich, full-bodied character. In Darjeeling, though, it is the fresh, aromatic style that makes it so unique, and the slower growth that comes with altitude is a prime contributor to this.

Darjeeling is a byword for attention to detail in the relentless pursuit of quality. Plucking rounds should be four to five days in mid-season or even three to four days earlier on (even other quality-obsessed parts of the world such as Assam are seven days at best). With such short intervals between visits to the same part of the garden, the leaf quality is peerless and the factory should have the very best chance of making good tea.

Darjeeling tea factories are easy to visit and there is a burgeoning industry catering to the tourist traveller, with former planters' bungalows now converted to tourist use, offering the chance to enjoy the region's teas, walks, temples and wildlife. The factories are quite unlike anything else, with the arguable exception of some small, high-quality Chinese factories. The tiny yields and limited land under the control of each plantation ensures that the volume of leaf taken in by a factory on a daily basis is modest at best. This gives rise to an almost Toytown feel to the equipment. Everything is scaled down to the optimum size for the crop (and the limited space available to set up any sort of factory on a Himalayan mountainside). If you wish to get a sense of the process of tea manufacture then you can do worse than start and end in Darjeeling, purely because you can see each key element of the process clearly in such close proximity, and because the factory managers there are amongst the most skilled and quality-focused in the world.

The most common misconception about Darjeeling is that there is a lot of tea produced here. The Darjeeling district makes around 8,000 tonnes each year, which is significantly less than 1% of India's tea. A commonly quoted figure is that four times as much Darjeeling tea is sold each year than is actually produced in Darjeeling. This is not all fraud and deception – some consumers had become

Tea plucking at Margaret's Hope Tea Estate.

accustomed to 'Darjeeling blends' that acknowledged non-Darjeeling provenance for a part of their recipe, and combined the high-grown aroma with the body of fine Assam, for example. However there does remain some adulteration and abuse of the name in less well-policed jurisdictions.

Thanks to the advent of a Protected Geographical Indication (PGI) for Darjeeling, major markets such as the EU can now only label a tea as such if it is composed 100% of Darjeeling tea. This is important as it goes some way towards protecting the district from the Nepalese competition only a few miles to the west where ostensibly similar tea is produced from younger and higher-yielding bushes off the back of lower wages.

Darjeeling's crop is unlikely to grow significantly any time soon as there is little incentive to invest. The political situation is perilous at best, as separatist Indian Gorkhas agitate for autonomy or statehood and the district is beset by *bandhs*. Yields are minimal, around a quarter of what you would find in Assam and as small as anywhere in the world, and the bushes are around the oldest of any planting district. Although there are a number of cultivars in Darjeeling producing excellent and characterful teas with refined clonal character much in evidence, it is the older seedling bushes that represent a valuable heritage and resource for the Darjeeling trade. As any farmer will confirm, old plants normally equal small yields, but they also equal a magnificent concentration of flavour and minerality, and it is for this that Darjeeling remains so extraordinary.

FIRST FLUSH

If elevation determines relative quality in Darjeeling, then it is seasonality that dictates style. Both a high and a low garden may make a version of first flush quality and one will be much better than the

BANDHS

A *bandh* is a strike, but a uniquely Indian one. A demonstration of civil disobedience on a local or a national scale, a *bandh* can be called by a political party, a union or a political affiliation of some other form.

The difference between a *bandh* and a strike is that the whole local population is expected to remain at home. Pickets enforce this at various points in the designated area, with the only permitted vehicular transport being by ambulance.

West Bengal (in which Darjeeling and Dooars planting districts are located) is the home of the *bandh*, with more per year than any other state.

It is not unheard of for illicit transit within tea areas under *bandh* to be undertaken by ambulance when it is not required on official duties.

other, but whatever happens, they are likely to be unmistakeably first flush in style. The season starts in late February when sunlight hours have started to increase, and the first warm days of the year entice the bush out of its winter dormancy and induce some growth.

First flush teas are primarily the province of the speciality trade, whether German, local Bengali or elsewhere, with vast sums of money being spent on the few early breaks of tea. The sought-after early invoice numbers, DJ 01 being most coveted of all, often change hands for almost five or six times what is produced just a couple of weeks later during the late first flush period. Why pay so much, when in theory the factory is still just getting going and ironing out its teething problems after a long winter?

The answer actually lies in that long, hard winter. The stress that the bush suffers on account of the cold months restricts photosynthesis; a side effect of this is that the bush enhances the concentration of secondary metabolites[4] which are compounds within the tea plant bringing volatile aromas and flavour. The aromas are *so* volatile that they can be detected even without needing to brew: in just smelling the dry leaf and inhaling the pungent greenish aromas, one gets a sense of the delights that are to come. The job is only half-done, though, as to get the full first flush experience the factory manager needs to ensure that he gives the tea a hard wither in order to more completely reduce leaf moisture and with it the oxidation potential. The higher altitude factories boasting cooler and dryer conditions (both factors that delay oxidation) will be more successful at achieving this hard wither. A gentle roll and a short oxidation time then follow, ensuring that the greenish volatile aromas are retained in the leaf and not converted to the more malty notes common in other black teas. This most effectively brings out the fresh, aromatic character of first flush Darjeeling, and gives the tea a chance to shine. The resultant leaf is greenish-khaki in colour with flecks of silver tip.

Brewing Darjeeling is very much a matter of taste. The brew you use for an Assam is not necessarily that you should use for a Darjeeling. Here I would experiment with water that is less hot (just off the boil), use a little more tea in the pot than you would for Assam, but consider a shorter brew time. The longer you brew, the more you will experience the tannins masking the sensual volatile aromas that emerge less stubbornly in the earlier stages of the infusion. The astringency is not for everyone, but a dash of honey can help here. Milk is no great friend of Darjeeling, especially first flush teas; I think it masks the quality (whilst in Assam, for example, a generous finger is essential to mellow down the strength). Some like a splash, though, and the later in the Darjeeling season you go, the better milk suits the style of tea produced.

First flush teas are light bronze in colour, an apricot yellow being typical, whilst the aroma is zesty and fresh. It seems that the tea factory itself can be smelt in Darjeeling aroma: a scent that balances floral notes with the raw pungency of fresh tea, it is all wrapped up in first flush Darjeeling. To taste, the teas have an astringency, but balanced by a length of flavour and intensity unparalleled elsewhere.

IN-BETWEENERS

If you were to walk into a tea shop you could easily come to the assumption that Darjeeling has a first and a second flush with nothing twixt the two. In reality there is a period between the spring and summer flushes during which teas are produced which cannot properly be said to observe the characteristics of either flush. These are often labelled *in-between* teas, and as they span the gap between the flushes they can tend towards either flush in style, depending upon the factory manager's inclination and the leaf he has to work with. An early in-betweener is likely to be given a hard wither and short oxidation in the first-flush style to create a tea of similar taste characteristics, providing a blender with a cheaper, but nonetheless very useable alternative to the vastly more expensive teas produced a few weeks before.

SECOND FLUSH

As spring turns to summer around the beginning of June, the temperatures rise and with them the humidity. Rainfall becomes more regular and intense, and the bush starts to respond to these improved growing conditions with a new flush. The leaf that emerges is very different in character to the precious green gold of only six weeks earlier. Second flush teas have not been forged in the stress of a Himalayan winter like their earlier brothers. The additional sunlight in particular has enabled them to photosynthesise more, and as a result there are less of the volatiles than are found in first flush teas, and hence less of a rush of aroma. Second flush tea is not inferior, it is just different and many consumers find it infinitely preferable. The longer oxidation that the factory tends to give a second flush tea makes for a more rounded, pleasantly fruity cup, coupled with a character that many describe as muscatel in flavour. If a first flush is a solo violinist: potentially brilliant but an acquired taste; then second flush is the string quartet: a more accessible, complete and rounded article.

Second flush teas tend to possess more body, and that oxidation results in a dark orange hue that sets them apart from their earlier brothers in the spring. They can take a splash of milk if needed, and the longer oxidation time makes them a more practical blending proposition if you like to match them with an Assam in order to marry the Darjeeling flavour with the Assamese body and power. However, if there is one word that is more overused than any when it comes to second flush Darjeeling it is *muscatel*, and arguably it is this distinctive character that helps to make Darjeeling the iconic tea that it has become.

The muscat family of grapes is vast and encompasses both table grapes and those destined for vinification; what is consistent, though, is a floral sweetness with elements also of raisin or apricot.

229

It is this character that one can tend to find in Darjeeling second flush teas, although it is by no means universal and even within one garden it can come and go. There are some cultivars in Darjeeling that tend to deliver the muscatel character and (uniquely for tea, which is never otherwise classified by the taste) such production is often specifically labelled *Musc.* in order to draw attention to the fact.

Many in the Darjeeling industry assert that the jassid population, at this time growing rapidly in the hotter, more humid temperatures and with no shortage of green leaf to feed off, is responsible for enhancing the taste. Bushes are subject to a sustained insect attack just as with champagne oolong, which possesses a similar character, albeit with less astringency. The claim goes that the resultant fruity taste comes as a direct result of the bush's reaction to the removal of leaf sap by the jassid; in defending itself, it creates flavours that surpass what was possible without the original attack. Whatever the circumstances, second flush teas should never be overlooked.

RAINS

The post-second flush period in Darjeeling is heralded by the arrival of the monsoonal rains. Starting in July and continuing through until September, it is this period that sees the annual crop reach its peak. Tea tends to grow best under conditions of sunlight and regular rainfall, but it does not necessarily follow that the optimum conditions for growth are the optimum conditions for quality. Rainfall tends to mean that much of the leaf entering the factory is wet, the handling of which in itself is an additional challenge for the tea-maker. Not only that, but fast growing conditions tend to dilute the unique character of the Darjeeling bushes, which require a little stress to deliver the distinctive teas that have made the origin so renowned.

Do not take this to mean that you should ignore rains teas – some of the better gardens make very good tea indeed throughout the monsoon, and you only need compare the prices with the earlier production to realise that if you can find a tea that suits you, then you can buy four or five times the quantity of July tea for the same money.

DARJEELING
at a glance

Plants

75% Camellia Sinensis var. sinensis. 25% var. assamica. Most Darjeeling cultivars are developed for a fine expression of flavour such as

Bannockburn 68

Bannockburn 157

Tukdah 323

Phoobsering 312

Ambari V2 -flowery character

Terroir

Sandy-clayey loam

800-2,000 metres

Seasonality

First flush in March and second flush in June

Harvesting

Manual

Yield estimated at 400-500kg made tea per hectaure

Processing

Black orthodox, small quantities of green, white and oolong

Drinking

First flush is best drunk without milk, second flush can take a splash if needed.

AUTUMNALS

Autumn in Darjeeling lasts from September to November and is characterised by a stark reduction in rainfall. Whereas at the start of autumn the rainfall of around 300 millimetres per month is more or less what one would expect during the monsoon, it drops off sharply in October and steadily declines further to around 25 millimetres per month in November. This reduced precipitation, coupled with lower temperatures, results in both drier leaf and marginally slower growth, resulting in a lighter-bodied cup quality in the teas. Autumn may be at the tail end of the season, but there can be some fine teas produced that are *more* and *better* than just late rains teas. When made well in the drier months of October and November they can have a quality all of their own, with a coppery colour, an almost oolong-like character and fuller-bodied liquor.

DARJEELING WHITE, OOLONG AND GREEN

It follows that a great producing area inhabited by some of the finest tea-makers in the world should also produce some fine alternative types. Dhajea's excellent version of fancy oolong, and some of the mango-scented greens from elsewhere in the Chamong stable are amongst the better known. The cooler climate and China jat plant type will always suit themselves to Chinese-style processing, but this should always remain a sideshow and is unlikely ever to compete with Darjeeling's raison d'être, which remains the production of singularly distinctive black teas.

A garden in the Kangra Valley.

SIKKIM

Located to the north of Darjeeling, Sikkim produces teas of ostensibly very similar quality to the mass of teas produced within its better-known southerly neighbour. The fundamental terroir and seasonality are that of Darjeeling, but with fewer of the real highs in quality that the very best Darjeeling estates can generate. Where Sikkim excels, though, is in the minority of standout estates manned by excellent, highly committed tea-makers who can offer Darjeeling quality at more modest prices. With less interference in their affairs due to the more peaceful underlying politics of the state, Sikkim tea producers are generally less harassed by the attentions of the politicians in their production of tea. Look out for Sikkimese tea; pound for pound it is often better than equivalent Darjeeling and a challenge to pick one from the other in a blind tasting.

HIMACHAL PRADESH/KANGRA VALLEY

Growing tea since the mid-19th century, Kangra, or Valley of the Gods as it is known locally, has as venerable a history as any growing district in India. Way up towards the north-western borderlands, only around 100 kilometres from Pakistan and with a shorter growing season than any other Indian planting district, Kangra is India's forgotten tea producer. With ample rainfall and, at 1,000 (3,280 feet), a relatively high altitude, it is perhaps surprising that tea has never moved beyond the local curiosity. That Kangra is known for its green teas perhaps says everything

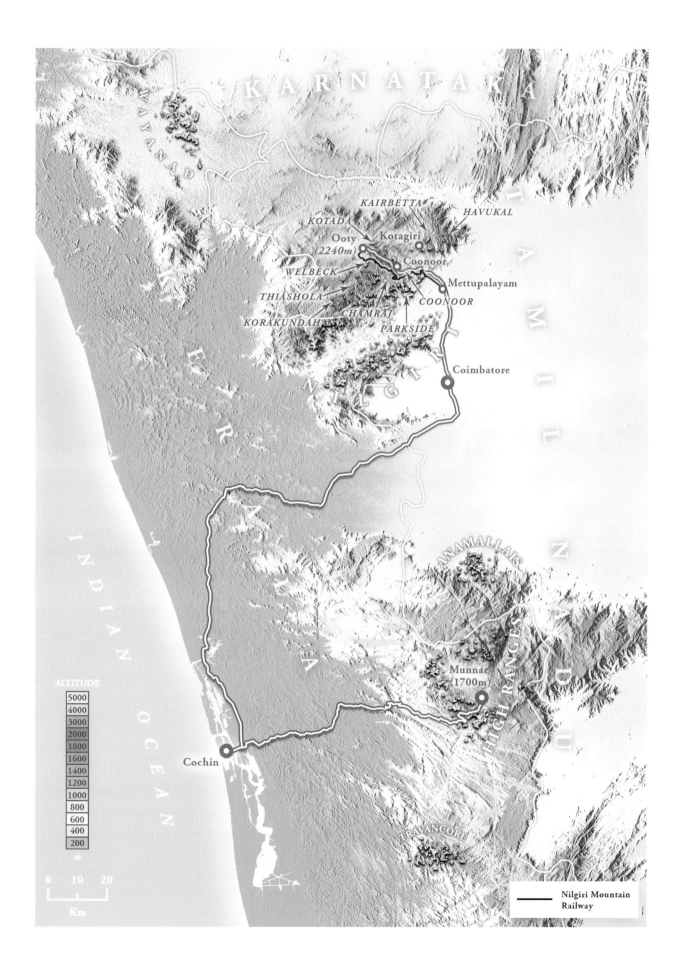

K A R N A T A K A

WAYANAD

KAIRBETTA

HAVUKAL

KOTADA

Ooty
(2240m)   Kotagiri

WELBECK   Coonoor

THIASHOLA   Mettupalayam

CHAMRAJ   COONOOR

KORAKUNDAH

PARKSIDE

NILGIRI

Coimbatore

T A M I L

ANAMALLAIS

Munnar
(1700m)

HIGH RANGES

K E R A L A

N A D U

INDIAN OCEAN

ALTITUDE

5000
4000
3000
2000
1800
1600
1400
1200
1000
800
600
400
200
m

Cochin

TRAVANCORE

0   10   20

Km

Nilgiri Mountain
Railway

Lockhart Estate in Munnar district.

about the district, a misfit in a land that has made itself the home of black tea. The predominantly China jat bushes have the potential to produce very good green and oolong tea, notwithstanding an early season black tea that has some of Darjeeling's style. A variety of oolongs are also produced all along the scale from floral Pouchong-style to the more fully oxidised style aping the Oriental beauty found in Taiwan.

As ever, particularly with the black tea, if you can locate an early tea produced in spring whilst the leaf is still soft then you can find some appealing flavour and delicate aroma. The challenge for any Western tea-drinker is finding any: with such limited crop and well-established local markets it is rare indeed for Kangra tea to make the exporter's consignments.

SOUTH INDIA

It is the south that completes India as a tea-producing nation – if Assam is about full-bodied, malty teas produced in massive volumes, and Darjeeling about finesse, aroma and boutique-style manufacture, then in many respects South India sits somewhere in the middle. There are the high-grown teas, few higher than the Nilgiri mountains, where tea produced at up to 2,400 metres (7,870 feet) eclipses even Darjeeling in altitude, but also some very mainstream CTC teas produced for price.

South India can be divided into five main tea-producing areas (if one excludes the limited tea production in Karnataka): in the western state of Kerala lie the High Ranges and Travancore, whilst

The Nilgiri mountain railway in Tamil Nadu snakes its way up from Mettupalayam on the plains up to Ooty by way of Coonoor. Steam locomotives can still be seen on the section between Mettupalayam and Coonoor, whereupon a diesel is substituted for the final section.

The route is an attractive one that provides numerous opportunities to see the local tea landscapes at their best. Further north in Darjeeling, the famous toy railway continues to ply its trade between Siliguri and Darjeeling.

in the eastern state of Tamil Nadu sit the Nilgiri teas and the Anamalais. Wayanad straddles both states. Whilst all are listed below, it is only Nilgiri teas that can rightfully demand a seat at the top table in international terms on the basis of their quality. There are pockets of brilliance elsewhere, but seldom with the consistency of the better Nilgiri gardens.

NILGIRI

Forming the southernmost extension of the Western Ghats, the Nilgiri hills vie with the Ceylon high-grown areas as one of the most accessible, tourist-friendly and beautiful areas to visit tea gardens anywhere in the world. The narrow gauge railway from Coimbatore on the plains up to the hill station of Udhagamandalam, better known as Ootacamund or just 'Ooty', is one of the best ways to see the tea and remains a masterpiece of Edwardian engineering. The evergreen attractions of the hill stations at Coonoor and Ooty have endowed the Nilgiris with numerous accommodation and sightseeing options.

The best quality lies in the areas around Ooty and Coonoor, and especially south west of Coonoor, where higher altitude and ample rainfall provided by the weather systems hitting the Ghats provide Ceylon-style high-elevation tea-growing opportunities.

Chamraj Estate in the Nilgiri hills.

Gardens such as Havukal, Kairbetta, Parkside, Chamraj and Korakundah make classic orthodox teas that provide pungency, briskness and fine, bright liquors. They drink well on their own or will blend successfully with Assams, and can bring a delightful mellowness to sometimes coarse African-based blends.

Some factories have gone further in producing boutique teas. Purpose-built areas are orientated around minute batches of ultra-high quality teas, into which only the very best quality leaf is routed, and with the expectation of a serious price tag on any teas emerging at the end of the process. The wine trade has a word for small-scale, ultra high-quality winemakers: *garagistes.* This is the tea equivalent, and you should look for the produce in tea shops because the batches are so limited that only small retailers can really stock it. Multitudinous types are produced – white, oolong, green and black – but pay especial attention to the lovingly handled leaf. Seldom outside of the realm of East Asian handmade produce has a tea been given more personal attention.

FROST TEA

The blessing of altitude is that with the lower temperatures at this height there is generally less pest activity, whilst the curse is that the tea planted in valley bottoms and hollows becomes more prone to frost during the cooler season. Whilst Darjeeling is equally high-grown (and cooler due to the influence of the Himalayas), it does have an off-season when temperatures drop so low that the bush becomes dormant. This means that one does not see the impact of frost damage in the tea, given that

Tea gardens in the High Ranges.

no growth is taking place. The Nilgiris, however, are much further south, with milder winters, and as a consequence the bushes are growing throughout the year (even if there is a period of much reduced crop during the earlier months). The prospect of frost is a worrisome one for the tea planter: the scorch that results can render the bushes unpluckable for the next four or five weeks at best, or at worst even kill off weakened areas entirely.

Enterprising planters have succeeded in turning this curse into a blessing. When frost is expected, the planter will know which hollows of his garden are more prone than others and have a team of pluckers readied the evening before. Frost will normally hit between 4.30am and 5.30am, so by 6am a special team of pluckers will be dispatched to gather as much of this leaf as they can and return it to the factory for withering whilst the cells are still frozen.

The thawing of the leaf cells is audible as a crackling in the withering loft; this helps the planter in achieving a natural wither without requiring mechanical intervention. One exposure to the seductive fragrance of any tea factory withering loft is enough to demonstrate how much aroma is lost during the mechanical wither stage of conventional tea manufacture. The frost has become a quasi-substitute for the withering process, which helps the tea-maker to achieve a very hard wither thereby retaining more of the top notes that are usually lost during tea manufacture.

HIGH RANGES

If Nilgiri tea at its best represents the ultimate in quality that South India can produce, then the gardens of the High Ranges in the Kanan Devan hills around Munnar are largely responsible for the everyday quality. Munnar tea is high-grown, good value and perfectly serviceable CTC and orthodox tea, well accepted in markets in Eastern Europe and the Middle East, but without ever scaling the heights of quality found further east in the Nilgiri hills.

The real pleasure here lies in a visit. Easily accessible from Cochin on the coast, and more recently celebrated in Yann Martel's novel *The Life of Pi*, Munnar is a wonderful base from which to explore the local tea gardens. Tea estates here are almost contiguous and form a beautiful contour-

Plants

80% var. assamica,
20% var. sinensis
CR6017- flavoury teas
2024- yield
B661 & B662- drought &
disease-resistant
Greenways- good green tea
TRI-2043- silver tips

Terroir

Sandy loam
600-2,500 metres

Seasonality

Best quality produced from
December to early February

Harvesting

90% shear
Yield estimated at 2500-
3000 kg made tea per
hectare

Processing

70% CTC, 25% orthodox,
remainder green tea

Drinking

High-growns can add
mellowness and aroma to
African-based blends. Very
high-grown Nilgiris work well
without milk.

Tea estates play host to a variety of wildlife, with the areas of indigenous forest that are often found in less viable parts of the gardens providing sanctuary to animals startled by plucking teams. In general most animals tend not to damage the tea, although porcupines are partial to the roots, especially those of the quality varietal CR6017. Leopards can still be seen in more remote areas where they help themselves to muntjac and sambar, but maintain a distance from humans. Sloth bears are occasionally seen and can be aggressive if disturbed. Bison in rutting season can do damage, as can elephants, although any real destruction is usually quite slight considering their size.

An Indian Gaur (or Bison) on Kotada Estate.

Organic gardens and those implementing certification are reporting an increase in insect activity and sightings of birds such as the hornbill in tea areas.

defining background to a drive through the region.

.

ANAMALAIS

Just across the hills from the High Ranges into Tamil Nadu lie the Anamalais. In reality the two areas are almost interchangeable as far as quality goes, producing everyday, workmanlike teas of medium quality. As with the High Ranges, though, the Anamalais is a beautiful hilly area that is worth visiting more for the scenery than the teas. The occasional patch of indigenous jungle is suggestive of what the area was like 150 years ago, and puts the efforts of the industrious pioneers into sobering context.

WAYANAD

Existing on the Tamil Nadu-Kerala border, Wayanad produces tea in the High Range style. In comparison with the Munnar teas Wayanad is unspectacular but eminently serviceable. Its lower altitude tends to give a little more body but rather less aroma to the liquors. The main reason to visit is the beautiful high-grown environment and abundance of wildlife protected by the neighbouring Mudumalai Wildlife Sanctuary.

TRAVANCORE

Another classic high-grown area of South India boasting not only tea plantations but also spices, coconut and coffee. The tea quality is fuller in body than the other South Indian types, but with modest levels of aroma.

NEPAL

*Best known for classic Himalayan orthodox tea often mistaken for Darjeeling,
but also a substantial CTC producer.*

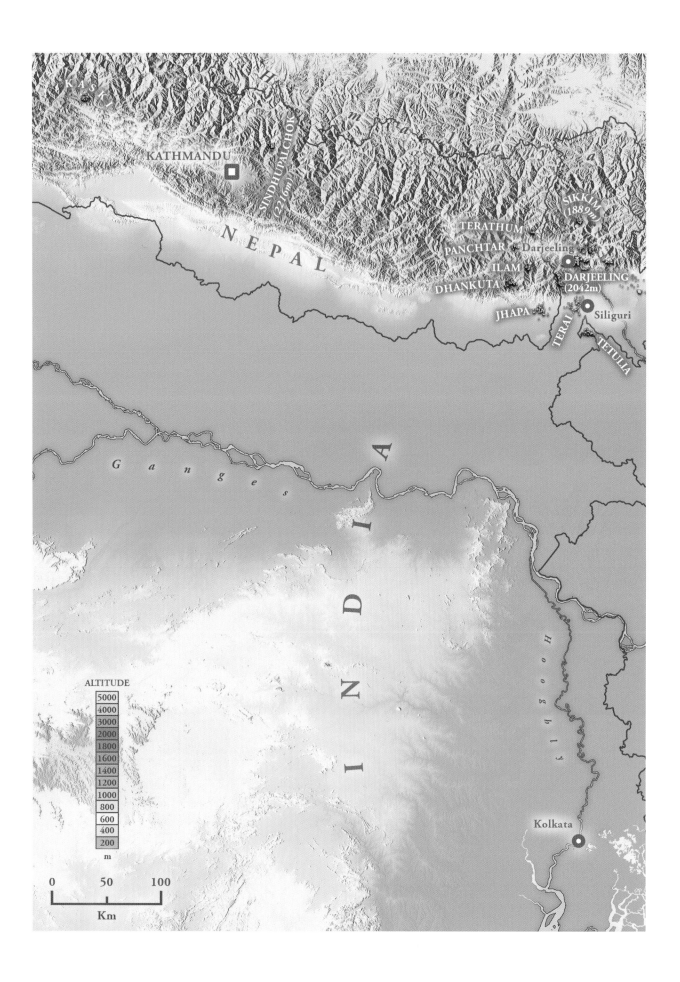

KASKI

KATHMANDU

SINDHUPALCHOK
(2216m)

NEPAL

TERATHUM

PANCHTAR • Darjeeling

ILAM

DHANKUTA

SIKKIM
(1889m)

DARJEELING
(2042m)

JHAPA

Siliguri

TERAI

TETULIA

Ganges

INDIA

Hooghly

Kolkata

ALTITUDE

| 5000 |
| 4000 |
| 3000 |
| 2000 |
| 1800 |
| 1600 |
| 1400 |
| 1200 |
| 1000 |
| 800 |
| 600 |
| 400 |
| 200 |

m

0   50   100

Km

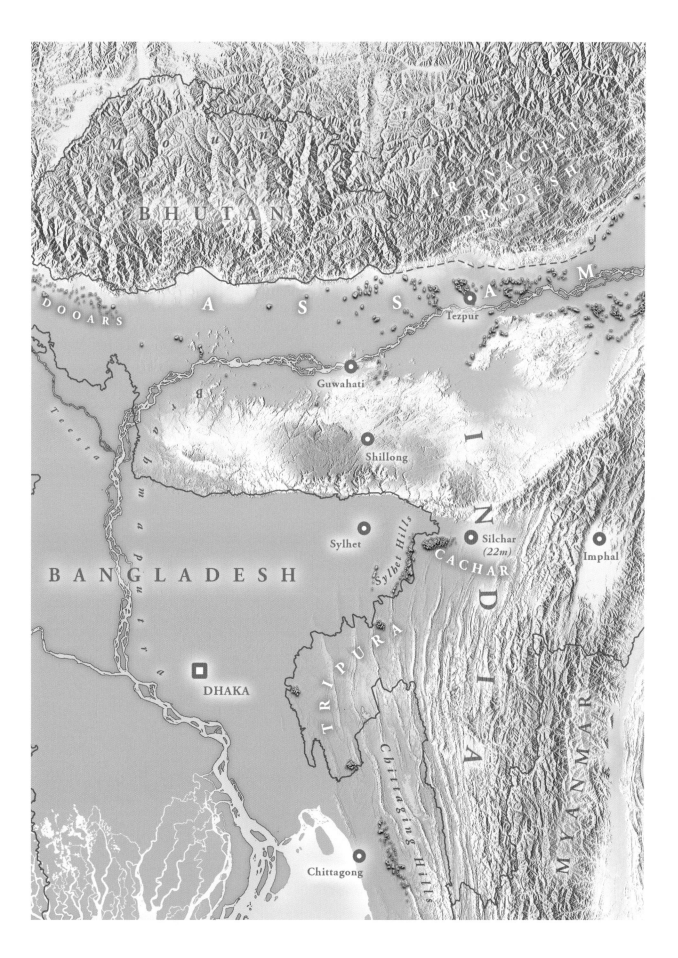

N EPAL SITS TWIXT THE WORLD'S two greatest tea producers, and although it can boast more than 150 years of tea-producing heritage, its relatively unstable history and bouts of governmental interference have ensured the industry a rougher passage than that of either India or China. With its Himalayan terroir and experienced tea-makers, Nepal is ideally located to produce world-class orthodox tea and increasingly features on the offerings of speciality sellers attracted by its refined, high-grown style, yet affordable price.

BACKGROUND

Nepali tea can trace its origins back to 1863, only a decade after the establishment of the Darjeeling industry. The comparison is not accidental, as they possess very similar terroir and quality potential, although the two countries have since followed differing courses. Darjeeling's tea has traced a trajectory taking it squarely into the stratosphere as far as pricing and brand equity are concerned, whilst Nepal has until comparatively recently made mass volumes of cheap CTC for the local market.

The early history of the industry involved state-owned and run tea gardens and factories. Whilst tea was processed internally, it is said that substantial volumes of leaf also made their way across the border to India, where they were processed and augmented the local crop. There was little in the way of dynamism until private gardens emerged with liberalisation in 1993. Such producers have become the trailblazers for quality, often with the help of Western NGOs and aid money, and you can see evidence of this most manifestly in the excellent orthodox teas. Although around 80% of the tea produced in Nepal is CTC, this is overwhelmingly local in consumption and if exported usually

Hariyali Cooperative in Ilam.

makes it no farther than India, where it is blended with similar Terai teas. It is the orthodox product that has inevitably captured the attention of the global trade.

NEPAL ORTHODOX

Tea processed in the orthodox style tends to show itself at its most characterful and distinctive at higher elevations. Here, at between 1,000 and 2,400 metres (3,280-7,900 feet) where the cooler Himalayan winds course down steep-sided valleys, sit some of the world's best high-grown tea producers. The cold winds restrict leaf growth and the icy winters ensure enough stress on the bushes to guarantee an exciting, piercing aroma on the first flush teas and equally appealing notes of tropical fruits during the second flush. There will be the inevitable comparisons with Darjeeling, and why not? The seasons follow a similar pattern, with Nepal having to wait only a week or two longer than Darjeeling for its flushes. The soil is the same loam but the bushes are on average much younger with potentially better quality of leaf.

Production is around a third to a half of Darjeeling's, but the value for money is excellent and without the snob value attached to some of the early invoices and better-known designer marks in Darjeeling. There is ample opportunity to procure world-class teas at excellent value for money. The eastern districts, especially Ilam, Panchthar, Dhankuta and Terhathum, account for the bulk of the orthodox crop. Panchthar itself sits on the border and is only 10 kilometres (6 miles) from Darjeeling, sharing its terroir most strikingly. Gardens or selling marks to look out for include Maloom, Kanyam, Mai-Ilam and Jun Chiyabari, all producing excellent black teas as well as the occasional fine floral-

Harka Tea Garden in the Jhapa district.

NEPAL
at a glance

Plants

Camellia Sinensis
var. sinensis
Tukdah 78- flavour
Tukdah 383- flavour
Teenali- early spring
flush
Bannockburn-157
flavour

Terroir

Shallow sandy loam,
some clayey loam,
1,000-2,400 metres
(high-grown tea),
100-300 metres
(Terai teas)

Seasonality

First flush in March,
second flush in June

Harvesting

Manual. Yield
1109kg made tea
per hectare

Processing

Orthodox black, CTC
black, some green

Drinking

Early season teas
best without milk,
later teas can take a
splash

scented green tea and limited volumes of bespoke handmade tea that can never keep pace with market demand. Guranse produces a tactile white tea, a green tea with notes of green apple, as well as world-class first and second flush types.

The future is exciting too: Teenjure is the first co-operative garden in Nepal and its skilled women have now started to pioneer the production of handmade tea. New plantings in Sindhupalchowk and Kaski further west represent a geographical expansion into potentially exciting high-elevation terroir, and will provide more classic Himalayan high-grown teas at eminently affordable prices in the future.

NEPAL BLACK CTC

Nepali CTC hails primarily from the Jhapa district, an alluvial area in the south east of the country. Although Nepal is known as a land of mountains, parts of the district of Jhapa are as flat as any producing area in the world. Here the floodplains of the Mechi river, which forms the border between Nepal and India, make for prime tea-producing country.

Tea gardens exist right up to the river within view of Indian territory on the opposite bank. The liquors are straightforward, strong and full-bodied, with a reddish fibre sometimes creeping in: more Terai than Assam in appearance, which is hardly a surprise as the terroir is identical. The seasons are much as for India: a first and second flush followed by rains and autumnal teas. These teas are honest, rich teas that demand some milk and are largely indistinguishable from their Indian neighbours.

Teenjure co-operative.

BANGLADESH

Shotty CTC tea of middling quality made for the local market. One solitary producer of orthodox and white tea in the northern border areas shows the potential that exists in Bangladesh.

BANGLADESH IS LITTLE KNOWN as a tea producer despite its substantial output and venerable heritage, mainly because its production is almost exclusively consumed domestically. With one notable exception, the tea is also of ordinary quality. Being both a populous country and one of enthusiastic tea-consumers, it is no surprise that the tea producers here do not unduly exercise the export statistician despite the government's best efforts. In many ways Bangladesh is a test case and it is experiencing now what India and Indonesia may one day experience – a growing tea-drinking populous with which its own domestic tea production cannot keep pace.

The local consumers demand a specific style well suited to the subcontinental habit of cooking the leaf in milk, to which a liberal dose of sugar is then added. Bold, shotty CTC teas are favoured, often much more attractive in leaf style than they taste, but then sugar can work wonders. In one of the poorest countries in the world, *cuppage* is important. Cuppage denotes the number of cups one can extract from a particular volume of leaf – clearly, the more cups, the more the tea may be favoured by a financially constrained consumer. This means producers will try to create as strong a tea as they can rather than moving mountains for specific clonal or seasonal characters that tea consumers of more premium persuasion may find important.

SYLHET AND CHITTAGONG

BLACK CTC

There are two main producing areas in Bangladesh which, although they themselves divide into a number of districts, can be regarded as geographically homogenous. The larger of the two is in the low hills around the town of Sylhet in Bangladesh's north-eastern corner. These gardens form part of the old British-established industry and sit on the border with Assam and Meghalaya. The teas

Plucking on the organic garden of Kazi & Kazi.

Plants

Camellia Sinensis var.
assamica
BT series of cultivars
(BT1 to BT13)- yield/quality

Terroir

Sandy loams in
Sylhet, alluvial
soils rich in
humus in Panchagarh, 20-
40 metres above sea level

Seasonality

Best teas produced
during second
flush in June

Harvesting

Manual, some shear
plucking. Yield
1223 kg made tea
per hectare

Drinking

Southern teas are best
consumed
with milk, speciality
teas
from Terai are
more versatile

are geographically close, and stylistically rather similar to Cachar types, with a touch less strength. The loamy soils here do not yield especially well, but this is also a factor of the large concentration of poor-cropping seedling bushes amongst the gardens. The season runs broadly parallel to that of Assam, although can extend a little longer owing to the more southerly latitude. The best crop in terms of body comes from the June flush, broadly commensurate with the Assam second flush, but even this is rather relative.

Further south there are further tea gardens inland from Chittagong on the slopes of the north-south range of hills that extend into the Indian state of Mizoram to the east. The soils are similar loams to those in Sylhet, and although the temperatures are slightly warmer and rainfall marginally lower, this does not make an appreciable difference to the quality of what is produced.

PANCHAGARH

ORTHODOX BLACK TEA, OOLONG AND WHITE TEA

The borderlands of Bangladesh and India are a plebiscite-derived mess. Hastily conceived as partition loomed, they trace around slivers of territory that at one time held a narrow minority observing one or other of the great religions. One such tract of land is the district of Panchagarh, a small finger of Bangladesh that juts into India like a peninsula. The tea garden of Kazi and Kazi lies in Tetulia (what the Bangladeshis call an *upazila* or sub-district of Panchagarh). Tetulia is pressed right up against the border: Panchagarh is surrounded by West Bengal on all three sides and is therefore much more within the terroir of the lower reaches of Terai than anything else within Bangladesh. Although it is only 25 kilometres (16 miles) south of the district of Darjeeling, the topography is flat and distinctly Assam-like. The humic, alluvial soils are identical to those of Terai, and there is no question that Kazi and Kazi is the jewel in the Bangladeshi tea crown.

Organically grown and featuring beautiful, tippy, orthodox black, mellow oolong with notes of apricot, and soft, delicate white teas. The small production here is produced almost exclusively for export. With a malty liquor, smooth, pungent aroma and a well-twisted leaf appearance, the Kazi and Kazi orthodox black teas do not rightfully belong with the remainder of Bangladeshi production and stand up well to much of what is produced only a few miles away in India.

SRI LANKA

Abundant variety of fine quality from an island that has become synonymous with tea.

COLOMBO

Kandy
(520m)

UDA

NUWARA
ELIYA

Ratnapura
(88m)

ATHERFIELD

VITHANAKANDE

MUTUWAGALLA

RILHENA

OPATA

ENDANE

KOPPAKANDA

KEKUNDENIYA

LUMBINI

AHINSA

POTHOTUWA

KALUBOWITIVANA

DAMPAHALA

ROTUMBA

ETAMBAGAHAWILA

Galle

Matara

Laccadive

Sea

ALTITUDE

5000
4000
3000
2000
1800
1600
1400
1200
1000
800
600
400
200

m

0   10   20

Km

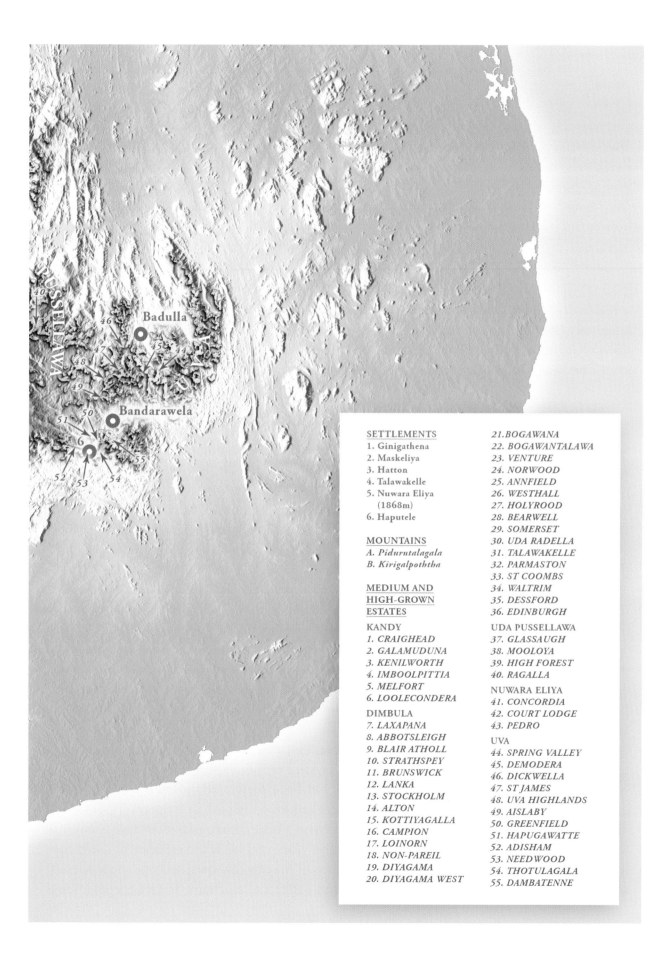

Badulla

Bandarawela

PUSSELLAWA

WHETHER FOR THE BEAUTY of its plantation areas, the teas themselves, or the warm welcome extended by its people, Sri Lanka is a resounding favourite for those who travel with tea. Meticulously manicured tea bushes define the contours of precipitous valleys, picture-book bungalows perched upon escarpments stand sentinel whilst waterfalls cascade through verdant gullies in a land fashioned with the romantic artist front of mind. Tea dominates the landscapes of the interior, its reach so broad that it occupies a significant place in the national consciousness of Sri Lanka.

There is a wealth of variety on offer. The island is roughly equivalent in size to Ireland, so it is certainly compact. Yet it succeeds in encompassing full-bodied, malty leaf teas much favoured in the Middle East within 160 kilometres (100 miles) of the light, bright, mango-scented delights of Nuwara Eliya. This shows the resounding impact of place on tea. Towering cliffs, home to leopards and sambar, lie within a relative stone's throw of the lowland jungles populated by peacocks, monitor lizards and elephants.

BACKGROUND

Sri Lanka's rural destiny seemed to lie in the hands of another beverage until as late as 1890. Coffee was widely cultivated by the earliest Scottish planters, for, as with Assam, it was largely Scotsmen who pioneered the clearing of the interior jungle areas. The earliest settlements took place in the 1820s in what is now referred to as the mid-country area south west of the ancient city of Kandy.[1] Over the 1820s, 30s and early 40s, the coffee industry boomed spectacularly before its equally dramatic collapse in 1847. Many proprietors were left either bankrupt, or in a position where they were forced to sell their once-prized land at a fraction of the former value.

The coffee trade managed to recover and flourished until the late 1860s when traces of coffee rust were spotted on the leaves. Within twenty years the industry was effectively dead as the orange blotches of *Hemileia vastatrix* laid waste to the vulnerable coffee plants in all-consuming fashion. Faced with the reality of revolution or ruin, planters had little choice but to uproot the decaying skeletons of the coffee industry and replace them with cinchona trees (the bark of which is used to make quinine) or tea plants. Whilst cinchona experienced the market crash one would expect of a market suddenly flooded with a product that could only ever sustain modest demand, tea was destined for a rosier future.

The first hero of the Ceylon tea story is a Scotsman called James Taylor who pioneered the planting of tea at a coffee estate named Loolecondera in 1867. Taylor, a well-built planter from Kincardineshire, wasn't the first to plant tea in Ceylon (tea seeds had been successfully planted in the botanical gardens of Kandy in 1839, and some coffee planters had experimented with the plant), but it was Taylor who had the courage and foresight to plant tea on a large commercial scale. This is no small feat as the plant yields nothing of use for at least five years, and his grand experiment could have left his employers with a worthless folly. The success of his experiments gave hope to those estate owners who had invested their hopes and capital in coffee and cinchona. In fact, the conditions

A typical Sri Lankan tea factory. The upper floors are devoted to leaf withering and the ground floor handles all other activities.

on the island were ideally suited for the plant, and those who had not sold up were again able to contemplate a profitable future. The stampede to tea that followed overwhelmed the modest supply of tea seeds that were available locally at the time and resulted in enterprising traders venturing as far afield as China to bring back suitable material. The achievement of the planters in rescuing the island from the coffee blight and the sudden rise of the Ceylon tea industry was such that Arthur Conan Doyle commented, *"Not often is it that men have the heart, when their one great industry is withered, to rear up in a few years another as rich to take its place, and the tea fields of Ceylon are as true a monument to courage as is the lion at Waterloo."*

Many, however, did decide to sell up. With plantation land going for a relative song it fell to the second hero of the Ceylon story to play his part. Sir Thomas Lipton was already a wealthy grocer with a chain of successful stores to his name, when en route to a holiday in Australia he broke his journey in Colombo. There Lipton spied an opportunity; if he could secure a good-value supply of tea by buying estates at knockdown prices, then he could make use of his retail outlets to bring tea to the masses at an affordable price. Before long he had bought twelve estates, tea from which went into packs bearing his name, selling at less than half the price of most other tea in the market. In bringing quality tea to the masses, Lipton became almost single-handedly responsible for the success of Ceylon as a brand of quality.

If Sri Lanka's principal distinction lies in the variety of its teas, then the main contributory factor is the mountains which dominate the heart of the island. It is these that provide the microclimates and variations in altitude; they define the average temperatures, the growth-inducing southerly aspects, and dispassionately act as both benign guardian and bringer of meteorological distress. They lend an epic, mythic quality to the landscape, such that one is aware of the potential greatness of the tea long

The Dimbula tea district is arugably the world's greatest concentration of top-quality tea production.

before it passes the expectant lips. Where there are no mountains, the humid tropical climate re-establishes control and lends a completely new dimension to the fruits of the soil.

The diversity of the produce has compelled the Sri Lankans to devise boxes in which to group their multitudinous teas. Ceylon teas tend towards terminological overload: low, medium or high-grown; liquoring teas or 'bright-lights'; Westerns, Nuwara Eliyas, Uda Pussellawas or Uvas. In order to demystify the Ceylon world there are some basics with which everything else falls into place.

ELEVATION: HIGH-GROWN TEAS

Of all criteria, elevation is the most significant in Sri Lanka. Altitude influences temperature, temperature impacts speed of growth, and speed of growth determines style and intensity of flavour and aroma. It is easiest to conceive of Sri Lankan elevation on the imperial scale; low-growns are officially from sea level to 2,000 feet (0–600 metres), medium-growns from 2,000 to 4,000 feet (600–1,200 metres), and high-growns above 4,000 feet (1,200 metres plus). Temperatures typically drop by around 1°C for every additional 100 metres (328 feet) of altitude, ensuring that the mean daily maximum temperature at Nuwara Eliya is 20°C whilst that at Ratnapura, only 32 kilometres (20 miles) away but 1,500 metres (5,000 feet) lower down, is 32°C. Temperatures aside, average annual rainfall at Nuwara Eliya is just over half that of the low-grown districts. Imagine this additional precipitation as a potential dilution of high-grown flavour and you begin to see how such a small area can play host to such variety.

At a mean temperature of 20°C, a typical high-grown Ceylon tea bush is existing at the extremities of its tolerance. Any colder and it will stop growing and go into dormancy, or worse still die. At this

Sri Lanka's hills have become a place of pilgrimage for many tea tourists; here on the Nuwara Eliya-Dimbula border there is hardly a spot without tea.

level of stress, nature decrees that in order to survive, a bush should not over-exert itself in growing foliage that it cannot support. What we get as a result is a fine concentration of flavours in the leaf. High-grown buds have taken three days longer to develop than at sea level, and the extra effort that the bush has had to make is evident in the tea. Aside from the temperature, the mountain soils are typically thinner than those at sea level, and the root structure has therefore to work even harder to extract the requisite nutrients from the poor earth. What results is a triumph. Faced with this adversity, the tea bush produces a tea of incomparable flavour. Startlingly zesty, the teas carry striking citric aromas that can be detected even on the black leaf, long before it has been infused.

Infuse the leaf, and a typical high-grown tea will immediately reveal an intense, tangy, citric aroma, suffused with freshness. Light-bodied and relatively thin on the mouthfeel, but with a charming mellowness and a briskness of flavour that is pure refreshment. Add a small dash of milk and the liquor becomes a bright pinkish yellow. This is classic afternoon tea, and a perfect foil to the stronger 'morning' blends from India and Kenya.

Within the sphere of high-grown teas there are four agroclimatic areas that, although they share some of the characteristics of high-altitude tea, are sufficiently distinctive to merit a description of their own.

WESTERN-DIMBULA

At the western limits of the high-grown area between the small towns of Maskeliya and Pussellawa lie the Western or Dimbula tea gardens. The names – Edinburgh, Holyrood, Strathspey – and the craggy peaks providing the dramatic backcloth help to explain how the early Scottish planters managed to make themselves feel at home here.

A well-made Western tea is a study in intensity of aroma in perfect balance with a mellow citric flavour. Year round, the district can be relied upon to produce beautiful, delicately flavoured teas of the finest sort; brisk and with a refreshing zing, these teas are prized all over the world either for drinking on their own, or to blend out the coarse flavour of African teas.

GEOFFREY BAWA

Bawa (1909–2003) is the greatest architect to have emerged from Sri Lanka, and many acknowledge him as the father of modern Asian architecture. During his career he designed not only Sri Lanka's parliament building and a number of eminent municipal *grand projets*, but also plantation bungalows. His early style is best seen at the Strathspey Estate bungalow in Upcot, at the foot of Adam's Peak.[2]

Between February and late March the region scales fresh heights of achievement as the north-east monsoon draws in. Whilst the monsoon brings rains to the northern and eastern sides of the island, it leaves the western areas to parch in the lee of the central mountains. The night-time temperatures drop and frosts start to make their presence felt, whilst daytime temperatures increase, rainfall dries up, winds start to blow and so the flavours concentrate in the leaf as the crop is cut in half by the climatic conditions. Although the entire period is unlikely to bring forth consistency of peak quality there is nonetheless generally a burst of one to three weeks when the liquors develop a heightened pungency, with subtly increased levels of sweetness to add to the already glorious 'standard product'. The village of Upcot to the western lee of Adam's Peak can boast the premier estates – teas from Alton, Stockholm, Brunswick and Strathspey stand the best chance of producing exceptional quality, but many other producers besides can match these on a good day. Deciding when in the season to buy is notoriously difficult, and determining when peak quality has been reached is only possible with hindsight.

NUWARA ELIYA

Heading east from Dimbula the A7 winds its way to the hill station of Nuwara Eliya, sometimes referred to as 'Little England'; for the past century or more it has been a thriving holiday resort, complete with racecourse and botanical gardens as well as its two grand, quintessentially English hotels, Hill Club and golf course. The town has since made the most of its enviable climate and the fertile soils that exist on the plateau, and supplements its tea and tourism income as the centre of the Sri Lankan market garden industry, the strawberries being exceptionally sought after.

Nuwara Eliya sits in the shadow of Mount Pidurutalagala (Mount Pedro), at 2,524 metres (8,281 feet), the highest in Sri Lanka. Although there are a number of gardens operating in the area, the most distinctive style of manufacture here is that of the 'bright-lights'. Tea factories manufacturing tea to this style allow almost no oxidation time. The tea is plucked, withered, rolled and then immediately dried when the leaf is still visibly green. The lack of oxidation seals in a distinctive raw character that can be an acquired taste; the Germans have acquired it and these teas are highly prized for their unique greenness.

To be drunk without milk and possibly with a slice of lime or orange, the teas are incredibly refreshing. In well-made teas, the greenish character is balanced by a lightness of body and pungency

Pedro tea estate in Nuwara Eliya.

that makes them very drinkable. The secret is the unique local conditions which produce a very dry leaf that has developed very slowly on thin soils. The leaf should be naturally low in moisture, having been stressed through its difficult growing phase. If it is a little too succulent then the factory manager will further stress it through giving the leaf a very hard wither to extract the requisite moisture through his own intervention. It is best to wait until December or January, when a paucity of rain and very low temperatures coincide to forge teas of unmistakeable class. Quality surges to the point where mango fruit flavours merge with the now heightened length of flavour to produce an astounding tea. The tropical fruit character is especially elusive and one occasionally found on Darjeeling green teas, but here in the season it is at its most evident. The best exponents of this art are the Court Lodge and Pedro factories, of which Pedro, being located a little higher, tends to produce the more exciting teas. Court Lodge teas are named as such; Pedro produce is sold as Lovers Leap and Mahagastotte in alternating batches.

UDA PUSSELLAWA

East of Nuwara Eliya and at a lower elevation sits the Uda Pussellawa district, producing a tea that is in many ways a halfway house between east and west. The defining characteristic is a floral character that is occasionally rose-like and coupled with a tangy citric note in the liquor. These teas share some of the characteristics of both of their neighbours without ever managing to reach the heights of either.

UVA

On the more sparsely populated eastern side of the island, the Uva district can almost be forgotten for nine months of the year, during which it produces teas which represent a bridge between the large leaf grades of the low-grown region and the brisk, flavoury liquors of the high-grown areas. However, the period between mid-June and the end of August sees the arrival of the south-west monsoon: clear

THE CLUB

For early planters dispatched to the most remote and isolated parts of the globe, a focus for social communion was recognised as a vital element in their wellbeing. The planters' clubs that were established in these pioneering days played a key role in providing a focal point for socialising. The managers of the early tea gardens would come from miles around on horseback in order not to miss out on 'club night'. Most of the clubs still exist, often with golf courses or even polo grounds in varied states of repair. The walls of the bar remain adorned with stuffed trophies, reflecting the different era in which such institutions were conceived. Visitors to remote tea-producing areas should try to support these clubs, which now struggle in the age of satellite TV and alternative forms of entertainment. Among the best of them is the Hill Club in Nuwara Eliya, which caters to tourists whilst succeeding in maintaining most of its most cherished traditions.

skies, dry weather, and a temperature variation of around 24°C between day and night. Perhaps most significant of all is the blowing of the hot, drying Cachan wind, so intense that householders weigh their steel roofs down with additional sacks of sand in order to prevent their removal by the stronger gusts.

Whilst the western districts suffer habitual deluges brought by the south-west monsoon season, the Uva district slowly bakes in the rain shadow cast by the central mountains. Production drops by 60% as the bush cuts non-essential growth and switches on its life support systems in a fight for survival. Leaf moisture slowly drops as the dry days and cold nights continue. Levels of methyl salicylate, which naturally occurs in any tea bush, steadily grow as the bush reacts to the changed conditions and endeavours to protect itself from attack.

Withers are hard in the Darjeeling style, the lower moisture content of the leaf ensuring that the aromatic top notes are retained to the max whilst oxidation is kept to the minimum, much less than quality teas in the western districts. Always night owls in any case, factory managers now produce tea exclusively at night when they can take advantage of the cool temperatures to maximise on quality.

Anticipation builds in the key markets of Hamburg and Tokyo as reports of the first signs of the hallowed, medicated notes found

FACTORY ROOFS AND THE RAF

Many Sri Lankan tea factories are recognisable from long distances by their code numbers, which are proudly emblazoned upon their broad expanses of corrugated steel roofing. The code numbers were reputedly introduced during the Second World War in order to assist RAF pilots with their navigation across the interior.

in the best examples of such teas filter through. When it comes it is scarcely possible to countenance that the character can be a product of a natural process, and the only really adequate descriptor is wintergreen (or Germolene®, the unmistakeable smell of a sports changing room). But this does nothing to represent the appeal of such teas, which are as genuinely unique as anything in the world of tea.

MEDIUM-GROWNS

These are the original Ceylon tea gardens. The mid-country estates lie in the swathe of land to the south of Kandy, the venerable cultural mecca that is Sri Lanka's second city. The rolling hills of Central Province have some of the manicured splendour of the high-grown areas but combined with the verdant jungle of the low-growns. The teas, too – aromatic, brisk high-growns crossed with the malty, thick, caramel-singed low-grown teas. The extra maltiness and body mean that milk is more welcome than in the high-growns, and the colour is noticeably redder. This middle ground could be seen as something of a handicap, not falling into either stall. Locals take quite the opposite view, seeing medium-grown teas as ideal drinking teas, and as such a higher proportion remains unexported.

RUHUNA AND SABARAGAMUWA

Low-grown tea used to be a world away from the pretentions of the high-grown product. Most of its drinkers lay far from the old Europe hubs of London or Hamburg. Its destiny was most likely a bazaar somewhere in the Middle East, where it would be sized up not on its taste, but entirely on leaf appearance, with different markets favouring different styles, whether well-twisted, shotty or tippy.

That was then; low-growns are now very much 'in'. The first tea-drinkers beyond the Middle East to appreciate their appeal were the Russians in the immediate post-Cold War period; they set a trend since followed by the Germans, who adore the black leaf appearance and deep reddish colour.

Low-growns are all about leaf, and such a concept is sometimes difficult for Westerners to understand. The idea that the appearance of the tea leaf can be so important, even more important than its taste, is anathema to many, but what is often forgotten is what modern marketeers would call the 'point of sale'. A low-grown tea will invariably be sold in a relatively crudely packed carton, or possibly even today straight out of a chest in a bazaar in the Middle East or North Africa. Whilst brand names exist, they are hardly expensively fashioned megabrands – favourites include a sometime Saudi brand dating to the dawn of the technological era called Mobile Phone Tea. The only way that the consumer can evaluate the tea is by looking at the leaf, and this is why it is so important that the factory manager has done his job in the sorting room properly.

Tea-drinkers in Iran favour tippy teas, where the leaf has a high proportion of gold (Indian) or silver (Sri Lankan) tips. Although these tips do not always impart much flavour, they are a sign that plucking has been discriminatory and due care has been observed in the factory, and more importantly, they are what generations of Iranians have told their children represent good quality. For the Turkish or Syrian consumer nothing can match the tightly rolled, shotty pekoe teas, each leaf tightly crimped into a densely-twisted pellet that in itself acts as a barrier to the ingress of moisture and oxygen, and ensures that the tea will taste better for longer. As it is the heaviest, densest pellets that command the highest prices, vast winnowing machines invariably occupy one corner of the factory specifically

The jungle-fringed tea gardens of the low-country

designed to sort the lightweight fluff from the peak quality destined for Damascus. Trying to satisfy these diverse markets is difficult enough before one factors in the demands of Iraq, Saudi Arabia, Jordan, Libya and Tunisia.

The low-grown sector is relatively young and owes much of its success to the expansion of the smallholder areas in Ruhuna and Sabaragamuwa. Whereas most of the high-grown estates are ex-colonial establishments owned by large corporations where the factory and the tea itself are under unitary ownership, the low-grown sector is primarily one in the hands of the smallholders. Competition amongst the many factories for the tea that the farmers harvest is fierce, and driving 50 or 60 miles in search of much-needed leaf is not unheard of. This would be unthinkable in many parts of the world, where any sort of bruising to the green leaf would unleash a tirade from the factory manager and the probable sacking of the unfortunate responsible. In the low-grown sector the fact that the market is interested in leaf appearance more than liquor means it is much less crucial to rush leaf to the factory in pristine condition. If it is not going to be tasted until it reaches the bazaars of Tehran, then what is the concern if a little pre-fermentation has occurred en route to the factory?

LOW-GROWN FACTORIES

A low-grown factory is an experience apart. Surrounded by jungle or swathes of rubber and tea. Tucked into a steamy valley side populated by boar, peacocks, kingfishers and monitor lizards. Corrugated steel cladding glinting in the intense tropical sun, windows flung wide open in a vain attempt to stimulate some ventilation, a well-tended flower garden outside, and a hovering assistant inside bearing a marigold garland to welcome guests.

The emphasis on leaf appearance brings about a distinctive layout in the factory itself. Although the sorting room is of a size befitting its status as the place where the crust is earned, to the uninitiated a Dante's inferno of chaos and confusion seems to prevail. Heaps of tea in every possible corner seem to demand the manager's attention. Technologies from the Victorian and the IT eras exist cheek by jowl, fibre-extracting machines spin and whirr, cripplingly expensive Japanese colour sorters examine each individual particle of tea, discarding anything of the wrong colour, sieves shake and rattle and an all-pervading dust hangs in the humid air, yet at the end of the room, somehow and seemingly against all odds, a pristine set of tea sacks is loaded with one of the ten or more different leaf grades that this particular factory produces.

LOW-GROWN TEAS

Despite this emphasis on leaf appearance over the liquoring qualities of the tea, there is considerable pleasure to be derived from a cup of low-grown tea. Start with one of the major leaf grades such as a BOP that will have been manufactured on a day-in-day-out basis (and hence has not sat around on the sorting room floor for days). Infuse, add a splash of milk and a warm, burnt chocolate-caramel aroma is the first taste sensation. This is the result of a high firing in the dryers (ordinarily to stabilise the product and halt oxidation, but in the low country this also helps to singe the leaf to a fine black colour). Tasting the tea reveals a full-bodied, malty character that is not dissimilar to Assam in style. There is no finesse here, more raw power and an honest, gutsy kick. Chew on a chunk of the local *kitul* or palm jaggery at the same time and any bitter caramel notes are swept away by a blanket of sweetness.

CREEPERS

An oft-overheard term in discussions with Sri Lankan planters is, 'I crept with so-and-so.' A 'creeper' is a trainee tea planter who shadows someone of greater seniority in order to learn as many aspects of the trade as possible.

SRI LANKA
at a glance

Plants
60% var. sinensis, 40% var. assamica (mainly in low-grown areas)
TRFK 6/8- quality
TRI 2025-yield, quality
TRI 2026-low country
TRI 2023-yield
DT1- yield, quality, drought tolerant
PK2- yield , disease-resistant
TRI 2043- silvery tip

Terroir
Red-yellow clay-loams, 50-2,000 metres

Seasonality
Year-round production with best quality March to April for Westerns, June to August for Uvas

Harvesting
Manual. Yield 1789 kg made tea per hectare

Processing
93% black orthodox, 6% black CTC, 1% green tea

Drinking
Westerns are good with milk and are ideal for mellowing down coarser E-African teas. Uvas work well without milk. Low-growns are good breakfast teas

Zealong tea garden in Waikato.

OCEANIA

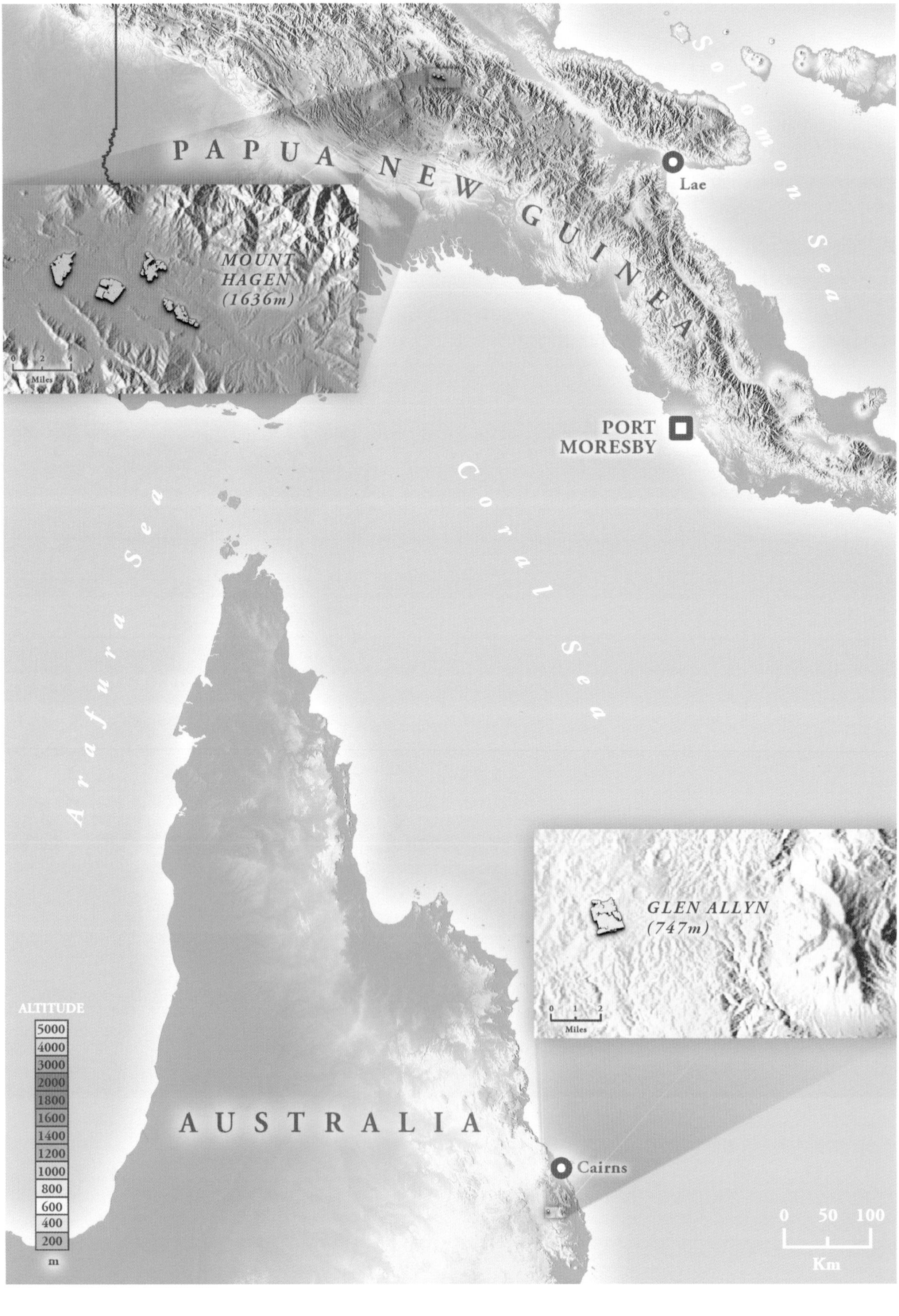

P A P U A   N E W   G U I N E A

Solomon Sea

Lae

MOUNT HAGEN
(1636m)

0   2   4
Miles

PORT
MORESBY

Coral Sea

Arafura Sea

GLEN ALLYN
(747m)

0   1   2
Miles

ALTITUDE

5000
4000
3000
2000
1800
1600
1400
1200
1000
800
600
400
200

m

A U S T R A L I A

Cairns

0   50   100

Km

PAPUA NEW GUINEA

THE WESTERN HIGHLANDS OF PAPUA NEW GUINEA (PNG) produce black CTC teas of relatively average quality, mainly for the Oceanian market. The teas work well when brewed in Australian water but can struggle elsewhere. The highlands are a tough place to operate a business, and such constraints hamper investment in quality.

The rich, well-drained fluvial soils of the Waghi Valley are surrounded by the mountains of the Western Highlands. Mount Hagen is the best-known peak in the area and has given its name to the main town of the region that serves as a base for a foray into the local tea (and better-known coffee). Mount Hagen is now extinct but the volcanic ash it and other volcanoes have left as a legacy to the area creates a fertile environment when mixed with the deposits of the Waghi river.

The tea estates in PNG were established in 1967, mainly on former swampland. The drainage of this land in the valley of the Waghi river represented a genuine achievement given that no suitable roads then existed and all equipment needed to be brought in by air. As the industry developed it quickly established itself as a prime supplier of mainstream tea for the teabags of the Australian and Malaysian markets.

The challenges of growing tea in PNG are profound. As their traditional way of life has been eroded and formerly separate tribes find themselves forced closer together, tribal conflict has become widespread and can spill over into the workforce at a moment's notice. Crime is a frequent reality in a land where many retain firearms for hunting. The logistics are primitive and as a result it can be difficult to expedite teas to the port of Lae for export. This is not an easy place to operate, but it possesses a genuine charm and beauty. The Waghi valley floor is home to used car lots and missionary churches, but another world entirely beckons beyond the coffee and tea estates at Bunum Wo. Remote jungle environments offering the chance to see a bird of paradise provide all the excuse one needs for a visit to the area.

PNG BLACK TEA

Relatively dull, reddish, coarse black tea that performs unexceptionally in European or USA water, but always seems one quality level better when tasted in Melbourne or Sydney. The best mark is Bunum Wo, which is the highest-grown of the estates and has a touch more brightness and aroma.

AUSTRALIA

Australia is home to a small number of tea gardens producing both black and green tea. The black tea producers are concentrated in the hotter, more humid environs of Queensland and northern New South Wales, whilst Japanese-style green tea is produced on a small scale in Victoria. Mechanical harvesting is part and parcel of this high-wage economy but the quality of the output is generally very good.

Yabukita tea surrounded by eucalyptus, a uniquely Australian tea vista at Two Rivers in Victoria.

BLACK TEA

Tea has been produced in Queensland for decades. The rich, red, volcanic soils of the estates of Glen Allyn in the Atherton Highlands produce a bright-liquoring, aromatic CTC. Glen Allyn is often sold as Nerada, although Nerada does pack imported teas as well. This is well complemented by Daintree, which sits amidst the rainforest somewhat further north and can produce a more mellow, orthodox style. The two blend well together and tend to give a brighter, more attractive cup than the PNG alternatives often found in Australia.

Further south where Queensland meets New South Wales, the Madura Estate is producing both black CTC and green tea, although as ever with estates of modest size it is difficult to find pure NSW tea that has not been blended with imported production.

GREEN TEA

Victoria has established itself as the home of a burgeoning green tea sector, where the cooler climate more closely resembles Japanese growing conditions. The aptly named Two Rivers plantation can be found where the Acheron and Goulburn rivers meet. A Japanese farmer would feel at home here, where a delicate *sencha* is produced from first-out-of-the-blocks Sayamakaori, classic Yabukita and the later-yielding Okuhikaori clones. The aromas and sweetness scream of Shizuoka whilst the leaf has all the polished-needle style expected of good *sencha*. The clear pick of the offerings is their early season Shincha, which offers more aroma and slightly more intensity than the already fine *sencha*.

North and east of Acheron sits the Kiewa Valley. Here the Alpine Tea Co. produces both Japanese-style *sencha* and roasted Chinese-style teas, also making use of Yabukita cultivars. Their best product is a delicate *sencha*, with the cooler climate giving it a slightly milder character than the Japanese equivalents.

Withering Leaf at Zealong.

NEW ZEALAND

New Zealand's tea output is too small to show up on the statisticians' tables, but what it lacks in quantity it makes up for in quality. The world-class jade oolong is a match for almost anything Taiwan can produce.

Planted just north of Hamilton in Waikato, New Zealand's only tea garden represents a winning fusion of the best of Kiwi food and drink heritage with Taiwanese oolong knowhow. The enthusiastic reception of quality Sauvignon Blanc and Pinot Noir on European and American shores has endowed the New Zealand brand with resonance, easing the path for other foodie products from the Land of the Long White Cloud.

The combination of the Pacific's maritime influence and North Island's more northerly latitude ensures mild winters and favourable rainfall. Although snow is unknown, frosts can sometimes threaten but the cooler winter ensures some genuine seasonality to stress the bushes into producing quality teas, especially during the spring flush.

Producing 20 tonnes a year from its 48 hectares (19 acres) of quality Taiwanese varietals, Zealong is a genuine jewel. Currently the garden makes three oolongs, a black and a recently introduced green tea from its three harvests – a spring flush in November, summer flush in January, and autumnals during March. The oolongs tasted so far have a classic Taiwanese jade oolong character, with pungent floral notes and a delicate sweetness. It is difficult to find the teas in tea shops, so limited is the output, but Zealong ships all over the world. Better still, for holidaymakers the garden has adopted the winery hospitality model and caters well for visitors.

Tea gardens in Rize.

TURKEY

Turkey is a large tea producer with an indifferent quality reputation. The teas are seldom seen overseas, but new quality-minded production of green and white teas is hoping to change all this.

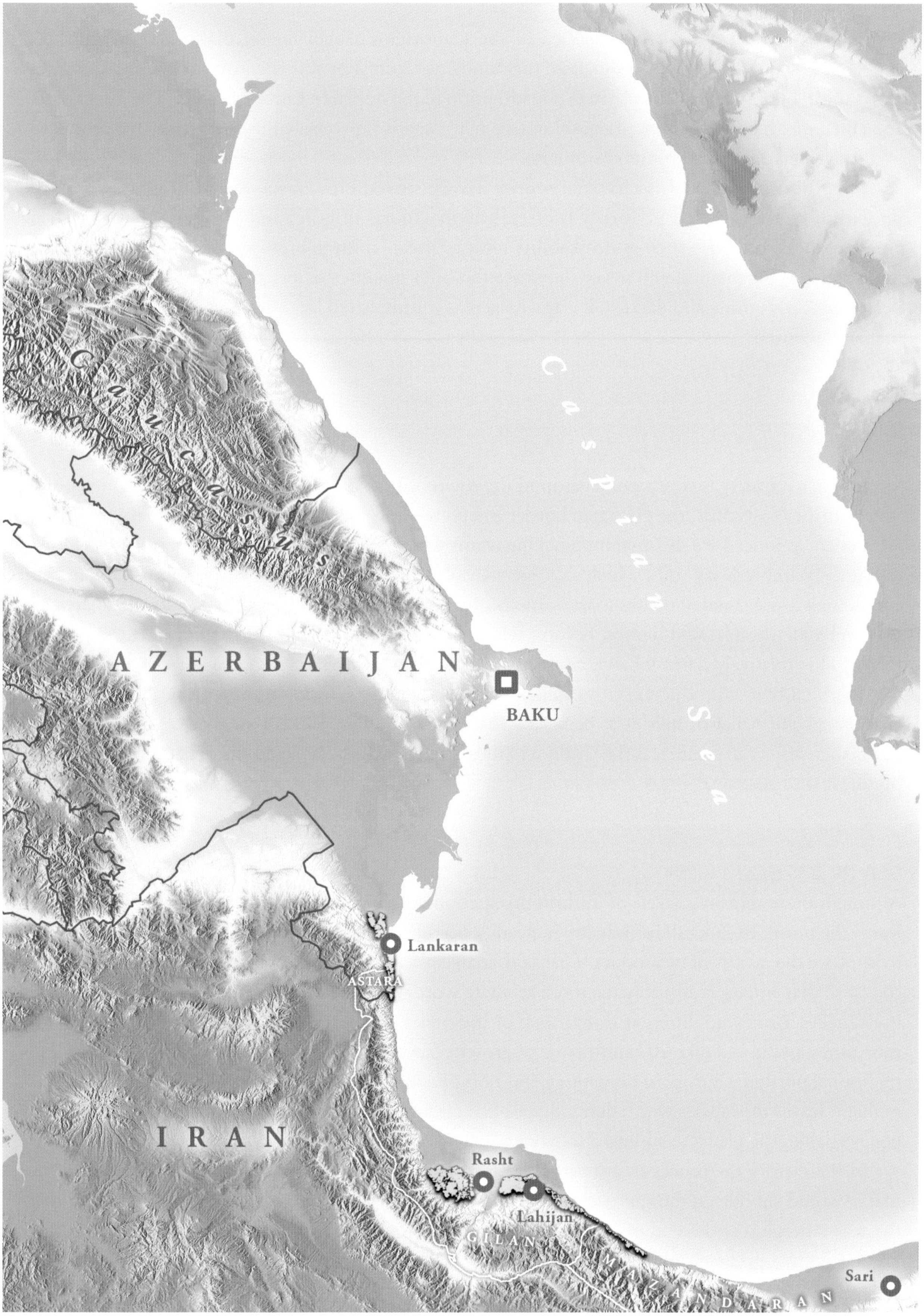
Caucasus
Caspian Sea
AZERBAIJAN
BAKU
Lankaran
ASTARA
IRAN
Rasht
Lahijan
GILAN
MAZANDARAN
Sari

THERE IS SOMETHING ABOUT the tea of the Caucasus-Caspian region that marks it out. It is possessed of a distinctive sour taste that tends not to matter if it is consumed with lashings of sugar, but renders it less-suited to consumption in the northern European style. The Turks brew and consume their tea in a singular fashion (see p90), and it is precisely this that makes tea produced in Turkey ideal for them but for few others.

The Turkish tea ritual is characterised by a very strong brew dispensed into glasses, topped up with hot water (which in Turkey is often heavily chloric in taste) and sweetened. Under such circumstances, qualities such as drinkability after a fifteen-minute brew are obviously of manifest importance. This method will never showcase the finer qualities of a seasonal Assam which would be undrinkably strong and dark, so it is the local teas (or imported large-leafed low-grown Ceylons) that are favoured.

RIZE

Turkey's tea industry is concentrated around the town of Rize on the Black Sea coast. If you venture much further eastwards, the Georgian border intervenes and the growing conditions here in Turkey are similar, as indeed are the migrant plucking teams which are often Georgian in origin. The rugged topography and red clay soils, which are especially acidic around Rize,[1] provide a comparable terroir and there is ample rainfall thanks to the same Black Sea maritime influence. Tea is cultivated between sea level and around 1,000 metres, beyond which it is not permitted in order to protect indigenous forest. This relatively narrow band, coupled with the size of the state-run Çaykur corporation and the interblending of production from all elevations and districts, makes it difficult to identify one or another specific valley or hillside as being any better than another. Turkish tea growers know that this limits their ability to create teas the world will recognise as world-class, and the debate about opening up forest land goes on.[2]

BLACK ORTHODOX TEA

Although there remain pockets of Turkish production where general lack of care and respect for the leaf is the norm, in general the industry is steadily becoming better at looking after its tea and seeking to improve the quality of its product. That said, coarse plucking with shears is the norm. In some cases so coarse that *pruning* is arguably the more accurate word. To pluck with shears is not unusual; this in itself makes Turkey no different from much of Indonesia or South India, but to pluck only three or four times a year and take 20 centimetres of growth hampers any potential for making tea suited to traditional northern European brewing styles. This plucking technique contrasts with tropical origins in that it leaves the bushes with a dome shape characteristic of more northerly producing regions, and better enables the plants to survive a snowy winter.

In the factory the processes are particular to the Caucasus; a Chinese tea master or Indian tea-maker would shudder at the approach to leaf handling, withering, rolling or oxidation. It is a feat that the teas emerging at the end of the line are drinkable at all, but they suit the Turkish tea-drinking tradition down to the ground. Greyish of leaf, pale tawny-yellow in liquor, soft and lacking any real

Plucking underway on a garden near Rize.

briskness, Turkish teas are seldom seen in the tins of a tea shop or the great blends of the European trade. However, for those who struggle with the astringency of more aristocratic offerings, Turkey's tea is often a surprise triumph in blind tastings for consumers turned off by strength and body. We should never overlook the fact that they are entirely suited to the Turkish market, so why under the circumstances would one do anything differently as a producer?

SINGLE-DISTRICT BLACK TEAS

There are some small areas where Çaykur has piloted production of small batches of organic or speciality types, Hemşin being one such district lying in a valley east of Rize. The black teas here are more floral in aroma and have less of the earthiness of their lesser cousins closer to the coast. The leaf is improved too, being slightly more twisted and less flaky, but relative to other speciality producers there is still some way to go.

GREEN TEAS

The green teas from Hemşin have arguably more potential still, not unlike a Chinese steamed green, but entirely organic. There is room for progress, but already these teas offer a great chance to set foot into the European speciality trade. Although such teas are seldom exported I believe we will see more of them as skills develop and awareness of the still rather dark art of good green tea-making becomes more ingrained in the Turkish tea community.

TURKISH WHITE TEA

If you are lucky you may find the odd batch of Turkish white tea. Some family businesses will still send out teams of pluckers with the express requirement to select only the buds. This is almost the only occasion in Turkey when you can expect to see manual plucking, and the white tea that results is certainly Turkey's best, and it falls very much into the boutique category. Production is so sporadic and difficult to obtain that to generalise on quality would be misleading, as each small batch is subject to the vagaries of weather and the will of the tea-maker. Whatever the case, an offer of Turkish white should not be spurned and each batch I have tasted has been both mellow and beautifully aromatic.

Turkish tea over-wintering under snow.

TURKEY
at a glance

Plants

Camellia Sinensis
var. sinensis and
some hybrids
Derepazari-7 [3]
Pazar-20
Tuglalı-10
Muradiye-10
Gundogdu-3
Komurculer-1
Fener-3

Terroir
Red clay,
50-1,000 metres

Seasonality
Spring

Harvesting
Mechanical, shear
and manual. Yields
3192 kg made tea
per hectare

Processing
Orthodox black

Drinking
Best consumed in
the local style..

GEORGIA

Former powerhouse of the USSR tea industry, and now one of the few remaining producers of handmade, genuinely artisanal tea.

See map on pp270-271

GEORGIA IS A TEA PRODUCER borne out of necessity. Necessity because it was one of the few regions suited to tea production at a time when the newly constituted Soviet Union was reluctant to spend its meagre foreign exchange reserves on tea. Although tea had been cultivated on a small scale in the Caucasus since around 1850, and with more gusto from the 1890s onwards, it was the advent of the USSR in the 1920s that saw the industry flourish. Always a tea-drinking culture, the cash-strapped USSR of the 1920s and 1930s wanted to avoid importing goods wherever possible, yet offer the proletariat the experiences of the former bourgeoisie. The wholehearted adoption of Georgian product fortified with a modest inclusion of barter-trade Indian tea was the direct consequence.

JACOB MCNAMARA

Georgia's tea industry is sometimes ascribed to the influence of a Scotsman named Jacob McNamara. McNamara was an officer on a ship that floundered off the Georgian coast during the Crimean War. The crew was held hostage by local forces for an extended period, an incarceration that cannot have been too hard on McNamara, who became engaged to and then married a local noblewoman.

Local cultivation of tea had commenced on a trial basis, and it was the Scot, as a keen tea-drinker, who is thought to have encouraged more widespread cultivation.

BACKGROUND

The Soviet era was the heyday of the Georgian tea trade. Massive expansion created large plantations. A paucity of labour and the need to keep costs under control resulted in real engineering advancement that is seldom given the credit it deserves. The first mechanical plucking devices originated here;[1] as far back as 1935 the tea industry was marvelling at Sadovsky's tea plucking machine, said to be capable of performing the work of twenty-five pluckers. Widespread automation in the factories was pioneered in Georgia, and substantial investment in tea research resulted in projects defined by genuine cutting-edge ambition. One such output that endures to this day is the *Kolkhida* cultivar that can flourish despite the often harsh winter conditions.

The downside of the Soviet era's need for tea was that a pricing mechanism orientated more towards quantity than quality encouraged rampant use of fertilisers and coarse plucking, with fundamental disregard for the ultimate drinkability of the resulting product. This was fine so long as someone would take the tea, but what if the market were suddenly to be opened up to international competition? This is the story of Soviet tea, but equally it could also be the tale of its automotive industry, or any other part of the empire that found itself in a completely different environment almost from one day to the next.

POST-SOVIET UNION

When the Soviet Union broke up, Georgia was forced to compete in an international market bereft of the protection it formerly enjoyed. The Caucasian tea trade declined from a peak of eighty thousand hectares under active cultivation in its early 1980s heyday, to around ten thousand

The hardy Kolkhida cultivar.

hectares by 1991.[2] A period of instability followed as much of the remaining tea reverted to forest or faced the ignominy of being grubbed up for less noble crops. By 1994 the industry had virtually ceased to exist as cheaper (and usually better) producing countries swamped the CIS states with their tea. The saviour emerged in 1996. Recognising the opportunity that Georgia provided, the German botanical extraction company Martin Bauer rescued the remnants of the local industry by buying twelve producing factories in order to turn the resultant tea into extracts for the burgeoning market in ready-to-drink tea (tea in a can). Although the financial crisis of the late 1990s severely threatened Georgia's ability to function effectively in any capacity, it weathered the storm and has since clung resolutely to its status as a net exporter of tea. Looking forward, there are many reasons to be cheerful…

Georgia as a country is an example of a microclimate on a macro scale, if such a description is permissible. By rights it shouldn't really be growing tea at all, being too far north to be credible as a tea-producing country. It is the benevolent presence of the Caucasus mountains we need to thank for Georgia's benign climate. The range acts as a barrier between the harsh, continental extremes of the northern weather patterns and the more tropical south, whilst westerly Black Sea winds laden with moisture ensure ample rainfall and the presence of the Black Sea itself helps to maintain a less extreme temperature bandwidth. The predominant soil type is red clay, in which the tea bush can flourish provided the drainage is adequate.

The conditions are very similar to those further west in Turkey; indeed the distances involved are relatively small and it is no surprise that the teas emanating from both countries bear striking similarities. Georgia is nonetheless lucky to be relatively far north – so far north, indeed, that the tea mosquito bug has not yet successfully penetrated, and yet with a wet enough climate that red spider is also not a problem. This may sound trivial, but in a world increasingly preoccupied with levels of agrochemical use, it is a happy set of circumstances indeed.

There is also a surprising amount of tea knowhow in Georgia. The Tea Research Institute at Anaseuli is a vast, crumbling complex that at one time housed hundreds of agronomists and scientists, all channelled towards making the most of the local tea opportunity. The projects and infrastructure that emanated from this investment demonstrate what could be possible again in Georgia with the right backers. By way of example, a sencha factory still exists, if in rather derelict state, its staff long since retired.

GEORGIAN GREEN AND BLACK TEA

A first encounter with Georgia's tea makes for a sorry sight indeed. The bushes in most of the gardens are overgrown with bracken and other weeds, though in some ways this is a blessing as at least the herds of cows wandering loose in the estates feast themselves on the weeds rather than the tea concealed beneath them. Weeding parties precede a plucking expedition, and the leaf they take in their three or four harvests per season will in all likelihood not be treated with great respect. The May-to-June crop is best (but this is not saying a great deal), and is usually sold as such, whilst the summer and autumn flushes are generally blended together. Does this matter? The manufactured tea in most cases will be extracted and find itself mixed with water and sugar for ready-to-drink iced tea in a can or a bottle, which is something of a leveller.

The split of production is more or less 60% green and 40% black, and although it is perfectly serviceable product it does nonetheless have a sour character that is mellowed only by the fantastically sweet mineral water found in most parts of Georgia, both bottled and via the mains. So far so good – this is not any different fundamentally from the product found in Iran, Turkey, Krasnodar or Western Azerbaijan: straightforward, black-leafed, pale-liquoring, slightly sour tea. The markets in which this is drunk will normally brew a more concentrated product in a samovar, which itself will be sweetened before drinking, so ultimately as with Turkey, the character suits the market.

COMPRESSED BRICK TEA

The production of 2-kilo blocks of brick tea for the Mongolian and Siberian markets was formerly a mainstay of the Georgian tea industry. There remain occasional producers manufacturing small volumes of tea, but as with much of the Georgian trade this is on a reduced scale. At its mass-market and most basic level this is usually rather coarsely plucked and processed as a steamed green tea before being pressed into bricks and allowed around a month to dry in a warehouse. The tea will then usually be consumed in a bowl with salt and butter, almost as a soup.

HANDCRAFTED, HIGH-GROWN TEA

Where Georgia really stands out is in the high-grown, small-scale production that is really more cottage industry in nature. Indeed, it is the epitome of cottage industry, taking place as it does in cottages at the hands of muscular housewives with years of experience of manual tea-making.

The origins of tea lie in the handmade artisanal production of inner China. Twisting and squeezing the leaf, either by hand or with their feet, the early tea producers were able to feel the process much more intimately than a machine operator could. They could sense the stage at which the leaf required no further abuse, and the tea was the better for it. The practice required a sensitive hand that could apply sufficient pressure to the leaf to break the cell walls and permit oxidation, but without damaging the product. Just as kneading dough need not be a violent assault, but a softer, more gentle process, so it is with fine handmade tea. It is this technique that continues in Georgia today, and can be found in some parts of the Caucasus mountains, where the higher elevation gives a finer quality to the leaf material to start with.

The tea that results is most immediately recognisable by its beautifully twisted appearance. If you place a couple of fingers into a sample tin of the dry tea and try to extract a little of the product, this delicate well-made style ensures that what you end up with is almost a handful, so intertwined are the leaves. If Gyukuro is the opposite extreme of the matrix in terms of its straight, needle-like leaf appearance, it is the handmade teas of Georgia that can stand up to anything from Ceylon or India on stylish leaf appearance and make. Levels of quality exist, with the AAA carrying the name of the artisan who handmade the tea, the AA (which is a blend all from the same village) carrying the name of the village in which it was produced and the A (which is more boutique factory than genuine handmade) carrying the name of the small factory.

With a richer and less sour character in-cup, as well as a more penetrating aroma, the teas are a mile away from their lower-grown distant cousins from the plains. If anything the taste is a little suggestive of Keemun, and the higher it is cultivated and processed, the more the flavour develops, with suggestions of Nepali character in the best teas, and it is certainly inadmissible to group it with anything else from the Caucasus.

High-grown Georgian leaf. This will be hand-processed.

GEORGIA
at a glance

Plants
Camellia Sinensis var. sinensis
Kolkhida- winter hardy

Terroir
Red clay soils,
20-600 metres

Seasonality
Best quality
from spring
teas in May

Harvesting
Machine. Yield
133kg made tea
per hectare

Processing
90% orthodox
black, balance
green

Drinking
Always best brewed in
Georgia's sweet
mineral water.
Handmade tea is
excellent in
afternoon blends.

IRAN

Neutral-tasting black and green teas that make a fine base for flavouring.

See map on pp270-271

RAN'S TEA INDUSTRY IS IN SOME DIFFICULTY. The twin threats of banking controls, which limit export opportunities, and competition from other crops, which impinge on crop, make for a bleak future. It produces classic soft and mild-tasting orthodox black tea and occasional useful green teas.

Iran's tea-growers produce tea for the budget end of a domestic market that prefers brisker, more astringent offerings from India and Sri Lanka, but is obliged to absorb a certain volume of domestic tea. 'Made in Iran' is not a big selling point in the world of tea, and the mild, soft teas are rarely exported. The gardens straddle the scenic hills of the provinces of Gilan and Mazandaran, bordering the southerly shores of the Caspian Sea where tea has been cultivated commercially for more than a hundred years.

The preferred model is of small farmers selling their green leaf to processing factories. These smallholders are subsidised, a lifeline without which the tea industry would struggle in the face of rising land prices driven by developers and competition with other crops such as rice or vegetables. Tea is often one of a number of options for such farmers and seldom their main priority, so the development of high-quality cultivars for uprooting and replanting is a rare undertaking. The smallholders approach their husbandry in varying ways – although the gardens in parts look much like they do anywhere else in the world, there are still some farmed in the classic form sometimes seen in northern latitudes of bushes pruned to a dome shape that would have been familiar to their forbears a century ago. Such a shape is more protective of the bush during the snowfalls of a cold winter, or spells of frost.

Although the presence of the Caspian helps to lessen the impact of the cold winters, the northerly latitude ensures a very short season with limited yields. In fact, at less than half the level of Turkey, these yields are pitifully meagre and say everything about the perilous state of the trade here. Harvests start in earnest in late April and are finished in October.

PRINCE MIRZA

Iran has Prince Mohammad Mirza to thank for its tea industry. The prince, operating as an ambassador to India in the latter part of the 19th century, managed to disguise himself as a French labourer and gain employment in the British-run tea industry. The British were jealously protective of their tea trade, built up as it was over years of disease-ridden jungle clearances, with success or failure very much a matter of trial and error. The enterprising Mirza managed not only to gain an understanding of tea production, but also make off with four thousand tea plants from Kangra Valley, all undisclosed to his British hosts, but afforded protection from discovery via his diplomatic immunity.

In such times this was no mere industrial espionage, but a heroic endeavour that brought wealth and employment to his people, who continue to cultivate tea to this day.

IRANIAN BLACK TEA

Although an appealingly fresh and aromatic first flush tea is produced during April and May, this is so sought after locally that it is seldom seen in Tehran, let alone outside of Iran. The majority of the tea is classic West Asian orthodox in the Georgia-Turkey-Abkhazia mould. The teas are light red to orange in colour, with little body, a soft taste and characterised by a general lack of astringency. The leaf is flaky and lightweight, with a lack of twist and style to elevate it above the budget category.

IRANIAN GREEN TEA

This is made-to-order Chinese-style pan-fired tea, and is much superior in relative terms to its black tea equivalent. Usually produced from earlier flushes, it is very pale in colour, light in body and neutral in aroma. It makes an especially interesting proposition for flavouring.

IRAN
at a glance

Plants
Camellia Sinensis
var. sinensis
Fashalam- yield
Iran #100- yield, quality[1]

Terroir
Brown clay,
100-700 metres

Seasonality
Best teas
produced in spring

Harvesting
Shear and manual
yield

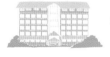

Processing
Orthodox black,
some pan-fired
green

Drinking
Best consumed in
the local style

Recently pruned tea bushes in Gilan.

OTHER CAUCASIAN PRODUCERS

See map on pp270-271

RUSSIA

RUSSIA HOSTS THE MOST northerly plantations in the world, producing commercial volumes of tea. The hardy, locally developed bushes ensure survival over the harsh winters, whilst the curiosity of tea grown in Russia provides something of a market for the teas, which are of intermediate quality at best. Since the demise of the Soviet Union and the advent of an independent and hostile Georgia, the tea in Krasnodar has assumed a little more importance in the consciousness of the Russian trade, but insufficient interest to guarantee its future.

Most of the plantations are located a short drive from Sochi but still very much within its environs, and within the foothills of the Caucasus range as it terminates into the Black Sea. The maritime climate provides the required rainfall and ensures a milder winter than areas further inland. This coastline has long been the haunt of Russia's elite, whether imperial, Soviet or oligarchic, and the Dagomys tea plantations adjoin the district hosting the Presidential Palace. The Winter Olympics of 2014 announced Sochi to the world, proclaiming its status as both a winter and summer playground, and more will be seen of Sochi via its annual Grand Prix and the 2018 World Cup. Hotels have sprung up along the coast, property developers have run rampant and land prices have soared. None of this makes for classic tea-growing country.

Whilst the Georgian gardens are protected from northerly weather by the Caucasus range, which traces the border with Russia for most of its extent, those of Krasnodar are a little more exposed and rely on proximity to the sea and hardy plants for their existence. That gardens exist here at all is a testament to Judas Koshman, a Ukrainian émigré whose plant research in the early 20th century resulted in bush cultivars hardy enough to withstand a severe winter yet still yield a remunerative crop. This research confounded the scientists who had always assumed such northerly latitudes to be unsuited, and infuriated the Georgian collectives who thought they had secured a monopoly on Soviet tea production. Although it is at best marginal, the location has some merits in that the harder winters do tend to eliminate a number of potential pests, meaning that the use of pesticides can be minimised. Koshman's Dagomys garden continues to yield small volumes of tea to this day as well as the Matsesta, Host and Solokhaul producers, who make a variety of types including some interesting green and yellow teas.

KRASNODAR BLACK ORTHODOX TEA
This is mild, aromatic, light-bodied tea with relatively low astringency. Liquors are generally a touch cleaner than the Georgian mass-produced teas.

Matsesta Tea Estate in Russia.

Produced in much smaller volumes, the style of leaf is relatively attractive but the quality of the liquors I have tasted suggests the bush is less suited than Chinese equivalents. There is less of the aroma and sweetness that such teas would ordinarily deliver.

AZERBAIJAN

Azerbaijan falls squarely into the classic Caucasian tea-growing cultures found between Iran and Turkey. As with neighbouring producing countries, the plants here need to be sufficiently hardy to withstand the harsh winter yet still productive enough to justify the inputs: compromises that limit the potential quality of the teas. When well-made, the teas are soft in liquor with a stylish black leaf, yet all too often they can tend towards an unpleasant sourness when consumed Western-style, requiring samovar-style brewing before they can be appreciated in full.

The heyday of Azeri tea was the 1970s and 1980s: investment was high and there was a ready market for the output, whatever its quality. Plans were made for a large expansion of the industry that would have tripled output from its 9,000-tonne potential in the 1980s in order to satisfy the ever-increasing Soviet demand.[1] The collapse of the Soviet Union intervened, followed by years of conflict with Armenia and underinvestment, which have done nothing for the trade. The annual crop is now less than 300 tonnes and as such cannot even satisfy the local demand, let alone allow Azerbaijan to feature as a significant player within the global trade.

The plantations sit in the coastal districts of the Lankaran-Astara regions, a southern finger of Azerbaijan which juts into Iran and benefits from its proximity to the Caspian Sea and the moderating effect this has on the otherwise extreme climate that much of the rest of Azerbaijan enjoys. Annual rainfall at around 1,300mm is just within the threshold needed for remunerative tea cultivation, but it is concentrated during the spring and autumn, with a dry summer occasionally causing problems for producers as the yellow, sandy loam does not retain moisture especially effectively and can tend to dry out.

BLACK TEA

May provides the major crop, a 'first flush' that boasts a mildly more intense character than the later crop which tends to flush in August. The orthodox leaf is attractive in itself but still sour, and with its even, blackish colour coming at the expense of an often over-fired character. The teas are at their best when prepared using the samovar method.

KENYA

Kenya plays Rome to India's Greece. A relatively young industry that has become a global tea powerhouse producing massive volumes of dependable, good-looking, high-grown CTC.

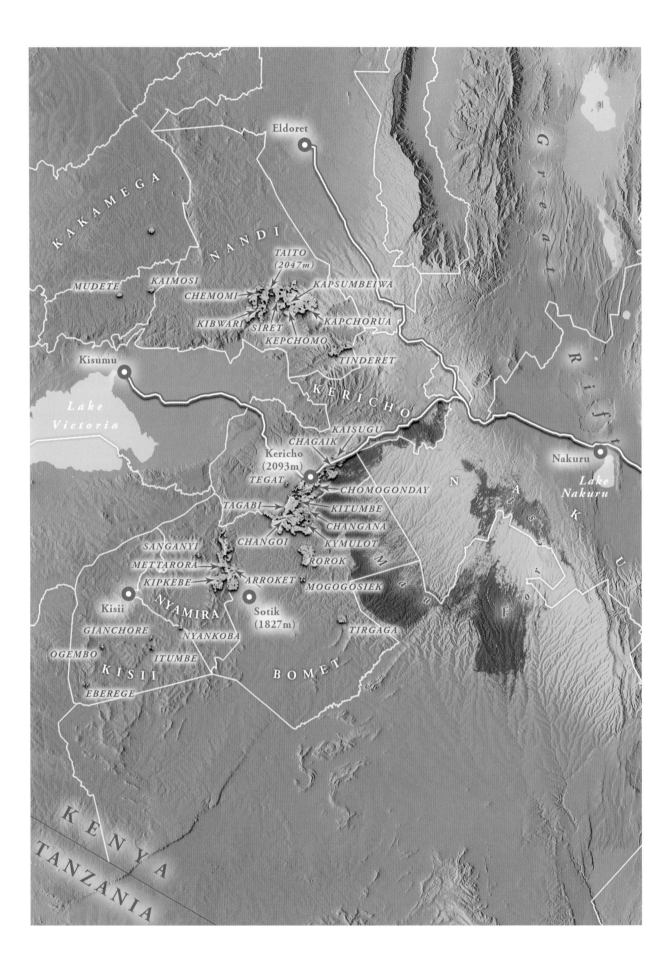

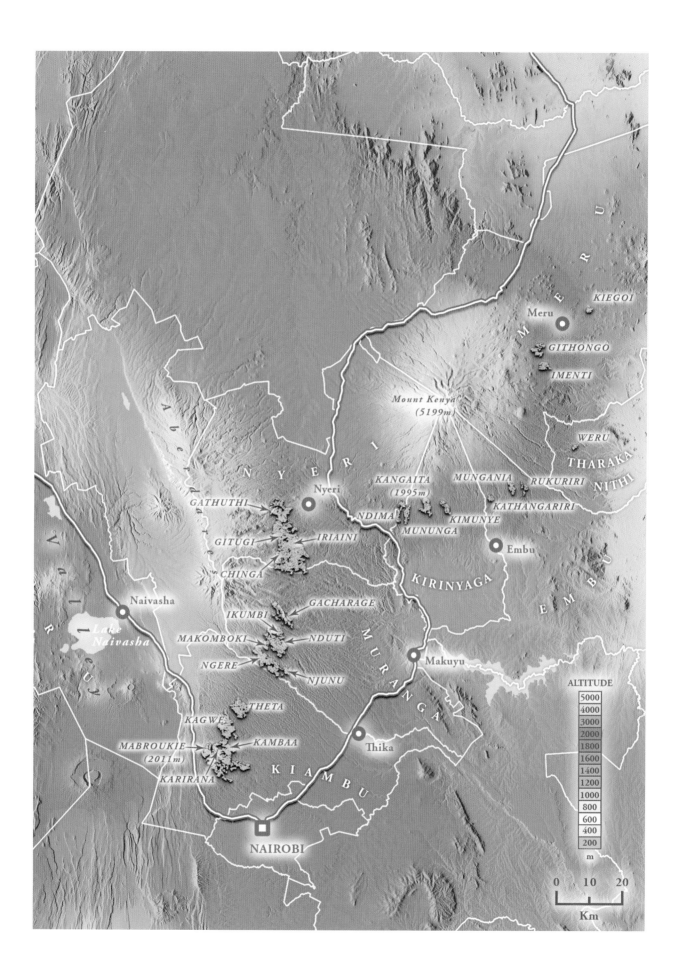

MERU

KIEGOI

Meru

GITHONGO

IMENTI

Mount Kenya
(5199m)

WERU

THARAKA

NYERI

Nyeri

KANGAITA
(1995m)

MUNGANIA

RUKURIRI

NITHI

GATHUTHI

NDIMA

KIMUNYE

KATHANGARIRI

GITUGI

IRIAINI

MUNUNGA

Aberdare

CHINGA

KIRINYAGA

Embu

EMBU

Naivasha

GACHARAGE

IKUMBI

MAKOMBOKI

NDUTI

MURANG'A

Lake
Naivasha

NGERE

Makuyu

Rift Valley

NJUNU

THETA

KAGWE

MABROUKIE
(2011m)

KAMBAA

Thika

KARIRANA

KIAMBU

NAIROBI

ALTITUDE

5000
4000
3000
2000
1800
1600
1400
1200
1000
800
600
400
200

m

0   10   20

Km

KENYA IS THE WORLD'S LARGEST tea exporter by some margin, a position it has reached off the back of rapid expansion of the smallholder sector and a relatively small local population that consumes only a modest proportion of the crop. Its mainstay is bright, reliably brisk, if sometimes workmanlike, CTC tea that is invariably a vital element of blends drunk with milk. Increasing volumes of good orthodox and green tea are also now being produced here.

BACKGROUND

Tea snobs tend to look down their noses at Kenyan tea. It is rare to see tins declared as such available for sale in any tea shop, and a scan of the shelves at the supermarket seldom reveals any Kenyan blends amongst the Assam, China and Ceylon packs on display. Yet for the 97% of consumers who regularly consume mainstream teabags, the chances are that Kenyan tea represents the largest single inclusion of the blend they drink and they should not permit themselves to be persuaded that they are being fobbed off with substandard sweepings from the floor.

Kenyan tea is almost exclusively CTC and doesn't boast the attractive leaf appearance and tactile quality of the grand old orthodox teas of the East. Although it is characterised by a quick-brewing, more astringent nature giving a brisk-tasting style that can lack the complexity, smoothness and refinement of the best orthodox teas, it is usually clean, well-made and reliable – one sees much less 'bad' Kenyan tea than its vast crop warrants.

Although not Africa's oldest tea producer, Kenya is by some margin its largest and now produces more tea than the rest of the continent put together. Kenyan tea (especially high-grown smallholder tea) should be a punch of brisk, fresh flavour. If you add milk to your tea then not much else comes close to the level of brightness that results. Kenyan teas look full of life and freshness when viewed alongside their more esteemed Asian cousins. So the message is not to ignore the riches that come from Kenya, but to embrace the local style for what it is: honest, clean, sharp, brisk, fresh 'morning tea'.

Kenya has a young tea industry in global terms. The first seeds, which had been brought from India, were planted in 1903 on a small farm near Limuru and it was not until the 1920s that the first large-scale commercial plantings took place. Brooke Bond planted a large area of land near Limuru and James Finlay concentrated on the Kericho district further west. That both companies still run successful tea estates in these areas is a testament to the skills of the original pioneers. However it was the post-war period that really saw the Kenyan tea industry take off. The prospect and then the reality of an independent India precipitated a move to secure land elsewhere within the empire where tea and other agricultural products could be produced under sterling company control. Kenya, which had demonstrated an evident suitability for tea production, was an obvious choice.

The area under tea in Kenya has experienced almost uninterrupted growth. Both large-scale estates and smallholders have seen the value in tea, often at the expense of coffee. Its enviable location on the Equator ensures that Kenya enjoys year-round production and thus year-round cash for the farmer. Blenders like Kenyan tea as a slick supply chain (pirates permitting) can ensure they receive consignments of consistent quality within weeks of production at any time of year, whilst accountants encourage their blenders in this as it means they do not have to pay for large volumes of seasonal tea

Kenyan tea planting divisions in Nandi lined with agapanthus;
immense pride is taken in a well-maintained tea garden.

in one hit. In short, Kenya is a tea-packer's dream and the love affair seems unlikely to cool for some time yet.

SMALLHOLDER TEA

The first thing to grasp when learning about Kenyan tea is the distinction between smallholder tea which accounts for two-thirds of Kenya's crop, and the balance of one-third which is grown on the large estates. Most Kenyan smallholders sell their tea through a parastatal organisation called the Kenya Tea Development Agency (KTDA). KTDA tea factories, wherever they are located – there are sixty-six of them at the last count – enforce a uniformly draconian standard on their leaf supply. Any leaf that does not comply with the two-leaves-and-a-bud standard synonymous with potentially fine tea quality is rejected out of hand before it can get anywhere near to the factory. This leaf is then transported to the factory from local collection points in specially made sacks designed to avoid leaf compression, and to ensure maximum air circulation. This all but eliminates bruising and pre-fermentation, both of which are certain to ruin what could otherwise have become perfectly decent tea. If good tea is made in the field, then this at least ensures that the leaf has travelled in club class to the factory, arriving in the best possible condition for withering.

The KTDA factory processes are sound enough to enforce a consistently high standard, and the equipment used is sufficiently high-spec to mean that there should be no barrier to the creation of the classic KTDA style: very dense, black-leafed, golden-liquoring, brisk and biscuity black tea. KTDA

TEA SMUGGLING

By dint of its sheer popularity, tea has always attracted the interest of the Treasury with duty periodically raised and lowered in order to finance the waging of war. As a result, smuggling has at times been rampant and by the mid-18th century more than half of the tea consumed in the UK was thought to have been smuggled.

Two of Britain's greatest Prime Ministers had a role in cutting duty and opening tea to the masses – William Pitt the Younger reduced duty from 119% to 12.5% in 1784, levying his Window Tax to make-up the difference. Then as Chancellor in his 1929 budget, Winston Churchill finally removed tea duty.

Smuggling thrives in Pakistan to this day where under the terms of a transit agreement with landlocked Afghanistan, tea may be imported into Pakistan for transport onward to Afghanistan, either via Peshawar or sent to Iran for transit to Afghanistan via Bandar Abbas.

The goods either reach Afghanistan before being turned around and filtering back across the border, or they disappear en-route whilst still in Pakistan.

In bull market periods it is thought that as much as 40% of the tea sold in Pakistan may have been smuggled.

teas are a classic tea bag mainstay and it really is difficult to go wrong with them. Their popularity is well illustrated by a look at market coverage: not only a favourite in Pakistan, Egypt and the UK, but also possessing the dubious but significant honour of being the most smuggled tea in the world, which has ever been a sign of indispensable quality.

PLANTATION TEA

Private estates (non-smallholder large-scale plantations) tend to have a more varied quality reputation. Some estates produce teas that approach the best that the KTDA have to offer, whilst others have a more inconsistent record. The only way to guarantee quality from these estates is to pick a name that suits you and stick to it.

Kenya as a country is geographically carved in two by the mighty Rift Valley, in Kenya's case more properly referred to as the Eastern Rift Valley. This magnificent geological feature extends more than three thousand miles (4,800 kilometres) from its northerly limits in the Lebanon to its most southerly point on the Mozambiqui coast, carving a swathe through the Red Sea and East Africa on the way. The Rift is the defining feature in the Kenyan tea map, and indeed on any map of East Africa. Typically teas produced to the east tend to be brighter and brisker than those produced to the west, although there are exceptions in both cases. The elevated land thrown up on either side by this great tear in the earth's crust is perfect for tea cultivation, and not just in Kenya: Rwenzori in Uganda and Thyolo in Malawi are both extensions of the Rift. The altitude and moist climate that results ensures benign temperatures and sufficiently slow growth to enable a fine concentration of flavours, whilst the equatorial location guarantees year-round production relatively unencumbered by the passing seasons.

EAST OF RIFT

The producing districts east of the Rift Valley (EoR) that account for about 40% of Kenya's tea are regarded by most as the choicest locations for tea cultivation. The eastern slopes of the Aberdares and the southern and eastern slopes of Mount Kenya provide the scenic backdrop. Skilled smallholders, thick, humus-filled volcanic soils, high rainfall and warm temperatures ensure healthy bushes, good crops and excellent, consistent quality. Although the immediate post-war expansion favoured the West of Rift areas more than the districts to the east of the valley, the EoR has nonetheless seen its own expansion, with Pakistan being the prime beneficiary. The ongoing antagonism on the subcontinent has been very much to Kenya's benefit in forcing the Pakistanis to seek alternative sources of tea to the Assams that would naturally be a perfect match for the local taste. East of Rift Kenyans are a good substitute; fine plucking and skilled manufacture result in strong, bright, coppery liquors, ideal with milk and with enough body to stand up well to the distinctive milk-based style of 'cooking' and drinking chai in Pakistan.

The market favours a very dense, black-leafed style, and here the EoR factories excel. Fine plucking is the first stage in ensuring the teas meet the exacting standards – if the leaf is too coarse then brown fibre will spoil the appearance and lighten the density. The manufacture process is carried out on standardised lines with the express aim of creating the signature bright golden liquors for which the KTDA is famed. An emphasis on creating a suitably black colour to the leaf ensures that the tea is fully fired in the dryer, and the tea displays its trademark biscuity character. The entire process is all about standardisation – of equipment, of processes and of quality – and it is difficult to argue that they haven't been successful. KTDA teas have a certain 'brand style' and you generally know you will get a tea of a certain class when you buy one.

WEST OF RIFT

Moving further west to the areas on the other side of the Great Rift Valley, one encounters many more of the private estates. This change in ownership is most apparent from the air. Whereas the tea areas further east tend to resemble a patchwork quilt, with tea inter-cropped with pasture, maize, coffee and vegetables, further west, particularly around Kericho, one encounters vast swathes of tea, threatened only in its predominance by the eucalyptus forests necessary to fire the boilers in the factories and the increasing number of greenhouses catering to the European demand for year-round cut flowers. If the altitude of 1,800-2,200 metres (5,900-7,200 feet) is less heady than EoR, it is still sufficient to make some very fine teas with good depth of briskness and brightness, if not of the elevated quality seen further east.

Kericho's carpet of green.

KERICHO

Even though Limuru claimed the first bushes to be planted in Kenya, it was Kericho that experienced the real zeal of the first planters in their quest to replicate Assam in the highlands of East Africa. Vast areas were cleared, and in many cases the bushes planted by the first pioneers are still producing tea today.

The county of Kericho around the town of the same name is synonymous with tea in Kenya. It just eclipses Bomet and Nandi if measured by crop, but feels somehow much more tea-orientated than its rivals. Nowhere else offers such spectacular vistas of tea stretching into the horizon; a lush carpet of green coating the rolling hills. This broad, almost English landscape is something akin to a dream environment for the tea bush. The classic deep green uniformity is interrupted only occasionally by the odd greenhouse, or the verdant forest in the valley bottoms, inhabited by the remaining Colobus monkeys. The altitude of 2,200 metres (7,200 feet) tempers the equatorial heat, and the reliably heavy rainfall that is a consequence of its proximity to the vast Mau Forest, combine to provide ideal conditions for tea plants.

Kericho more than any other district in the world can claim to represent an unparalleled 'share-of-throat' for the British consumer. Its bright and brisk, reddish-hued teas are ideal companions for a splash of milk. The year-round crop guarantees continuous supply as well as a constant flow of green leaf through the factory, ensuring that the peaks and troughs in crop that seem endemic in less equatorial longitudes are avoided (and with them the consequent quality variation that comes with

A family of Colobus monkeys inhabiting the neighbouring forest.

ebbs and flows in the factory). In short, although Kericho tea may not be the most glamorous of offerings, and although it seldom makes it into the top five of the discerning expert, it is a staple and a reliably good one at that.

NANDI

The rich, red volcanic soils and mild temperatures of the Nandi Hills combine to make for excellent tea cultivation conditions. The average quality of Nandi teas is typically superior to those in Kericho, with Nandi tending towards a brighter, more golden style of tea; also arguably a touch brisker and much favoured in Pakistan.

BLACK ORTHODOX

Although known for its CTC teas, Kenya produces more and more orthodox tea each year. The Kangaita factory in the East of Rift area is the best-known source, taking its leaf from producers on the slopes of Mount Kenya, but there are notable producers also in Nandi (Emrok, Kaimosi and Tinderet) as well as Milima in Kericho, which is made at the Kitumbe factory.

Most obviously compared with its forerunners in India, orthodox Kenyan tea is varied in style and difficult to pigeonhole, although whatever the type, the best quality seems always to

KENYAN ATHLETES

The Kalenjin tribes which stem from the tea-producing areas in the highlands west of the Great Rift Valley have produced a disproportionately large number of Olympic medal winners. A drive through Nandi's tea-growing areas will often pass by large training groups out running, and any attempt by keen amateur athletes to exercise can result in painful scenes involving keen competition from local enthusiasts. Being overtaken on a morning run by an eleven-year-old girl in flip-flops carrying both her own and her younger sister's schoolbooks is a particular memory.

It is said that there are parts of the Nandi district where one can see the homes of seven or eight Olympic medallists from one point, an activity impossible anywhere else in the world.

come from the dry weather periods. Kangaita and Milima strike a fine balance between the body of the lower-grown Assams and the brightness and aroma of the higher-grown South Indians, whilst Tinderet's offering is suggestive of a high-grown western Ceylon. Emrok is the pick of the bunch, the leaf is more Darjeeling first flush in style, yet during dry weather it carries the aroma of an Uva Ceylon. The liquors are all mandarin and clementine notes, and whilst lacking the body and richness that only a good Assam can deliver, they make up for it with classic high-grown flavour.

GREEN AND OOLONG

The burgeoning speciality market has also made its impact felt in Kenya, where the demand for oolong and green tea, and loss of faith in some of the more mass-produced China green teas, has led to the establishment of a number of small-scale operations (usually tucked away in the corner of a black tea factory). Kangaita again is a great example and will produce both green tea and oolong, either of which is worth a try as the Kirinyaga altitude gives a fine level of aroma to the tea.

Further west in Kericho, James Finlay produces a bright, clear, beautifully clean CTC green tea sold as Kijani. It is unusual to find CTC green tea, and probably best to adjust your brew a little, given that it can seem overpowering if you make it in the usual way. A shorter infusion time coupled with a smaller volume of tea should help here. In Nandi, the Tinderet greens show wonderful clarity coupled with attractive brightness and clean aromas on a more traditional orthodox style of leaf.

THE FUTURE

Kenya has been a boom country for tea in the past sixty years, and this pace shows little sign of slackening. As the trade enters a new era of diversification into orthodox and green teas, the country has an assurance and confidence born of its place at the top tier of global tea production. Those who have hitherto dismissed Kenyan tea need to revisit, because its teas will play an ever larger role in global blends whether they like it or not. The more the Indian and Chinese domestic populations consume their own teas and restrict exports, the more we will come to rely on Kenya. Kenyan tea is here to stay, and we should rejoice at it.

PURPLE TEA

Only currently available in small quantities but increasingly planted out in the Kirinyaga district is clone TRFK 306/1. Distinctly unsexy in name but potentially something to watch closely in the coming years, 306/1 is an anthocyanin-rich tea that yields a purple-coloured liquor from tea bushes that themselves are greenish-purple in appearance. It is both drought and frost-resistant, is high-yielding, and claimed to have a high antioxidant load. The purple colour comes from the anthocyanin pigments – the same pigments that turn autumn foliage red. When processed it is let down by a rather bitter character, but it has some of the fresh-tasting characteristics of newly manufactured black tea, combined with the typical astringency of a green tea.

TRFK 306/1
The purple tea cultivar.

UGANDA

Producer of ordinary black CTC rising steadily from its Amin-induced nadir.

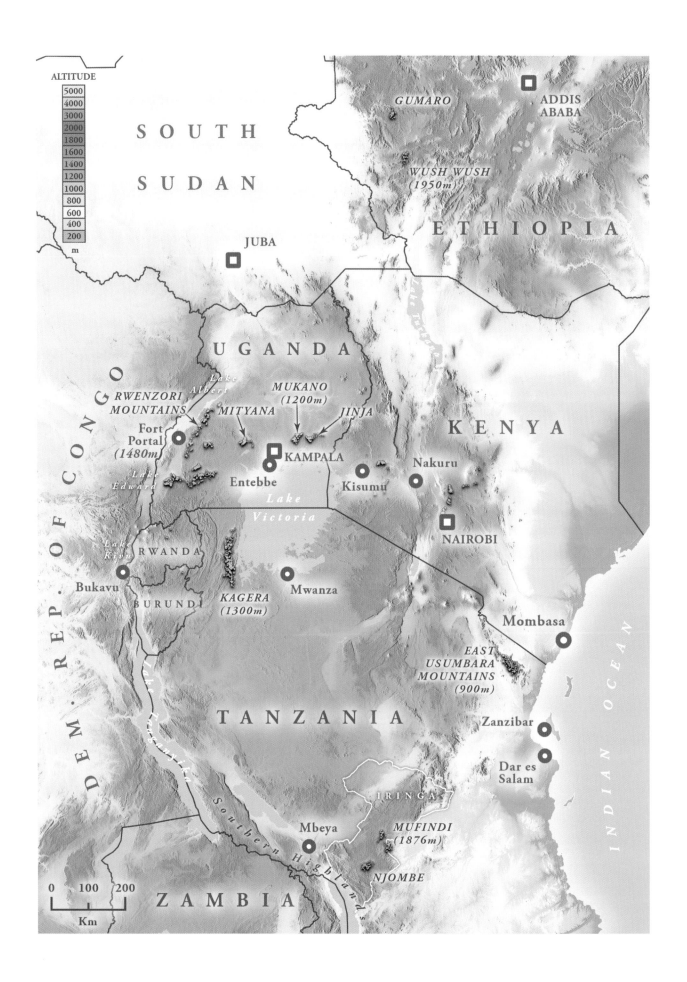

ALTITUDE

5000
4000
3000
2000
1800
1600
1400
1200
1000
800
600
400
200
m

SOUTH

SUDAN

GUMARO

ADDIS
ABABA

*WUSH WUSH
(1950m)*

ETHIOPIA

JUBA

UGANDA

KENYA

*Lake
Albert*

*RWENZORI
MOUNTAINS*

MITYANA

*MUKANO
(1200m)*

JINJA

Fort
Portal
(1480m)

*Lake
Edward*

KAMPALA

Entebbe

Nakuru

Kisumu

*Lake
Victoria*

NAIROBI

*Lake
Kivu*

RWANDA

BURUNDI

*KAGERA
(1300m)*

Mwanza

Bukavu

Mombasa

*EAST
USUMBARA
MOUNTAINS
(900m)*

TANZANIA

Zanzibar

Dar es
Salam

INDIAN OCEAN

IRINGA

*MUFINDI
(1876m)*

Mbeya

NJOMBE

0   100   200

Km

ZAMBIA

THIS LEAST KNOWN AND VISITED, yet in many ways most promising of the East African big three, has suffered an unenviable recent history, even in the context of a region known for volatility. Uganda underwent a generation of apocalyptic decline, moulding nadir and tiger-like resurgence, such that we can only marvel at what could have been achieved without the bloodshed and persecution of the 1970s. Like almost any Ugandan story, tea's history here falls into two parts: pre- and post-Idi Amin's era of tyranny and destruction.

BACKGROUND

Uganda's tea was conceived in the early years of the 20th century, endowing it with a no less venerable history than neighbouring Kenya, which is now vastly more significant in tea terms both in quality and quantity. As global interest in tea developed, local Asian and European-owned and run tea gardens grew steadily in number and productivity, initially with the dawn of independence on the subcontinent, then in Uganda's brave new post-colonial economy. Although never entirely untouched by the smear of corruption, it was at least an environment to which foreign businesses felt they could entrust their money, and investment in Uganda's agrarian sector was healthy. It has been said that Uganda could feed all of Africa were its resources only properly managed, so rich is its potential.[1] The future looked bright…

Then came Amin. He apart, there is no real reason why Uganda's tea should not have followed a similar path to that of Kenya's, endowed as it is by comparable soil, altitude and climatic conditions. This optimism was dashed by Amin's coup of 1971 and the subsequent years of near anarchy. The Ugandan tea industry fell apart from 1975 as the persecution, appropriation and chaotic mismanagement of the regime destroyed almost the entire industrial and agricultural base of the once promising country. An industry that had for years generated valuable foreign reserves for the state now lay neglected and dismembered as its bushes became trees and its factories stood stagnant and silent, stripped of their equipment and awaiting what an uncertain future would bring. The industry remained shunned by a Western world unwilling to invest in Amin's folly, and why would you?

By 1981 and Amin's flight to Libya, Uganda was producing just 5% of the tea it made in 1974, a figure not untypical for many similar Ugandan industries at that time, but a catastrophe for anyone formerly reliant on tea as a livelihood. The publicly owned tea industry stuttered on into the late 1980s, when foreign donor funding brought much-needed investment as a prelude to privatisation in 1994. Commonwealth development money combined with the international expertise of James Finlay in rehabilitating the once great estates.

It is no easy feat to restore a tea estate. Squatters need to be evicted. Bushes that have become trees need to be pruned in a two-stage process to create a plucking table. Factories, long since empty shells, need rebuilding, birds and bats smoking out, power supply reconnecting. Roads need regrading, workers retraining…

And they have largely managed it. Progress has been made, massive progress if we regard the industry as dead thirty years ago. From a *Stunde Null* in 1981, Uganda is now again Africa's second producer, eclipsing even Malawi's output, and it won't stop there as its old bushes continue to improve their output and new areas are planted out with higher yielding varietals. Yet somehow Ugandan tea has never really managed to reach the heights of its East African brothers. The leaf quality and appearance is often excellent – blackish and dense – but liquors lack the briskness and point of their

Tea gardens in the Rwenzori Highlands.
The stripes reveal the recent activities of
mechanical plucking machines.

Kenyan cousins and come nowhere near the brightness of Rwanda and Burundi. At best Uganda stumbles along, vying with lower-grown Tanzanians to avoid the East African wooden spoon.

The industry now can be very roughly divided into two planting districts: a fringe around the western and north-western shores of Lake Victoria, and a belt of tea on the Congolese border extending from the areas around the southern shores of Lake Edward to Lake Albert. Of these areas it is the tea on the higher land approaching Congo that offers the greater potential.

RWENZORI HIGHLANDS

Fort Portal, gateway to the Rwenzori Highlands, serves as a useful base for exploring the Ugandan 'Mountains of the Moon', and forms the best start point for an exploration of Uganda's higher-grown tea. Notably it is this extension of the Western Rift, locally known as the Albertine Rift, that gives us the high mountains on which the great teas of Burundi and Rwanda have been forged. Majestic escarpments tower over the great Lakes Edward and George in the south and Albert in the north, bodies of water that are small by local standards but nonetheless still epic in their scale and scenery. The estates are scattered over a 300-kilometre (190-mile) line along Uganda's western fringes immediately north and south of the Equator. A visit to these parts is a splendid experience, with a real sense of moving into the African interior as one nears the Congolese border. Extensive vistas of tea reward the determined visitor, all surrounded by horizons of indigenous forest, much of it the Queen Elizabeth National Park. The roads are predictably terrible, being so poorly connected and inadequate for the climate that almost any drive in the more rural areas becomes a lengthy affair. But that is a part of Uganda's charm…and its development challenge.

The teas here are made with the Egyptian and Pakistani tea-drinker very much in mind. Blackish and grainy in leaf appearance, yet still soft and unexceptional in liquor, rarely with quite the brightness of a Kenyan, the potential is there but is not often fulfilled. The attractive leaf comes at a cost of frequent over-firing, and these teas look better on the leaf than they taste. The preconditions are there for teas that liquor well, and with the fertile volcanic soils and combination of rainfall and altitude we are likely to see a steady improvement in quality. When it comes, it will be in the Rwenzori areas that we'll see it first.

LAKE VICTORIA

The areas around Lake Victoria tend to be rather lower in altitude and, with an as yet not especially well-coordinated smallholder sector, they cannot boast the quality of Kenyan smallholder teas or the investment of the better-resourced estates in the Rwenzori areas. However, there is still room for the dedicated producer to make fine-quality blending teas on excellent soils when the factories are alert and well-managed and plant material good. With more and more tea now planted out we should see a steady improvement here, albeit from a relatively modest start point.

We may not know Uganda as a quality producer yet, but what is for sure is that more and more of its teas will find their way into blends in the future. As they do and the industry gains in confidence and experience we will see it go the way of Kenya: self-assured, independent of thought and carving a unique niche for itself in the world of tea.

Predicting the future in a country like Uganda is a dangerous business, not least in an agronomic world where shifting temperature and rainfall patterns wrought by climate change are rendering lower-altitude tea-producing areas potentially unproductive.[2] What Uganda does have going for it is a reliably wet climate, a heady altitude, rich, volcanic soils, and the blessing (at least in its central and southern regions) of a year-round growing season. We may not see many Ugandan teas available as self-drinkers, but can be sure that Uganda will produce ever more tea in the coming years, and as the industry regains confidence, those teas will improve.

Plants
Camellia Sinensis
var. assamica
TRFK 6/8- quality/
yield

Terroir
Volcanic soils in
Rwenzori, 1,200-
1,800 metres

Seasonality
Year-round
growth with best
teas in July and
August

Harvesting
Mix of manual
and shear. Yield
1809 kg made tea
per hectare

Processing
CTC black

Drinking
Blending tea

TANZANIA

Picturesque planting areas dispersed across the country, producing classic East African black tea and occasional batches of orthodox and green tea.

See maps on pp302 and 336

TANZANIA'S MAINSTAY IS CLASSIC EAST AFRICAN tea: bright yet coarse CTC of fine but unexceptional quality; but it is increasingly attracting attention for the small volumes of orthodox and green tea produced in the Southern Highlands around Mufindi.

BACKGROUND

Tea was first planted on a trial basis by German colonial settlers in 1902 around Tanga, at the same time as the British were also trialling tea in their own East African colony. The Tanga trial was very slow-burning in its success – it was not until the 1920s that the first meaningful commercial planting started, by when it had become British-administered under a League of Nations mandate. Growth continued under British control much as it did in Kenya, with large-scale, foreign-owned estates the preferred route. Independence came in 1961, and whilst Kenya's tea industry flourished in the brave new post-*Uhuru* world, most especially its smallholder sector, Tanzania's followed a less dynamic path.

A glance at the industry now is encouraging. Although much of Tanzania is too dry for tea, there are a number of potentially excellent sites yet unplanted. The crop is recognised as a potentially valuable bringer of wealth and employment to rural areas. With the help of organisations such as the Wood Family Trust the future promises sustainable growth, especially amongst smallholders.

There are three main planting areas in Tanzania: those in the Southern Highlands around Mufindi and Njombe, the plantations of East Usambara in Tanga region close to the coast, and the areas around the south-western shore of Lake Victoria in Kagera. In Tanga and Kagera the seasonal pattern is even, with relatively constant temperatures across the year and two distinct rainy seasons: the long rains

Bulwa factory in the East Usumbara.

Pluckers at Luponde.

Kwamkoro Estate in the East Usumbara.

TANZANIA
at a glance

Plants

Camellia Sinensis
var. assamica
TRFK 6/8- quality
BBT 207
BBK 35- quality/yield

Terroir

Volcanic, rich
with humus,
900 metres in
Usambara to
2,200 metres in
Southern Highlands

Seasonality

Quality peaks between
July-September
in north, November-
December in south

Harvesting

Machine, shear
and manual. Yield
1466 kg made tea per
hectare

Processing

More than 98%
CTC black tea

Drinking

Adds brightness
and briskness
to blends

between March and May and the short rains between August and December. These two rainy seasons provide the bulk of the crop in the northern areas. Teas from both regions typically end up in the mainstream blends of the European and Pakistani markets, where the CTC output is most at home.

The Southern Highlands tea falls into a moderated version of the Malawian seasonal pattern, characterised by a cold winter between February and August and one rainy season between November and April, during which most of the crop is to be found. The most exciting teas here are made at Luponde, which at an altitude of 2,200 metres (7,200 feet) is one of Tanzania's highest, and also its only organic producer. Although the higher elevation helps to restrict the number of potential pests that are able to survive, organic cultivation is still a struggle here. Luponde has diversified into fine green, white and orthodox black teas produced in small batches, and this in itself makes the estate worth singling out. The orthodox tea is bright and mellow, with an attractive leaf appearance enhanced further by the use of superior tippy clonal leaf. The green is a beautifully subtle steamed tea with an attractive aroma, a pleasant freshness and clean flavour. The white tea is a classic silver-tipped tea much like a Chinese white downy, that is the result of hours of plucking for minimal weight of leaf.

Elsewhere in the Southern Highlands there is fine tea grown at an elevation of around 1,700–2,000 metres (5,600-6,600 feet) by both smallholders and estates. Such elevation usually augurs well for the appearance of the liquor, and gardens such as Kibena can make fine, bright, brisk tea using 100% mechanically harvested leaf. This level of mechanical intervention may run counter to the romantic artisanal ideal of many, but these producers are a harbinger of things to come in the tea industry and the fact that Kibena can produce attractive teas from such leaf is encouraging.

DEMOCRATIC REPUBLIC OF THE CONGO

A bright future beckons for Congo as Indian investment and orthodox manufacture expertise elevate quality levels.

See map on p316

ONGOLESE TEA HAS A POOR REPUTATION. Decades of conflict have done little for the industry, which is a fraction of its early 1970s size, but the better estates lie on the same geological ridge as the Rwandan and Burundian tea gardens, and there is no real reason why good tea cannot be produced there in the future.

BACKGROUND

Congolese tea was first planted by Belgian pioneers in the 1940s, with factories processing tea on the Legg-cut method designed originally for tobacco. The teas could boast very bright liquors at the cost of, by and large, dreadful quality of leaf. Liverpool and its environs proved to be an especially well-suited market, with the Horniman's blend in particular exploiting the affinity that the local water had with Congolese teas. As the industry grew through the 50s and 60s the teas acquired a reputation as reliably bright and brisk blending teas. Tea continued to expand in a modest fashion during the 1960s as the newly renamed Zaire took its first steps as an independent nation. But by 1970 economic stagnation set in as Mobutu Sese Seko's policy of indigenising foreign-owned businesses started to gather pace. Any meaningful foreign investment was deterred; a situation little improved by the civil wars that followed Mobutu's regime and subsequent cross-border conflict with Rwanda. Only comparatively recently has the Congolese trade started to attract the attention of foreign investors that it deserves.

The gardens are located near the towns of Bukavu, which is at the southern end of Lake Kivu, and Butembo, which sits north west of Lake Edward. Of these it is the Bukavu properties of Mbayo and Madaga which benefit from the superior terroir. Here the tea is only 35 kilometres from Rwanda, and at 1,950-2,150 metres (6,400-7,050 feet) only marginally lower in elevation. The properties have recently come under Indian control and quality has improved – not yet to Rwandan standards,

Mbayo's recently rehabilitated bushes.

but in the long term the potential is there. The compost-rich volcanic soil makes an excellent tea-producing base and the rainfall is suitably reliable as westerly weather patterns hit the mountains of the Albertine Rift.

BLACK CTC AND ORTHODOX TEA

CTCs are bright although relatively soft in taste, and lack the briskness and length of flavour of their Rwandan neighbours. Orthodox tea production has started, and given the heritage that the new owners, M. K. Shah, have in Indian orthodox tea we can expect some genuinely interesting teas to emerge in the future.

Further north in Butuhe where a black CTC is produced, the quality has never reached that of Mbayo and it is unlikely that these teas will trouble the exporters' statistics for some time.

CONGO

at a glance

Plants

Camellia Sinensis
var. assamica
A number of cultivars of
unknown parentage believed
to be from Kenya
and Rwanda

Terroir

Volcanic soils,
1,900-2,200
metres

Seasonality

Best teas
produced
in July

Harvesting

Manual

Yield

551 kg made tea per
hectare

Processing

CTC and
orthodox black

Drinking

Orthodox can be
consumed unblended
without milk, CTCs are
blending teas

RWANDA

Sparkling, golden teas of matchless lustre and consistently fine quality.

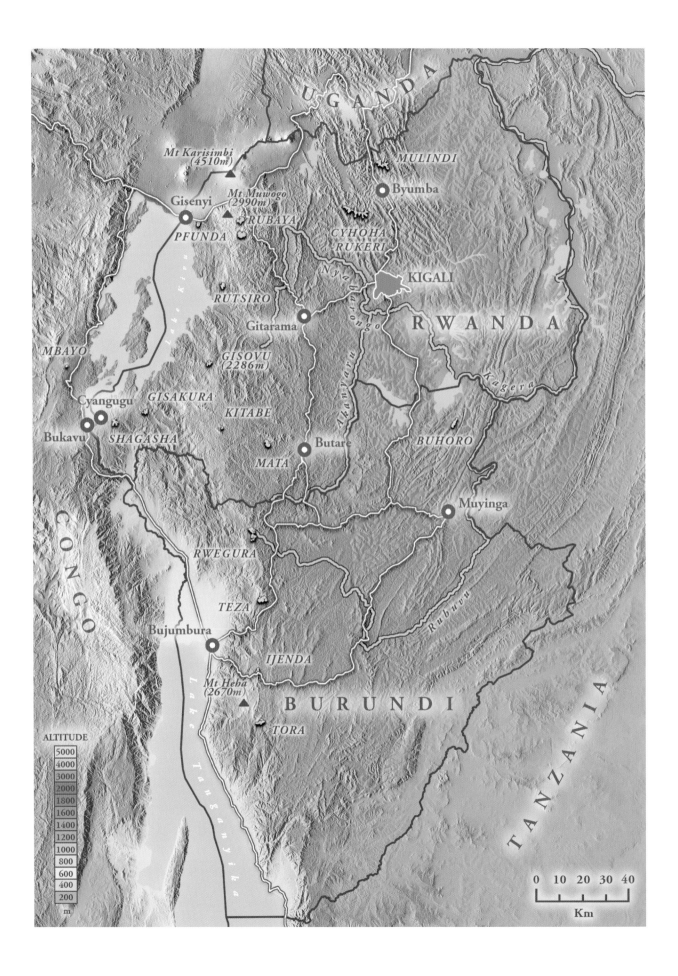

UGANDA

Mt Karisimbi
(4510m) ▲

MULINDI

Byumba ◉

Mt Muwogo
(2990m) ▲

Gisenyi ◉

RUBAYA

CYHOHA
RUKERI

PFUNDA

KIGALI

Lake Kivu

Nyabarongo

RUTSIRO

RWANDA

Gitarama ◉

MBAYO

GISOVU
(2286m)

Kagera

Akanyaru

GISAKURA

Cyangugu ◉

KITABE

SHAGASHA

Bukavu ◉

MATA

Butare ◉

BUHORO

Muyinga ◉

CONGO

RWEGURA

Rubuvu

TEZA

Bujumbura ◉

IJENDA

Mt Heba
(2670m) ▲

BURUNDI

TANZANIA

TORA

Lake Tanganyika

ALTITUDE

5000
4000
3000
2000
1800
1600
1400
1200
1000
800
600
400
200

m

0 10 20 30 40

Km

RWANDA IS UNSURPASSED in producing the world's most attractive teas, with incomparable golden liquors that only ever enhance the appearance of a blend. Whilst there is great depth of quality here, the variety is also widening with the advent of some fine orthodox and green teas. The land of a thousand hills has every right to claim the honours in any assessment of Africa's best teas. There is much to love in Rwandan tea.

That the teas are not often acknowledged in blends or on the front of a pack is pure snobbishness, or perhaps, put in marketing speak, 'a lack of consumer traction'. Where tea-drinkers acknowledge Ceylon or Assam as origins with a marketable heritage, Rwanda is known more for its troubled past than the excellent teas that will help it towards a better future. This needs to change because Rwanda has every right to sit at the top table with these better-known producers.

THE MOUNTAINS OF THE MOON

Many locals claim the Virunga range on Rwanda's border with Congo as the authentic Montes Lunae of Ptolemy's ancient history; a fact disputed by the Ugandans, who believe the ancient texts point to their own Rwenzori mountains.

The merchant Diogenes was the first to assert that he had traced the source of the Nile to the glacial meltwater of a range of mist-shrouded mountains, improbably capped with snow so close to the Equator.

The mythic range now makes for excellent tea land, its fertile volcanic soils, high elevation and reliable rainfall all key factors in the fine, bright teas Rwanda produces.

TEA'S HISTORY IN RWANDA

The first tea planted out in Rwanda during the 1920s proved to be a false start, and it was not until the 1950s that planting of tea could be shown to be a clear success. The spread of tea has since reached the point that it now represents Rwanda's most significant foreign exchange earner after coffee. The gardens are scattered right across the country, but with a greater preponderance of producers along the Congo-Nile crest in the north, south and west. Rwanda's heady altitude is ideally suited to quality tea cultivation, with the range from 1,600-2,500 metres (5,250-8,200 feet) providing on average the highest tea land in the world. This elevation helps to moderate the otherwise scorching equatorial temperatures, the mountains help to capture much-needed rainfall, occasional mists bring daytime moisture, and the cold nights bring a level of stress to the bush that responds with distinctively flavoury teas as a result.

TERROIR

Tea can be found on hillsides as well as in well-drained peaty marshland, with only the drier eastern districts unsuited to its cultivation. This has served to encourage ever more smallholders to plant tea and the crop is growing at a rapid rate, well supported by the philanthropy of backers such as the Wood Family Trust which has helped to provide factory investment and industry expertise. The ample rainfall and free-draining, porous volcanic soils on the hills form an excellent basis for tea cultivation, enabling the roots to penetrate deeper and absorb more nutrients. The peaty marshland forms an alternative terroir, the large volume of organic matter forging teas with attractive bright colour and mellow liquors.

Plucking teams at work in Rwanda.

BLACK CTC

The CTCs produced here are still Rwanda's stock in trade. Entrepreneurial producers recognise the keen demand from quality-minded tea-drinkers for such qualities. Long favoured by the Irish as well as the more discerning of the British and Pakistani consumers, it is their sparkle and brightness, especially when made with milk, that marks them out as special.

As tea-drinkers we like to think that we are influenced predominantly by our palates and are largely immune to other influences, but Rwandan teas challenge this convention. Our eyes are incredibly influential in assessing quality, whether consciously or not. It is this visual check that suggests to us whether or not it is of the style and strength we expect. Is it bright with hues of gold or red? Or is it dull with coffee-like shades of grey and brown? A Rwandan tea will always tip the balance towards the golden end of the scale and we love them for it.

But Rwanda is no one-trick pony; the teas have a delightful aroma and taste pretty fine as well, even if they can sometimes lack a little body or thickness. The hill teas such as Gisovu and Kitabi tend to deliver a little more length of flavour, combining all of the briskness and biscuity character of the best Kenyans with a dash of enhanced smoothness and almost bubblegum notes of refined flavour.

Although there are few producers that do not excel in Rwanda, the organic garden of Rutsiro commanding majestic views of Lake Kivu is arguably the pick of the bunch, with sublime length of brisk, fresh flavour, well-balanced body and sparkling golden orange colour. The pristine, state-

Tea on drained swamp at Sorwathe; such land requires constant maintenance to prevent flooding.

of-the-art factory's current CTC production will soon be augmented by orthodox and steamed green tea.

BLACK ORTHODOX

The Sorwathe factory, selling teas under the Cyhoha and Rukeri marks, nestles in drained papyrus peat marshland north of Kigali. These are amongst the few tea soils in the world to dip below a pH of 4.0 and demand occasional lime in order to maintain their viability. In such potentially boggy environments, the demands on drainage channels are high and the continued success of the estates is a testament to the skills of those who established the plantation decades ago. Rukeri is worthy of note for its composition of a relatively high proportion of China jat bushes, which creates opportunity and variety not open to producers with fields solely planted from Assam jat leaf, and ensures a distinctive aromatic mellowness in the made tea.

In recent years an orthodox line has been commissioned producing a beautiful wiry black tea with lashings of tip and a fine zesty character.

Although they have relatively little in the way of factory rolling equipment, the expertise is there in spades via Sri Lankan factory management and dedicated, well-drilled field staff. Rukeri orthodox is arguably the best such tea in Africa, with the flavour easily a match for medium-grown leafy Ceylons, yet possessing of largely superior leaf and a more attractive colour when brewed with milk.

LIGHT-BRIGHT BLACK TEAS

Sorwathe processes small batches of leaf in limited quantities into an unoxidised tea labelled *Tumba*. Locally understood to be a variation of CTC oolong, the tea shares a number of characteristics with the Nuwara Eliya light-bright black teas that also carry a minimal oxidation time. Tumba is processed as a CTC but then moved directly to the dryer, much as a tea may be at Pedro or Court Lodge in Sri Lanka. Although they can seem a touch maritime in aroma on first encounter, the teas carry an intense freshness and can blend very effectively with both green and black teas. Tumba shows the versatility of some African producers and reassures that the spirit of innovation is alive and well in Rwanda.

STEAMED GREEN TEA

As one should expect of a garden composed of a large number of China jat bushes, Sorwathe produces small parcels of delightfully aromatic steamed green tea. The peaty soils and China leaf material tend to create an appealing vegetal-samphire character.

SILVER TIPS

Like any such *bai hao*-style tea, Rukeri's silver tips are a study in painstaking commitment to quality. Plucked only in the mornings and following a process of minimal intervention, they are gently withered, dried and immediately packed. The slow withering that can take up to forty-eight hours ensures that the process is as gentle as possible and preserves as much of the notoriously fragile and sensitive buds' natural flavour.

RWANDA
at a glance

Plants

Camellia Sinensis
var. assamica
Main cultivar:
TRFK 6/8- quality

Terroir

Volcanic soils on
hills
Peat in drained
swampland
1,600-2,500 metres

Seasonality

Year-round
production with
best quality July to
September

Harvesting

Manual plucking
Average yield:
1452 kg made tea
per hectare

Processing

98% CTC 2%
speciality orthodox

Drinking

Orthodox Rwandan
tea is excellent
on its own CTC
adds brightness to
premium teabags

BURUNDI

Surpassed only by Rwanda in its production of beautiful bright CTC teas.

See map on p316

BURUNDI

at a glance

Plants

Camellia Sinensis

var. assamica

TRFK 6/8- quality

SFS 204- attractive liquor,

resistance to helopeltis

Terroir

Volcanic soils,

1,900-2,100 metres

Seasonality

Year-round

production with

best quality

July-September

Harvesting

Manual. Yield

1133 kg made

tea per hectare

Processing

Black CTC

Drinking

Adds brightness

to premium

teabags

BLACK CTC

The industry was not established until the early 1970s, which makes it amongst Africa's most youthful. This apparent lack of heritage has not held the country back from its ascent to a reputation rivalled only by Rwanda for the production of quality tea. Burundi's tea sits on the same range of mountains as Rwanda's: the Albertine Rift, which exists here as a ridge forming the watershed between the great rivers of the Congo to the west and the Nile to the east. The elevation of 1,900 to 2,100 metres (6,200-6,900 feet) is comparable to that in Rwanda, although being located slightly further south begets the double-edged sword of more seasonality. Seasons are loved and loathed in equal measure by tea devotees. The variation and quality they create bring us some of the world's finest teas, but for those earning a crust from plucking and selling green leaf, a cool, dry season can mean weeks without the bonus payments that big crops can boost. The dry period between July and September tends to form the lowest cropping period, but also boasts the best quality.

Tea here is predominantly grown by smallholders; only about 20% hails from larger estates. The state-owned Office du Thé du Burundi provides the co-ordination needed to produce and market tea from smallholder leaf. Given the proximity it is no surprise that the teas are much like Rwanda's, being characterised by brisk, fresh liquors and a sparkling, golden appearance. Although classy and with great potential, the teas seldom manage to scale the heights of the better Rwandan gardens, a browner leaf appearance often responsible for the discount they realise in the market.

When compared to Rwandans, the greater seasonality and associated stress on the bush in Burundi could yet create the opportunity for superior quality, which estates in private hands could exploit even more effectively. Burundi has the capability of producing world-class tea in even greater volumes, and is a producer to keep an eye out for.

MALAWI

Africa's most venerable producer is a must-have in many British and Continental blends.

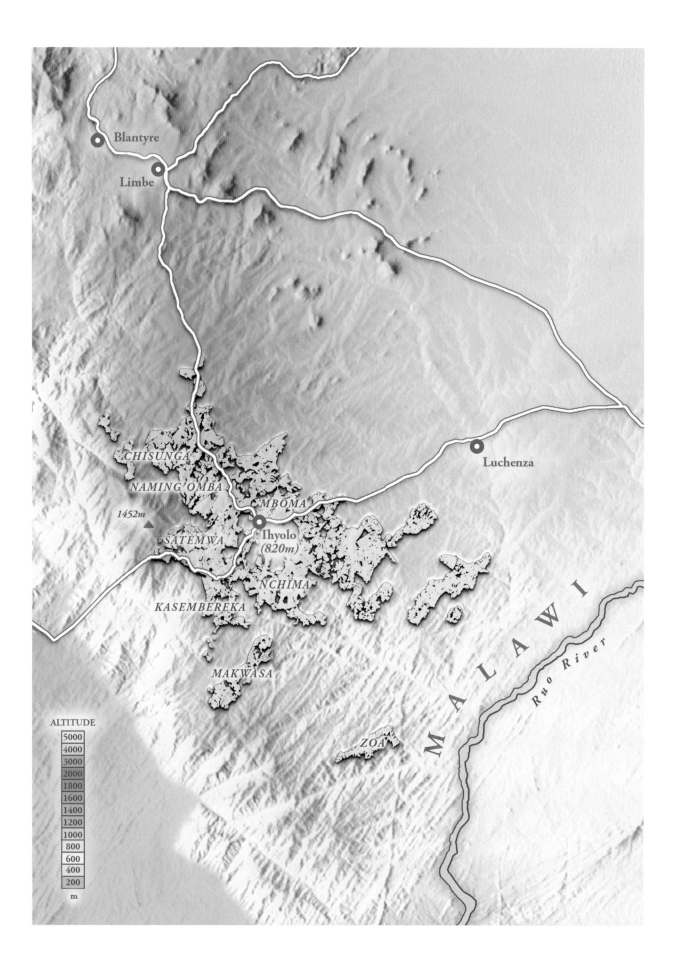

Blantyre

Limbe

Luchenza

CHISUNGA

NAMING'OMBA

1452m

MBOMA

SATEMWA

Thyolo
(820m)

NCHIMA

KASEMBEREKA

MAKWASA

ZOA

M A L A W I

Ruo River

ALTITUDE

5000
4000
3000
2000
1800
1600
1400
1200
1000
800
600
400
200

m

CHITAKALI

Mulanje
(650m)

ESPERANZA

LAUDERDALE

MINI MINI

SAYAMA

ELDORADO

LUJERI

PHWAZI

BLOOM
-FIELD

RUO

CHISAMBO

LIMBULI

Mount Mulanje
3002m

MOZAMBIQUE

M O Z A M B I Q U E

0   5   10

Km

Africa's oldest producer may yet represent the future. It has long produced classic teabag types which endow their blends with a beautiful red colour, but there are early signs that it can produce speciality teas on a par with Asia's esteemed offerings.

In tea terms Malawi is something of an enigma. Who is aware that Malawi even produces tea, yet it can boast the most venerable tea industry in Africa, with a history that stretches back almost as far as Ceylon's. Seldom boasted about on-pack or in tea shops, yet the better Malawis are included in all of the major British blends for their rich red liquors. Malawian tea is a must-have inclusion in many teabags, so although not necessarily conscious of it, most tea-drinkers have definitely drunk it.

Tea is important to Malawi, vitally so. It employs many thousands of people and is (with tobacco and sugar) one of the few export cash crops bringing in vital foreign exchange to a country often listed amongst the world's poorest.

Malawi does not enjoy much of a reputation for its tea quality, but this is an unjust state of affairs for a producing entity whose only essential crime is that it is not Kenya. The fact that Malawi has for a long time suffered in comparison with its showier northern counterpart is a shame as it has much to be proud of; one especial quality is that the gardens are amongst the most accessible in the world, being only a short car journey from downtown Blantyre and well-located close to the Zomba plateau and Mount Mulanje, themselves both significant tourist meccas.

BACKGROUND

Tea was first brought to Malawi (then Nyasaland) by the gardener to the Blantyre Mission of the Church of Scotland in 1878. Although the initial attempt failed, a subsequent effort with some seeds from Kew Gardens in 1886 produced two successful germinations. This showed that tea could survive in Malawi, but it was not until Henry Brown, a failed Ceylon coffee planter, arrived with a view to cultivating coffee in Mulanje that the first commercial plantings took place. Initially a parcel of twenty seeds from the Kirk were planted at the Thornwood and Lauderdale estates. The benign climate and deep red acidic soils well suited the plant, and before long plantations were also being established closer to Blantyre in the rolling hills around Thyolo.

The teas were never regarded as much more than middling quality, being mainly of *assam-sinensis* hybrid stock producing thin yellowish liquors. This was less important than the sheer availability of cheap tea to British blenders, who appreciated the presence in the southern hemisphere of a producer able to ship teas during the off-season in the Assamese winter. The industry grew as the burgeoning consumer market of the early 20th century lapped up the opportunity of an inexpensive offering to draw new consumers into the world of tea at the value end of the market.

The advent of the teabag age provided Malawi with new opportunities. Its ability to produce no-nonsense teas that coloured quickly and provided a robust blast of brisk flavour was highly valued by convenience-minded consumers revelling in their liberation from the perceived shackles of loose tea. The Tea Research Foundation worked hard to produce cultivars from the 1960s onwards, and Malawi eventually became the go-to producer for the reddish-coloured teas that look so wonderful with milk.

As technology developed, Kenya dispensed with orthodox rolling technology and moved to CTC. Malawi's planters followed a different path with the introduction of the Lawrie Tea Processor (LTP), an absurdly noisy maceration device that relies upon a succession of knives and beaters to break down

green leaf. Regarded by many as being more suited to the local conditions, where the precision lathes required to sharpen CTC rollers on a regular basis are both expensive to import and requiring of highly-skilled operation and maintenance, LTP processing gives what is ultimately a cruder leaf, but is to all intents similar in liquor and it seems well-suited to the Malawian plant material.

Malawi's tea trade flourished, but more significantly so did Kenya's and it has long since overtaken Malawi as the key producer for anyone interested in consistent quality tea available all year round. Malawi has played second fiddle in Africa since 1962, and it is inconceivable that it could ever wrest the initiative back from Kenya. Its relatively small area and already overused land preclude expansion, whilst the limits of shallow-rooted cultivars in areas of unpredictable rainfall ensure that replanting will continue only in areas where the topography and mountain-fuelled watercourses permit the excavation of reservoirs for irrigation.

THYOLO

Malawi's two main planting districts, Thyolo and Mulanje, each claim a broadly similar annual crop. Areas of Thyolo, which sits to the south east of Blantyre, were first planted out in 1908. The gardens are as easy to visit as any in the world of tea, an hour's car ride from downtown Blantyre on a good day and well worth the visit. Thyolo's attractive topography, characterised by rolling hills punctuated with granite outcrops, belies a comparatively heady altitude.

The terra rossa (which derives not from a red but from a dark grey dolerite rock) is a classic tea soil, and when conditions are right, the Thyolo estates have the potential to produce some very nice teas, and in particular some very nice-looking teas, with deep red, sparklingly bright liquors that beg to be blended with a dash of Ceylon and Assam and drunk strong at breakfast with a heavy splash of full fat milk.

Thyolo's great handicap, though, is a lack of watercourses providing irrigation or damming opportunities. This hampers estates in their ability to plant out higher-yielding cultivars, and limits their ability to extend their season into the drier periods through irrigation. As climate change leaves Malawi with increasingly erratic rainfall patterns, and local deforestation leads to localised lack of rain, it is increasingly an area under threat.

GREEN/WHITE/OOLONG/PU ERH

At altitudes of between 750 and 1,250 metres (2,500-4,100 feet), Satemwa can boast the highest altitude tea in Malawi. So long as the consumer pays up for reddish-liquoring black tea, this altitude is of relatively modest benefit, but when it comes to orthodox black tea or beautifully aromatic green teas then this is potentially very significant as an advantage. White tea, for example, is almost unheard of on the African continent, but such precedent has never stopped the Kay family or Custom, the aptly named speciality tea-maker. As a consequence the visitor will be rewarded with not only Satemwa white tea in both silver needle and Pai Mu Tan form, but also a hand-rolled 'pearl' type that will slowly unfurl under multiple Gong Fu-style brewings, a roasted green tea going by the name of Zomba with an attractive, toasty bite and piercing freshness, a jade oolong with a sweet mellowness and notes of cut grass known as Bvwumbe Twist 'n' Dry, and the only Pu Erh-style Shou dark tea produced in Africa. A particular highlight is Satemwa Antlers, prepubescent upper stems taken before the bud has formed and very slowly dried with no further intervention. Antlers are a prime example of the argument that the inclusion of stalk need not necessarily be a bad thing. The floral aroma and distinctive caramel character is genuinely unique, and a just reward for the painstakingly intricate and skilled plucking required to select the appropriate raw materials.

Whilst the speciality types are always interesting, the essentially artisanal production methodology will always limit their mass availability on the global market, so in some ways the most interesting tea to emanate from Satemwa is their early-season orthodox black tea, labelled TSFBOP1. Malawi's great challenge has always been its extreme seasonality which seems to worsen by the year, shortening the remunerative cropping period with disruption to climatological patterns. But here Satemwa has turned it to its advantage by producing what is essentially a first flush tea maximising on the distinctive character that winter stress brings to the bush in much the same way as an early Darjeeling. The bush has fought to survive a lack of rainfall coupled with the cold, damp Chipperoni fogs that drift in from Mozambique during winter, a stress that manifests itself in a deep concentration of fresh, aromatic notes in the leaf. The whole-leafed black tea is blessed with an uncharacteristic (for Malawi) citric-zesty character that has much of the piercing aroma of a Darjeeling, but with a more rounded and approachable mellowness. There is perhaps

Hand rolling a speciality tea at Satemwa.

Tea plucking in Thyolo.

not a better orthodox tea in Africa, and such teas stand on an equal quality footing with India's better-known specialities. Other gardens may be bigger, better financed or producing redder-liquoring teas, but I challenge any visitor to walk away from Satemwa without a warm feeling for a long-standing family business producing excellent speciality teas of genuine world class.

MULANJE

Mount Mulanje forms the epic backdrop to the planting districts of the same name. A broad granite massif reaching 3,000 metres at its highest point, it is a challenging ascent for those interested in hiking, requiring ideally a couple of days set aside to scale and descend its flanks. Standing as a mountain island dominating the plains around, the massif acts as a rain barrier forcing clouds to deposit their contents around its broad summit. The planting districts around the base of the mountain and up to around 800 metres may not always benefit directly from the rains, but the innumerable streams and rivulets that rise here are a fine basis for the numerous tea gardens to dam, thereby enabling irrigation of their high-quality bushes.

Although Mulanje is generally lower in altitude than Thyolo, it receives about 30% more rain and it is because of the reliability of the rainfall and the opportunity to irrigate that planters with the opportunity will always favour Mulanje. Here you can find some of the most prized teas in Malawi. Clonal gardens such as Sayama produce excellent red-liquoring brisk teas that, when made with milk, produce some of the most beautiful liquors in the world: you don't need much clonal Malawi tea to turn an otherwise greyish-looking Assam into a beautiful, rich-looking breakfast blend. Malawi clonals are perhaps the 'airbrushes' of the tea world: always in the background, unseen, unheralded, but when used in a blend they permit teas with much more eminent reputations to blossom and shine.

Malawi is poor, indeed the poorest country in the world judged by World Bank statistics. Although tea workers may be better off than other rural workers, wages and benefits in the tea sector here are lower than anywhere in the world, and there is an urgent need to elevate the pay of those in the Malawian industry above the World Bank Extreme Poverty Line. There are some genuine innovators and visionaries within the country doing their utmost to remedy this whilst making excellent teas in desperately trying circumstances.

The best way to support those who depend on tea for a livelihood is to actively seek out Malawian tea and pay up for it, support the small speciality sector, or visit the country itself. Visitors will find that the sense of joy and welcome quite belies its development problems and statistical poverty.

Plants

Camellia Sinensis
var. assamica with
some China jat
SFS 204- attractive liquor,
resistance to helopeltis
SFS 150- hardy, drought-
resistant
PC 105- attractive liquor
PC 108- attractive liquor

Terroir

Alluvial red soils,
650-1,250 metres

Seasonality

Best quality produced during
early season in
November-
December

Harvesting

Mainly manual
but also a mix
of shear and
machine. Yield
2361 kg made
tea per hectare

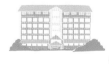

Processing

CTP and LTP
black tea,
small volumes
of boutique teas

Drinking

Cultivars bring an
attractive colour
to blends

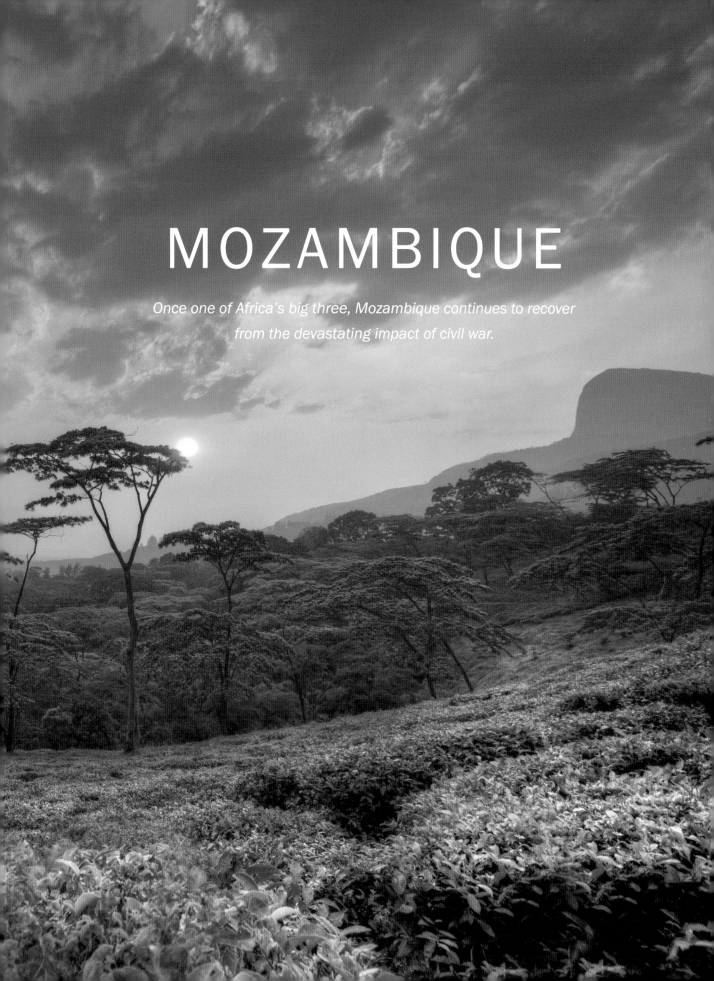

MOZAMBIQUE

*Once one of Africa's big three, Mozambique continues to recover
from the devastating impact of civil war.*

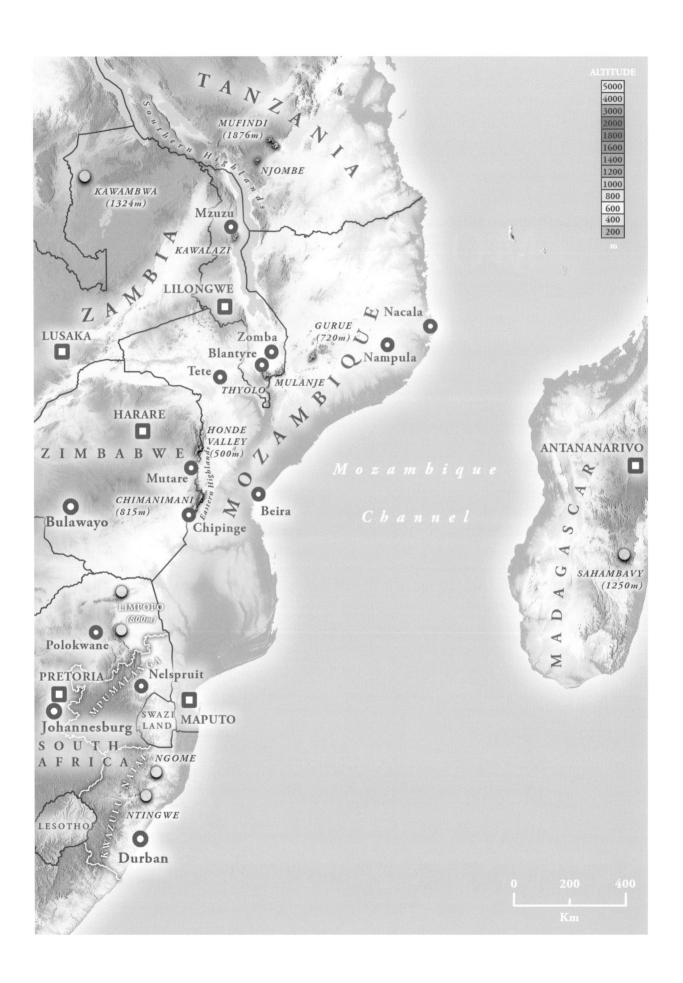

ALTITUDE

5000
4000
3000
2000
1800
1600
1400
1200
1000
800
600
400
200

m

T A N Z A N I A

*MUFINDI
(1876m)*

NJOMBE

Southern Highlands

*KAWAMBWA
(1324m)*

Mzuzu

KAWALAZI

LILONGWE

Z A M B I A

LUSAKA

Zomba

*GURUE
(720m)*

Nacala

Blantyre

Nampula

Tete

THYOLO

MULANJE

M O Z A M B I Q U E

HARARE

*HONDE
VALLEY
(500m)*

Z I M B A B W E

ANTANANARIVO

Mutare

Eastern Highlands

*CHIMANIMANI
(815m)*

Beira

M a d a g a s c a r

Bulawayo

Chipinge

M o z a m b i q u e

C h a n n e l

*SAHAMBAVY
(1250m)*

*LIMPOPO
(800m)*

Polokwane

PRETORIA

Nelspruit

M A D A G A S C A R

MPUMALANGA

*SWAZI
LAND*

MAPUTO

Johannesburg

*S O U T H
A F R I C A*

NGOME

KWAZULU NATAL

LESOTHO

NTINGWE

Durban

0   200   400

Km

MOZAMBIQUE'S GARDENS IN THE GRANITE-topped hills around Gurúè produce an unexceptional black tea for the southern African and export markets. Many gardens are only now becoming rehabilitated after the civil war that followed independence from Portugal. Although there are encouraging developments in replanting and investment in green tea production, production remains a fraction of the potential.

BACKGROUND

The Mozambiqui tea industry is analogous to the Congolese: a once glorious status as a producer of some significance is now a distant memory. It is focused upon the area around Gurúè, which is only 200 kilometres from Mulanje on the Malawian border, although the dirt roads turn this into a full day's drive. This part of Zambezia province, with its healthy rainfall and more moderate temperatures, is where Portuguese colonial tea businesses first started planting tea on an experimental basis in the 1920s, and then with abandon in the mid to late 1930s. The enthusiasm was such that by 1950 there was more land under tea in Mozambique than in any other African country, an honour it retained unbroken until overtaken by Kenya in 1960. Although there was much tea in the ground, this never yielded very efficiently and the volume that was actually produced was always eclipsed by Kenya and Malawi. The industry never grew beyond its 1960 area, although yields did improve somewhat to a peak in 1981, by when the country had started to succumb to civil war.

Soon after independence had been achieved in 1976, the governing FRELIMO party declared Mozambique to be a socialist one-party state, nationalised businesses and gave Portuguese residents a ninety-day ultimatum to remain and take local citizenship or leave. These measures precipitated a rapid exodus of the majority of the white Portuguese community which had been involved in financing and managing much of Mozambique's economy. Civil war followed in 1978 as neighbouring countries defended interests through local proxies. The fifteen-year conflict proved devastating to vast swathes of the country, and continues to cast a shadow over many agricultural industries forced to deal with the legacy of landmines, destroyed infrastructure and an exodus of expertise. As a result tea production collapsed from 22,000 tonnes in 1981 to just 1,500 by 1988.

By the mid-1990s came the first efforts to get the tea gardens back on their feet, a process that continues to this day. Producers have struggled to make ends meet as they battle with the costs of rehabilitating tea and factories following the war. A number of buildings remain empty shells, some scarred by mortar or small arms fire, and with little immediate prospect for tea processing. Most of the gardens were planted from seedlings (rather than special cultivars), and given the intervention of

BED TEA

The factory manager's first pot of tea in the morning should always be the tea produced only hours earlier in the night, and provides him with an opportunity to assess quality before he even emerges from his bed. For other household visitors not burdened with quality control responsibilities, bed tea is enjoyed in the knowledge that there is nothing fresher anywhere in the world, and this imparts an incomparable sense of pleasure at the relish of consuming something genuinely local at the point of its conception.

the war, these bushes have been permitted to become trees requiring rehabilitation. This has presented the producers with problems, as the cost in man hours required to restore an area of old seedling bushes may not always be compensated for within a remunerative timescale, whether through yield or quality. The yields in Mozambique remain a fraction of what the nearby Malawian estates are able to achieve with modern clonal varieties, while the quality also lags some way behind.

The strongly seasonal production pattern of a long, cold, dry season between May and September means that 75% of the tea is produced between October and April, placing considerable pressure upon the factories forced to manage this glut and the field workers who have to pluck it. The season frustrates any attempts to retain workers on permanent contracts, and it can have a knock-on effect on labour relations in general. This is not an enviable situation as seasonality is a wonderful thing where producers are able to take advantage of it (as in Darjeeling, for example), but it does little for the Mozambiqui trade.

CTC BLACK TEA

Because the overwhelming proportion of the gardens is dry land seedling tea (non-irrigated tea planted from seed), the quality is potentially similar to Malawi tea of seedling provenance grown on the same red clay. Mulanje, for example, receives almost exactly the same rainfall and enjoys similar temperatures yet produces much the better tea. The variation comes with the attention that this tea is given in the factory, where many producers are still finding their way with the manufacture process. Where they are well-run, the teas are relatively soft in taste, clear-liquoring when drunk without milk, relatively bright and pinkish with milk and with excellent leaf. Periods of heavy crop tend to result in stalky brown leaf and a deterioration in liquor, arising from overloaded, withering troughs and dryers.

MOZAMBIQUE
at a glance

Plants

Camellia Sinensis
var. assamica
SFS 204- attractive liquor

Terroir

Silty loam,
700-900 metres

Seasonality

Early season
in November-
December

Harvesting

Shear and
machine. Yield
1851 kg made
tea per hectare

Processing

CTC black tea

Drinking

Blending tea

ZIMBABWE

See map on p336

BACKGROUND

Tea was first planted in Zimbabwe, then Rhodesia, in 1924 in the same Eastern Highland areas that remain the heartland of current tea production. The industry grew slowly but steadily for the next thirty years before a period of accelerated growth in the 1960s and 1970s in which the area under tea more than doubled and crop increased tenfold. As throughout the Zimbabwean agricultural sector there was further progress during the 1980s and 1990s until self-inflicted economic catastrophe intervened in 2007. Crop declined by 80% as producers struggled with the inflationary consequences of the regime's economic policy.

Zimbabwe has a small tea industry concentrated around the eastern border areas abutting Mozambique. The largest estates are located near Chipinge below the Chirinda rainforest, and further north beyond Mutare in the Honde Valley. The rugged hills topped with rainforest trap considerable rainfall, the free-draining sandy loams are excellent tea soils and the rivulets running throughout the highlands are an enviable power generation resource. On the face of it, this is a combination of blessings but the stewardship of any business in Zimbabwe has seldom been smooth in the last decade.

In a local context, Zimbabwe is at the front of the curve as far as worker remuneration is concerned and it is the Eastern Highland gardens that have paved the way for full mechanisation and correspondingly higher wages for skilled employees. Although this is a situation forced upon the estates following large-scale migration to urban areas, it provides a fine example of what can be done to elevate living standards in rural communities.

Plucking teams in action in the Eastern Highlands.

BLACK CTC TEA

Zimbabwe has always been capable of making very fine CTC teas, not of Rwandan or Kenya Tea Development Agency quality, but certainly of mid-range Kenyan standard. Honde Valley teas are fine mainstream CTC teas for the classic teabag markets, clean and increasingly well-made. Further south, around the Tanganda river, the style is a little brighter and a good match for the style produced in the Kericho district of Kenya.

ZIMBABWE
at a glance

Plants
Camellia Sinensis
var. assamica
PC 168- yield and
good liquors

Terroir
Red clay loam
with some
sandy loam
700-900 metres

Seasonality
Best teas
produced during
early season in
November-December

Harvesting
Machine. Yield
2576 kg made
tea per hectare

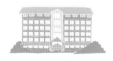

Processing
CTC black tea,
small
quantities
of LTP black tea

Drinking
Blending tea

OTHER AFRICAN
TEA PRODUCERS

See maps on pp302 and 336

ETHIOPIA

Tea has been cultivated in a half-hearted way in Ethiopia since 1957, but until the mid-1970s it was more as a curiosity than with any serious commercial ambition. Ethiopia is coffee country; in fact it is regarded as *Coffea arabica*'s birthplace, so any serious ingress of tea will always be more culturally difficult here where traditions run so strong. Despite this, since tea planting started in earnest in 1973, two well-run estates have been established, producing substantial volumes of bright, high-grown tea. Wush Wush sits in the Kaffa Zone at about 1,900 metres (6,200 feet) and Gumaro is a little more distant from Addis Ababa in the Illubabor Zone at 1,700 metres (5,600 feet). Both estate leaf and smallholder-supplied leaf is used. There is adequate land and potential for further growth, so it is likely we will be hearing more of Ethiopia's tea industry.

The teas are typical high-grown African CTCs with brisk, biscuity liquors and an attractive golden brightness when brewed with milk.

CAMEROON

Cameroonian tea was for many years a mainstay of the British and continental market. The teas produced at the gardens of Tole, Ndu and Djutitsa were regularly sold in the London Tea Auctions. The July to September rainy season in West Africa and the resulting heavy crop at that time complemented the concurrent dry season in Zimbabwe and Malawi very effectively. Although the liquors are bright and lively, the coarse and workmanlike character limits the appeal somewhat.

The gardens are well distributed across the highlands of the south-western corner of Cameroon, with Tole in particular most spectacularly located in the lee of Mount Cameroon, a 4,000-metre active volcano. Generally the soils are volcanic and well drained, although less acidic than is usual in tea gardens which can make demands upon yield and the health of the bushes.

The 5,000-hectare estate of Ndawara is now arguably the premier garden in Cameroon, and one of the largest in the world. It boasts a wealthy and influential backer, ready investment in a modern factory and as a consequence can claim the highest proportion of clonal bushes, but its passage has been far from smooth. The Fulani cattle herders who have made their home here from across the border in Nigeria assert that their former grazing land now plays host to the expanding estate, whilst the proprietor claims he provides much-needed jobs for thousands of local villagers.

Cameroonian economic disruption has resulted in a stuttering supply of teas into the traditional export markets and it is rare now to find Cameroonian tea in Europe and North America. They may not care, though, as Cameroonian consumption of tea grows faster than any other country in the world.

NIGERIA

The Mambilla Plateau of Nigeria has been producing black CTC tea since 1982, [4] almost unknown as a tea producer to the rest of the world. The bushes benefit from the more temperate climate that the 1,400-1,600 metre (4,600-5,200 feet) altitude brings. At 1,400 millimetres (55 inches) there is just enough rainfall to make the tea viable, although the lengthy dry season does create problems. The bushes are all of Kenyan origin and the red clay soils are similar to those found in Malawi, but the smallholders growing the tea are hampered by a lack of cash for fertilisers, resulting in what is amongst the world's lowest yielding tea. Growers also suffer from an absence of any embedded tea culture to bring about improvements in husbandry. The factory is hindered by poor power supply, whilst any outside investment is dissuaded by Nigeria's domestic strife. Against all the odds, then, a perfectly drinkable tea is produced, although it lacks any real export potential. Liquors are a little dull, and the soft teas do little to offend, but not much to attract.

Tea gardens on the Mambilla Plateau.

ZAMBIA

Zambia's tea is located in the north-western corner of the country in the Kawambwa district bordering Congo. The red-brown soils derived from laterite are quite heavily acidic, even for the normally acid-tolerant tea bush, but the heavy rainfall and 1,000-metre (3,300-feet) altitude, which provide a slightly cooler daytime temperature, are otherwise well-suited to *Camellia sinensis*.

Tea here has enjoyed a troubled recent history – promises made by incoming investors have been broken and workers left unpaid – although some cause for optimism remains in the shape of the publicly-held Zambian Forestry Corporation, which has pledged to plant tea on a large area of land under its control. There remains a potential in Zambian tea, but long-term commitment and investment is needed if the quality is to approach the level of Zimbabwean and Malawian tea.

SOUTH AFRICA

Tea has a long history in South Africa: the earliest planting dates back to 1877,[1] making it even more venerable than Malawi as a producer. Being well-developed and possessing of world-class agronomists and engineers, with a sizeable local market and good logistics, South Africa would appear to offer great potential as a tea producer.

This long history has not been without its problems. Tea is a demanding mistress if it is to be effectively farmed, and South African wages have frequently been too high in comparison with its neighbours to permit adequate numbers of workers to be engaged. Even as far back as 1911, planters were complaining of the cost of production[2] and its hampering impact on the growth of the industry. Somehow, though,

Tshivhase Estate in Limpopo province.

although never booming with the enthusiasm of Malawi's trade or even that of Mozambique's, the South African tea industry grew steadily to the point where by the mid-1980s it was producing about 10-12,000 tonnes of good quality tea each year, a figure it more or less maintained until 2003. By then the impact of rising production costs, new minimum wage levels and cheaper imports started to catch up with the trade, and production plummeted as factories shut in the face of the rising costs. By 2003 it had sunk to just 2,600 tonnes,[3] a shadow of its former self.

Tea production now is restricted to a handful of producers in Limpopo and Kwazulu-Natal provinces, where the compulsion to mechanise has made them standard-bearers in factory technology. The South African estates are very strongly seasonal, a reality that inevitably further compounds their lack of competitiveness, but as with many seasonal origins, such extremes of climate, brought about by the latitude, can be an advantage in sheer quality terms. A bush emerging from its dormancy tends to produce teas of distinctive character; the more extreme the conditions during its dormancy, the greater the potential (within reason).

The limited remaining South African tea is of fine overall quality, and is an example of the excellence that can come from fewer, more highly remunerated and highly skilled workers. Teas are strong with attractive body and brightness, with the spring crop from the October-November period being the best of the lot.

MAURITIUS

At one time Mauritian tea was a mainstay of British blends. Planting of the gardens in the interior commenced in the 1920s but accelerated in the post-war years in line with many African producing countries. By the 1970s Mauritius was a producer of some significance, but the growth of the tourist industry has fuelled domestic demand, just as it has challenged the viability of a people- and land-heavy tea industry on a small island of increasing affluence.

The main plantations, Bois Cheri and Chartreuse, are located towards the centre of the southern part of the island, which receives the most rainfall. The reddish humic latosols are comparable to those found across tea-growing regions of southern Africa. The seasonality is related, too: a cooler, drier winter from June to September provides an off-season and the warm, wet November to May summer period is responsible for the overwhelming bulk of the tea crop.

The teas themselves are very pleasant, bright, classic CTC types. Although a commonplace Maldive speciality is to blend locally grown vanilla into the tea, one does also sometimes find a very attractive natural vanilla note in some teas, which adds to the appeal.

MADAGASCAR

There is one producer of significance growing tea at around 1,250 metres (4,100 feet) in the Central Highlands of the island. The estate of Sahambavy occupies an enviable location on slopes which descend to a lake of the same name. The garden was first planted in 1970, its red iron-rich soils and heavy rainfall offering ostensibly similar conditions to Malawi, although the more maritime conditions in Madagascar provide a little more rainfall and less seasonal variation in temperature. The main produce is ordinary, honest black tea, which from time to time can carry a Brazil-like coconut character. The green tea is a more recent innovation and volumes remain very limited.

Bois Cheri in the Mauritian foothills.

EUROPEAN PRODUCERS

A tea estate in Porto Formoso, Azores

Title page: Tregothnan in Cornwall

EUROPEAN REPRESENTATIVES IN THE tea-producing community are often said to be curiosities more than tea producers of size and scale. However, those producing tea at this latitude, and against the odds of location, culture and history, are often even more committed than their more southerly counterparts, and to use the word *curiosity* does these artisans a disservice.

AZORES

The Azores represents Europe's most commercially significant producer, and the only European tea that one can realistically buy at supermarket prices. Producing both a green bohea and a black tea, the Azores have climate squarely on their side. The scale is such that, given European rates of pay, mechanical plucking is the only realistic harvest method, and as practised here, brings with it quality concerns when set against the benefits of manual plucking. The Azorean bohea is a classic green tea in the Chinese pan-fired style. Although it is a little toasty and suggestive of an ordinary Chun Mee, the quality of the leaf is insufficient to elevate the liquor to the point that any genuine comparison with China is possible.

The Azorean orthodox black is a flaky, almost Turkish-style tea of thinnish body and low astringency, but mercifully without the sourness. It works well without milk and appeals to those who find teas from more traditional origins too brisk and pungent.

ITALY

The Lucca botanical gardens around Sant'Andrea di Compito are home to a small-scale tea plantation manufacturing limited quantities of green and black tea, although not on a scale to represent anything more than an entertaining diversion from a Tuscan holiday. The Tuscan climate would seem on the face of it to offer inadequate rainfall for tea cultivation, and it will be interesting to note how the venture fares.

SWITZERLAND

The southern slopes of the Alps create numerous excellent microclimates: good sunshine hours, wet springs and summers and the protective influence of the Alps ensure fine growing conditions. The establishment of a small tea garden on Monte Verità in the hills above Ascona stands testament to what can be done with geographic good fortune, intense care and skilled manufacture. They do things properly in Switzerland, and the plucking and manufacture is expertly overseen by Kotaro Tanimoto-san of the Japan Tea Exporters Association. The miniscule tea crop is as good as one should expect from a country that wears its Swiss Quality badge proudly.

UK – CORNWALL

Tregothnan Estate, just up the Truro river from Cornwall's county town of the same name, represents the UK's best-known foray into tea production. The family seat of the Boscawen family boasts a two-hundred-year heritage of successful camellia cultivation, skills that the current head gardener, the irrepressibly enthusiastic and visionary Jonathon Jones, has pressed into use in the first plantings of *Camellia sinensis*. Small parcels of tea are planted in fortuitously located spots in the grounds of the country house, as well as across the estate, always making best use of sheltered, sunny microclimates and maximising on the abundant rainfall and warm temperatures that Cornwall can boast. These microclimates are vital because, although it is one of the UK's warmest and wettest counties, it is some way behind the major subtropical origins in terms of mean temperatures and rainfall.

Tregothnan is an ancient family estate and it has a correspondingly long-term vision for its tea cultivation. The ambition is clear in their marketing efforts, and the sheer force of personality that Jones brings to the enterprise shines through every communication. The teas are manufactured in miniscule quantities and fetch a substantial price premium, even over the most noble of Darjeelings.

SCOTLAND

It may seem improbable, but the small yet beautiful output of Scotland's producers can put many better-known origins to shame. Tea in Scotland is the brainchild of Tam O'Braan, an agronomist with a record of successful cultivation in marginal conditions, and spawned out of research into super-high-antioxidant teas for recovering chemotherapy patients. With 6 hectares (14 acres) of tea, Scotland is still very much in the realms of the artisan, but those 6 hectares are spread across multiple terroirs and production styles are such that the teas genuinely speak of their birthplace.

The first winter of any tea plant in a marginal environment is always a concern, but that of 2012-2013, defined at Dalreoch in Perthshire by extended periods of sub-10°C temperatures, was as stern a test as any new tea garden should undergo, well outside of any textbook's advice on viable tea cultivation. O'Braan's fledgling plants seemed to succumb, and with them his hopes of establishing a viable tea garden. By spring 2013, though, when all hope seemed lost, the bushes began to sprout anew and Tam knew that he was onto something special.

O'Braan's example has encouraged producers right across the country, assisted by the supportive umbrella of the not-for-profit Tea Growers Association. Experiences are shared amongst the membership, purchasing power and marketing spend is pooled, and the nascent industry benefits as a consequence. Tea is now growing on five different gardens encompassing red Aberdonian clay, Dumfries and Galloway's sandy loam, the Isle of Mull's peat and Perthshire's stony clay, none of it protected by polytunnels or any other sort of artificial microclimate. Such regional variation forges teas of great distinctiveness.

The sea-level teas produced on the warmer, wetter west coast near Stranraer are fast-growing, with a flush every two to three weeks during the season, a fertile environment ideally suited to black tea manufacture. In Dalreoch, the 750-metre (2,500-feet) altitude is more suited to white tea, with the resultant fruity peach notes more akin to a fine Bi Luo Chun. The local expertise in the cold smoking of salmon has also resulted in their white smoked tea, recently garlanded in Paris. The Isle of Mull's sea air forges teas ideally suited to Japanese-style green tea processing, such that their salty, umami character is suggestive of Shizuoka's senchas. We point at the sea, but Mull's peaty terroir is not dissimilar to the drained papyrus bogs found in parts of Rwanda, which also produce a green tea with marine taste notes in entirely different climatological conditions.

A new factory is planned in Perthshire, its central location offering growers the prospect of a more systemised opportunity to process leaf and support the industry's growth. More is on the way, with a dark oolong tea expected as well as the promise of citrus-tinged pan-fried green tea from Aberdeenshire. Given that much of the world's tea and its planters emanated from Scotland, tea is coming home.

Scottish tea plants.

ARGENTINA

South America's foremost producer specialises in teas well suited to iced tea.

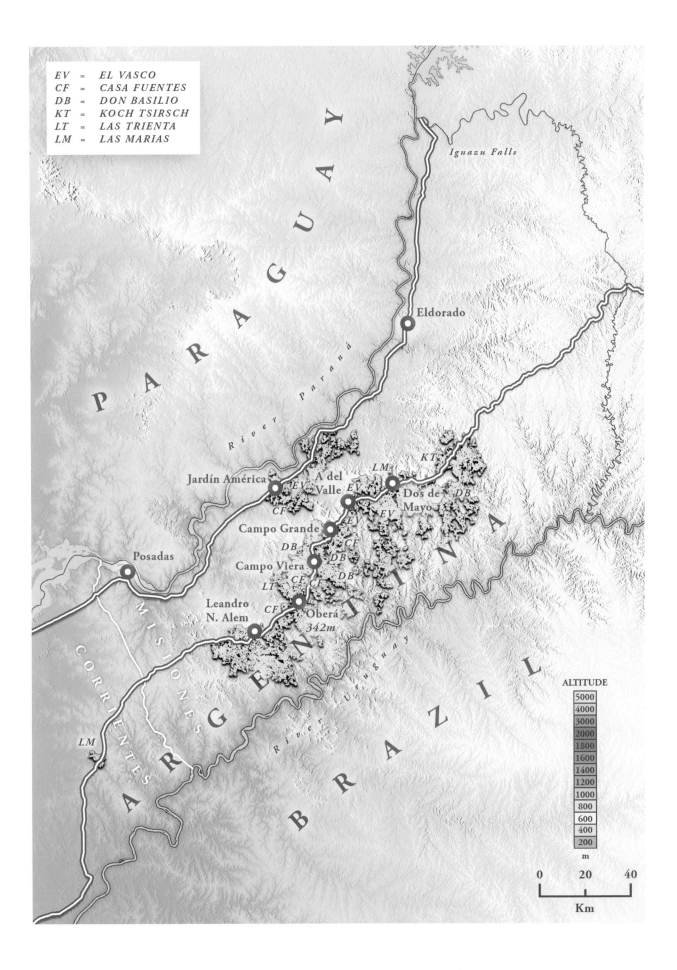

EV = EL VASCO
CF = CASA FUENTES
DB = DON BASILIO
KT = KOCH TSIRSCH
LT = LAS TRIENTA
LM = LAS MARIAS

PARAGUAY

Iguazu Falls

River Paraná

Eldorado

BRAZIL

Jardín América
A del
Valle
KT
LM
EV
EV
CF
Dos de
Mayo
DB
Campo Grande
DB
EV
EV
CF
DB
Campo Viera
DB
LT
CF
CF
DB
Leandro
N. Alem
CF
Oberá
342m

Posadas

MISIONES

CORRIENTES

River Uruguay

ARGENTINA

LM

ALTITUDE
5000
4000
3000
2000
1800
1600
1400
1200
1000
800
600
400
200
m

0   20   40

Km

WHILST WELL KNOWN for its *yerba maté*, the gauchos' preferred beverage, Argentina is seldom seen in evidence across the supermarket shelves or in the tins of specialists. It produces a prodigious volume of tea to have remained under the radar of most tea-drinkers for so long. Argentina is a tea-growing land quite unlike any other, and a visit is always a pleasure.

BACKGROUND

Argentina has been growing tea since the 1920s, but with real enthusiasm since an import ban in the 1950s generated vast demand for domestic produce. It now produces a lot, much of it about as unsuitable for hot tea blends as anything else in the world. Argentina's black tea is mostly dull and brownish, flat, earthy, sometimes iodine-like, often with a suggestion of mustiness and rarely worthwhile using for hot tea drinking. But tea is a broad church, and a Stateside visit to the porch of a house in the USA's Deep South during the scorching summer reveals the joys of *iced tea*.

Brewed in the morning, placed in the fridge to chill and then poured over ice with a squeeze of lemon and a sprig of mint in the evening, it becomes the perfect thirst-quenching sundowner, and Argentina arguably does it best of all.

MISIONES

Argentina's tea hails primarily from the province of Misiones, a finger of Argentina that extends into Brazil and Paraguay. Misiones is a tourist magnet by way of the magnificent Iguazu Falls which lie on its northern border with Brazil, but it is rare for tourists to venture any further south into the province. A shame, as Misiones can boast beautiful rolling hills, impenetrable indigenous forest, and broad vistas of tea and maté.

The red soils of Misiones are home to a number of farmers who tend to grow tea, yerba mate or tobacco, and often a combination of the three. In a land of high labour costs with no prospect for anything other than mechanical harvests, these farmers inevitably orient themselves around quantity rather than quality of leaf. For the Misiones Argentine, four leaves and a bud constitutes fine plucking but curiously, it is just this that is responsible for the characteristic Argentine style.

To look at an Argentine farmer through the prism of an Asian tea schooling one would say that the plucking standard in Misiones is one of the worst in the world. Machines are never as discriminatory as hands or shears, but in Argentina the ride-on machines are much less selective than the handheld machines largely employed outside of South America. When the period of at least three weeks between harvests is also factored in, then the age and relative tenderness of the leaf can be well imagined.

However, Argentine estate workers are better remunerated than any others, and Argentina's producers have been at the forefront as routes to more sustainable employment practices are concerned. What starts in Argentina is often seen elsewhere in the industry, so we should be careful about dismissing the plucking standard before we see how other tea economies will cope with the impact of rising wages.

Strange as it may sound, the merit of Argentine as an iced tea lies precisely in this coarser, older leaf that the long plucking rounds and non-selective machinery provide. It is a characteristic of tea that the infusion process results in some of the soluble constituents of the leaf dissolving into the

Las Treinta's Don Henrique Estate in Misiones.

water during the brew. It is these solids that endow tea with its 'mouthfeel' characteristics: generally the more 'soluble solids' that a tea has, the more body the liquor will possess. What is less well known unless you have experimented with making iced tea is that these solids start to precipitate (or emerge out of the solution) as the tea cools. We see this in Assam with the process known as *creaming down* (see p219), making it eminently unsuitable for iced tea-making.

The concentration of solids in a particular tea is down to a number of factors: elevation, seasonality, plucking standard, leaf quality and manufacture style. It is a combination of these factors in the Argentine case that makes the tea so perfect for iced tea (and so poor for hot tea), but chief amongst them is the preponderance of old leaf and stalk in the leaf entering the factory.[1] It is known that older leaf contains less soluble solids and caffeine, and by dint of manufacturing four leaves and a bud or older, the factory only maximises the potential clarity of the tea when made iced: hot tea's loss is iced tea's gain.

When looking for Misiones tea there is not a great deal to separate one factory from another. A number of estates have planted cultivars from which sizeable crops are derived, some producing up to 5 tonnes per hectare which is a prodigious yield for a seasonal origin with fields lying dormant for six months of the year. The commoditised nature of the industry has led to the formation of large groups catering to the international trade, most notably Casa Fuentes, Don Basilio, Las Treinta and El Vasco, which can claim more than half of the total output between them. There being no real boutique trade here, your choice should be governed by the characteristics you are looking for. My own experience is that, clarity aside, iced tea requires a level of redness which is best found in Casa Fuentes or Koch Tschirsch. The starting point is all-important as the addition of ice and lemon to a brew dissipates the colour, iced tea-drinkers tending to favour reddish-orange rather than yellowish hues. Taste comes comparatively low down the list as lemon, and often also fresh mint or sugar, will act as seasonings and mask any tea character.

Misiones is as commoditised as a tea industry gets, but we should not knock it for this. It has long since abandoned supplying tea for price to cheap private label tea packers in Europe, who can now find much cheaper options elsewhere. It produces a reliable product offering an ideal base for iced tea-making, and neither the teas nor their producers have any pretensions that they do otherwise. Even were it to double its quality it would never see the rewards in price terms, so it continues doing what it has always done best. Even if you don't drink iced tea, don't malign the Argentines for producing it – they make a pretty good job of it.

CORRIENTES

Misiones' southern neighbour, Corrientes, is much less significant as a producing region, but in Las Marias and its owners, the Navajas family, it can boast a quality focus. Finer plucking standards are enforced and generally better clonal bushes have been planted out on the garden. The highly mechanised factory has long acted as a harbinger of things to come in the global industry, and the

Las Marias Estate in Corrientes.

care and attention taken there is a further reason why its teas are preferable for hot tea-drinking to the teas from the north.

It is pushing the boat out to favour Las Marias over a well-made African tea, or even closer to home, a Brazilian, but it remains the only Argentine tea that I would seriously contemplate drinking hot. Corrientes offers enhanced levels of brightness and briskness over the Misiones teas, and a touch of aroma.

Mechanical harvesting at Las Marras in Corrientes.

ARGENTINA
at a glance

Plants
Camellia Sinensis
var. assamica and
var. sinensis
Main cultivars are
bred for yield, iced
tea quality, and
drought-tolerance
chiefly Gyayuvira and
Japanese Jazmin

Terroir
Red clay soils,
200-400 metres

Seasonality
Early season
in November

Harvesting
Ride-on machine.
Yield 2011 kg of
made tea per hectare

Processing
CTC and LTP
black, 5% green

Drinking
Ideal as iced tea

OTHER AMERICAN
TEA PRODUCERS

TE CHIRREPEC

LOS
ANDES

MEXICO

HONDURAS

NICARAGUA

COSTA RICA

PANAMA

VENEZUELA

GUYANA

SURINAME

FRENCH
GUIANA

NORTH

ATLANTIC

OCEAN

AGRICOLA HIMALAYA

BOGOTÁ

QUITO

COLOMBIA

ECUADOR

SANGAY

PERU

TINGO MARÍA

BRAZIL

LIMA

SANTA TERESA

SOUTH PACIFIC OCEAN

BOLIVIA

BRASILIA

PARAGUAY

REGISTRO

CHILE

MISIONES

URUGAY

BUENOS
AIRES

ARGENTINA

ALTITUDE

5000	
4000	
3000	
2000	
1800	
1600	
1400	
1200	
1000	
800	
600	
400	
200	

m

0   500   1000

Km

USA

INTEREST IN DOMESTIC CULTIVATION in the USA has accelerated in recent years as consumers have learnt to identify with locally rooted, more artisanal teas produced in smaller batches than the major brands have been able to accommodate into their businesses. This trend is perhaps not tea-specific, as craft brewers and speciality coffee roasters would testify, but it does provide new avenues for consumers to encounter tea on a bush rather than in a cup.

Although tea has been cultivated successfully in the USA since 1888, the intensive labour requirement has always acted as a brake on any large-scale developments given the level of wages in the USA when compared to some other producing countries. Despite this, smaller-scale planting has accelerated, much of which is commercially available, and it is now said that there is tea under cultivation in some form in every state.

The Charleston Tea Plantation on South Carolina's Wadmalaw Island boasts the USA's most significant crop. The plantation at Wadmalaw has grown from a potato farm in 1963, to a commercial enterprise and visitor centre producing both black and green tea from its bushes, which are direct descendants of the bushes imported into the USA in 1888 by tea pioneer Charles Shepard.[2]

Elsewhere in the USA, of a number of planting ventures all run with passion and pride, there are two states to watch for. In Mississippi, The Great Mississippi Tea Company is applying expert agronomic research in its pursuit of a viable organic plantation, and in Hawaii the volcanic soils have for some time now yielded excellent green tea and Taiwanese-style oolong from a multitude of producers.

Agricola Himalaya in Colombia.

A vew of Sangay volcano from the tea estate.

GUATEMALA

This coffee-producing country has a number of qualifications for tea production. The warm average temperatures and abundant rainfall create favourable growing conditions which have been exploited in two districts. Te Chirrepeco is a co-operative at an elevation of about 1,300 metres (4,300 feet) near to Cobán, producing small batches of black orthodox tea for the local market. Further south and west, at the base of the spectacular (and still active) volcano Mount Atitlan, sits Los Andes, which produces small quantities also of orthodox black tea, some of which finds its way overseas. The teas are red-liquoring yet mellow, light-bodied teas, and can perform well as iced teas. The low astringency ensures that they drink well without milk.

ECUADOR

Sangay is an active volcano of classic conical shape, and provides one of the tea world's most spectacular backdrops. The volcanic soils that form the basis of the Sangay Hacienda at around 1,400 metres (4,600 feet) are fertile and well-drained, whilst the Andes ensure more than adequate rainfall is harnessed from the moisture-laden winds that blow from the Pacific. Sangay produces bright, mellow CTC tea.

A plucking party returns, Agricola Himalaya.

The liquors are clean, neutral and relatively soft, although the leaf can be somewhat light in weight. It makes good iced tea and hot tea.

COLOMBIA

Colombia's tea is well located within the Valle del Cauca, which drains the local Andean Mountains into the nearby Pacific. The confusingly named Agricola Himalaya has always produced high-grown CTC black and pan-fired green teas primarily for local consumption, but is increasingly looking towards speciality production. The small fifty-one hectare garden sits amidst indigenous forest at between 1,800 and 2,050 metres (5,900-6,700 feet), and can boast not only China and Assam *jat* bushes, but also *Cambod*, hence there is really exciting diversity in the plant material. Himalaya is trying to build upon this by developing local Colombian cultivars that thrive in the volcanic soil rich in organic matter. These teas speak eloquently of their high-grown origins, with some parallels to the Indonesian higher-grown teas from similar soils. With an eye on development of a more appealing local style, they are increasingly converting to orthodox manufacture. Their whole leaf *Te Negro* is well-made and wiry, smooth and clean and fired to perfection. It has some of the characteristics of a Sri Lankan whole-leaf OP, yet without the preponderance of over-fired character that can dominate low-grown

Ceylons. The steamed *Te Verde* is of a similar leaf size, although slightly maritime in character. On the leaf it promises much, with fresh and fruity notes, and shows the potential that exists in Colombia.

PERU

Peru has a long heritage of tea cultivation dating back almost a century. The initial seeds were supplied by Japan, which has long enjoyed a close relationship with Peru. One would think these plants more suited to green tea manufacture, but Peru has always been more of a black tea producer. Further impetus was given with the recruitment of Sri Lankan planting and manufacturing expertise from 1928,[1] which cemented the Ceylon high-grown orthodox style as dominant.

The gardens are located on the eastern side of the Andean Mountains at altitudes of around 1,800 metres (5,900 feet). The main production is centred around Tingo María in the region of Huánuco, and Santa Teresa and Huyapata in Cusco further south. The current cultivars used are primarily African in origin, and as a consequence of the altitude the teas exhibit all of the brightness of high-grown production. Liquors are relatively pale, and whilst they do not boast much in the way of body, they are more astringent than Colombian or Ecuadorian teas. Peruvian teas are much superior to Argentines for any hot tea consumption, and the potential exists to produce some excellent teas from the high-grown terroir even if current quality can be hit-and-miss.

BRAZIL

It may be a coffee country at heart, but Brazil can also make some very good tea when the stars are in alignment. The tea gardens lie amidst banana plantations in the hills around Registro, around 150 kilometres (240 miles) down the coast from Sao Paulo. Run by members of the Japanese community long since naturalised in Brazil, they produce modest volumes of tea in a classically distinctive style.

Brazil's tea is relatively old as an industry. Dating back well into the 19th century and formerly reliant on slave labour, it has developed since the 1920s into a modestly sized, mechanised industry with a more qualitative focus than its Argentine neighbour, and its product has an ability to be enjoyed both hot and iced.

For a number of years, Brazilian tea could safely rely on its long-standing European and North American customers for its business, and its reliable southern hemisphere October-to-April growing season and reliable rains for its supply. The unique character could not be found anywhere else in the world of tea (although there are some Ugandan and Malagasy teas which are at times suggestive of the Samba style).

The hills around Registro now play host to an industry in crisis. Declining yields, disappearing markets and quality concerns have all combined to shake the confidence of those involved in the trade. This is a crying shame, for the teas have always been able to hold their heads up high in any comparison with East African teas. Bright and golden in colour, with a characteristic marzipan-coconut character, the teas are brisk, yet without real coarseness, and can be drunk without blending if needed and you wish to relish the unique style.

GLOSSARY

Bai (China). Chinese tea nomenclature meaning 'white', and suggestive either of white tips in the leaf, or a white tea itself, sometimes also written as *pai*.

Bhanji. Leaf shoots that have entered a period of dormancy.

Bloom. Satined leaf appearance characteristic of well-made black orthodox tea. The sheen is derived from the coating of leaf juices upon the downy hairs covering the green leaf. The more a tea is handled, the more this bloom is rubbed off and the leaf becomes dull and greyish in appearance.

Chun (China). Meaning 'spring', and suggestive of the cropping period of the tea in question (although this is interpreted liberally).

Congou (China). A classic Chinese style of black tea traditionally made from the fifth leaf. Now often used as a catch-all term to describe a larger-leafed Chinese black tea.

Creaming down (India). A quality assessment method in India by which un-milked teas are left uncleared in tasting rooms after the taste assessment. After a period of hours the teas containing the highest proportion of solids which precipitate in cold water will take on a golden, creamy appearance, as if milk has been added. Experts regard these teas as having the greatest body and strength.

CTC. Crush Tear Curl – a tea production style invented in 1930 but in popular use from the 1950s to achieve strong, thick, full-bodied teas that brew quickly. In this method, withered leaf is forced between sets of two sharpened rollers, being soundly crushed in the process. This style is well suited to teabags, where a quick brew is regarded as desirable. A consequence of this process is that the tea can lose its complexity and subtlety, with colour, strength and power being the overriding characteristics. CTC production is prevalent in Africa, most of Assam, parts of South India and Indonesia and pockets elsewhere in the world.

Cultivar. Also known as clonal, and produced using the principle of vegetative propagation, as opposed to the planting of seedlings. Creating a cultivar is little different to taking cuttings from a favoured garden plant and allows the planter the opportunity to select for drought resistance, taste, crop, distinctive tip or any other favoured characteristic particular to a bush. Because of the nature of the root development after propagation, clonal plantings can be less successful in drought-prone areas as they lack the deep tap root common to plants which have developed from seed. Clonal plantings can easily be identified when viewed alongside seedling areas, showing up usually as a uniform colour.

Dhool. A batch of leaf that has been removed from the rolling phase for oxidation in a tea factory.

Dryer Mouth (or DM). A mixture of leaf grades and stalk that emerges from the mouth of the dryer. The leaf is visually unattractive as it is irregular in size, but the liquoring characteristics are usually good because it has not suffered additional handling through the sorting process.

Epigallocatechin gallate (ECGC). A polyphenol present in large concentrations in green tea. ECGC is a type of catechin and is considered by many academic studies to be responsible for the positive health benefits of green tea.

Famous Teas (China). A list of China's ten most preeminent teas, more or less corresponding to the best examples from across China's varied processing styles.

Fibre. Particles of stalk or leaf veins (rather than leaf) remaining in the tea at the end of the process are known as fibre. Fibrous particles normally show up as a yellow-brown colour in black teas and as a pale yellow or white in green teas. In most cases producers will endeavour to remove all fibre through electrostatic action to create an offgrade.

Flush. Flushes are periods of leaf growth often punctuated by interludes of dormancy. Seasonal origins such as Assam and Darjeeling in North India, for example, are especially famed for the elevated quality produced during the 'first flush' and 'second flush' periods.

Golden Flower (China). Found on Fu brick tea. Small, yellowish spots of *Eurotium cristatum* bacteria found on good Fu bricks are known as Jin Hua, or Golden Flower.

Helopeltis theirora. A leaf-sucking insect also known as tea mosquito bug. *Helopeltis* attacks are especially aggressive during wet, overcast periods, with the weakest, most stressed bushes succumbing first. Assam has been a notable victim of such attacks in recent years, which can decimate a flush.

Hu (China). Lake.

Huang (China). Meaning 'yellow', and often either a description of the manufacture process or the colour of leaf or liquor.

Hyson (China and India). Leaf description used in green tea manufacture for larger OP-sized leaf grades, originally describing China teas but now often also used in Indian green teas.

Jat (India). When used in relation to tea, *jat* describes the variety of the bush, whether China jat (*Camellia sinensis*) or Assam jat (*Camellia assamica*).

Jin Hua (China). See Golden Flower.

Lawrie Tea Processor (LTP). Tea-processing machine now seldom seen outside Malawi. The LTP cuts and crushes leaf through the action of revolving sets of knives and beaters. The leaf is usually less stylish than CTC, but the machines are cheaper to buy and requiring of less skilled maintenance.

Legg Cut. Tea-processing machine that is derived from tobacco-cutting equipment. Typically leaf was cut into strips and rolled, quickly oxidised and then fired with little requirement for withering in advance. The resulting leaf appearance is predictably poor, but the liquor very bright. This was a common method for some time in Dooars and Congo, but is now all but extinct.

Liquor. The name given by tea experts to the liquid that results from the infusion of tea leaf in hot water. This is more commonly referred to in consumer parlance as the brew.

Looper caterpillar (Buzura suppressia). A tea pest that eats young leaf. Looper caterpillars start at the outer edge of the leaf and work inwards.

Maingrade. A grade of tea containing predominantly black leaf derived from the leaf of the tea plant as opposed to fibre derived from the stalk and veins. In a tea factory sorting room, fibre extraction will remove stalk from the bulk tea in order to create maingrades and offgrades. Maingrades are also known as *primary grades*.

Mao. Descriptor sometimes used in Chinese tea nomenclature to denote a downy leaf appearance (e.g. Mao Feng). *Mao* refers to the tiny hairs on the buds.

Mashdana (India). Leaf description often used in green tea manufacture. Roughly approximate to a shotty or gunpowder style.

Mongra (India). Leaf description used in Indian (especially South Indian) green tea manufacture to refer to broken-leafed teas.

Offgrade. Grades of tea containing large amounts of stalk or fibre. Some markets (such as Somalia) specifically seek out offgrade leaf as it suits their consumption style. Offgrades are almost always cheaper than their equivalent maingrade. Offgrades are also known as *secondary grades*.

Orthodox. A traditional tea production method that loosely mimics the traditional handmade style of manufacture. Tea is placed in a drum which either rotates above a fixed, flat table, upon which specially-shaped batons have been arranged, or (in double-action rolling) it rotates against this table which itself is moving in a contrary direction. The action of the tea rubbing against the batons under different degrees of pressure creates a twisted leaf. The object of the process is to coat the leaf with its juices and squeeze open the leaf cells, exposing enzymes to oxygen, thereby initiating oxidation. Compared to the CTC method, orthodox teas tend to be mellower in character, more complex in flavour, paler in colour and slower to brew. Orthodox production is prevalent in Sri Lanka, Darjeeling, particular factories and during early season in Assam, most of South India, Indonesia, Vietnam, China and parts of Argentina.

Outlots. Lots of tea that have been withdrawn from an auction due to failure to secure a bid above their reserve price.

Packer. A company engaged in the activity of packing tea into either loose-leaf packs or teabags. Packers may also be contract packers, involving the packing of teas for supermarkets or brands.

Primary grades. See *maingrade*.

Pruning (also known as *skiffing).* Pruning can be deep or shallow according to a number of predetermined depths, and will follow a set cycle over a period of three to five years. Skiffing helps to develop better quality of green leaf as well as prevent the bush creeping to an inconvenient height for plucking.

Qian (China). 'Before'. For example, a She Qian tea has been produced before the She Ri festival. This is especially important in denoting early spring cropping hierarchies in China.

Quimen (China). The original Pinyin name for the Anhui tea-growing county that has since been anglicised to Keemun.

Reconditioning. The practice of removing secondary grades after sorting, grinding them to a powder, and then adding them back before the CTC phase of black tea manufacture. The proportion of a factory's secondary grades is reduced as a consequence and a grainy leaf is created, albeit one with compromised liquoring characteristics. The practice is most prevalent in South India. Teas produced in this method are often labelled *RC*.

Red Spider Mite (Oligonychus coffae). A very small insect that attacks tea bushes (and other plants) by sucking juices from individual cells in the leaves. Red spider attacks are most common during hot, dry periods.

Rotorvane. Leaf preparation device usually found immediately before the CTC or orthodox stage of a production line. A rotor fitted with a number of vanes revolves within a casing that propels tea leaf forwards against the resistance of metal plates that project from the casing. The action of leaf against plate disrupts the cell structure and better prepares the leaf for orthodox rolling or CTC.[1]

Secondary grade. See *offgrade*.

Seedling. A bush that has been cultivated from seed rather than as a cultivar.

Sencha. Steamed method of tea manufacture typical to Japan. Tea leaf is exposed to steam, which deactivates the leaf enzymes. A series of rolling and drying processes then follow, followed by leaf sorting (usually in a different factory). The classic taste profile of a well-made sencha tea is umami.

Selling mark. The name under which a tea is sold. Often this is the same name as the factory in which it is produced, or the estate from which it comes. Occasionally multiple selling marks are used to differentiate different cultivars, manufacturing equipment or leaf standard (see *Tipping leaf*).

Shan (China). Meaning 'hill' or 'mountain', and used to denote the origin of the tea. Hence Lu Shan tea was cultivated on the Lu mountain.

Skiffing. See pruning.

Souchong (China). Now used to describe any number of types of black tea. Originally described smaller types of leaf. (From *xiaozhong*, or small kind.)

Spring crop. A key period for producers of quality teas in strongly seasonal origins such as Darjeeling and China. The long winter period permits the bush no opportunity to grow – indeed, it retreats into dormancy when shorn of the requisite rainfall and temperatures. In the act of protecting itself against this stress, the levels of antioxidants in the leaf build. This change in the chemical nature of the leaf creates unique aromatic characteristics in the first spring harvests of the year.

Standard number (China). Many Chinese teas are sold in bulks of homogenised quality known as standards. This helps the trade regulate the quality of what is sold, and assemble meaningful quantities of teas at different prices and quality levels. This standardisation generally starts below the best versions of the famous teas; hence, where sometimes one may expect to see a name upon a tea shop's tin, one instead encounters a number.

Sumi (India). Leaf description used in North Indian green tea manufacture for fannings-size teas.

Superior cultivar. See Cultivar.

Theaflavin. An oxidised polyphenol formed during the black tea oxidation process. TFs tend to bring brightness and briskness to the liquor.[2]

Thearubigen. An oxidised polyphenol formed during the black tea oxidation process. Thearubigens are responsible for black teas' reddish liquor, body and strength.[3]

Tipping leaf. The first growth after a bush has been pruned. When processed, teas from tipping leaf tend to be thin and light, hence an alternative selling mark is often used.

Ye (China). Meaning 'leaf' and often used to describe either the tea or the bush it comes from, *Mao Ye* being 'downy leaf'.

REFERENCES

AT A GLANCE

Unless otherwise stated, yield statistics are three-year averages reproduced from the *Annual Bulletin of Statistics* with the kind permission of the International Tea Committee, London.

THE TEA GARDEN

1. Vijay Rani Rajpal, S. Rama Rao, S.N. Raina. *Molecular Breeding for Sustainable Crop Improvement*, Volume 2. Springer. pp.105-106
2. Jane Pettigrew interview with Michael Adams. (1998) *Green Tea and the scent of orchid*. The Free Library. *Lockwood Trade Journal*
3. Luohui Liang. (2010) *The Tea Forests of Yunnan.* United Nations University http://ourworld.unu.edu/en/the-tea-forests-of-yunnan
4. Angiosperm Phylogeny Website. Retrieved March 2016. http://www.ncbi.nlm.nih.gov/Taxonomy/Browser/wwwtax.cgi

THE TEA FACTORY

1. P. Sivapalan, S. Kulasegaram, A. Kathiravetpillai (Ed). *Handbook on Tea.* (1986) Tea Research Institute of Sri Lanka. p158

TASTING TEA

1. ISO 3103. (1980) *Tea – Preparation of liquor for use in sensory tests.* International Organization for Standardization
2. *Ibid*

BLENDING AND FLAVOURING TEA

1. Rekha S. Singhal, Pushpa R. Kulkarni and Dinanath V. Rege. (1997) *Handbook of Indices of Food Quality and Authenticity*. p466. Woodhead Publishing Ltd
2. EFFA Guidance Document. (Chapter 1) *Regulation (EC) N° 1334 of the European Parliament and of the Council on flavourings and certain food ingredients with flavouring properties for use in and on foodstuffs.* http://www.effa.eu/en/legislation

BREWING AND DRINKING TEA

1. http://languagelog.ldc.upenn.edu/nll/?p=3282. Retrieved January 2016
2. Lu Yu. (780 AD) *The Classic of Tea.* Chapter 5. Numerous modern publications of this classic work exist.

[3] Dr Ronald Fisher. (1925) *Statistical Methods for Research Workers.* Oliver and Boyd, Edinburgh

CHINA
[1] Solala Towler. (2010) *Cha Dao: The Way of Tea, Tea as a Way of Life.* p9. Singing Dragon
[2] Bret Hinsch. (2008) *The Ultimate Guide to Chinese Tea.* White Lotus Co. Ltd
[3] Jung Chang and Jon Halliday. (2006) *Mao, The Unknown Story.* p398. Anchor, London
[4] Su Feng. (2011) *Study on Fu-brick Tea Fermented by Eurotium cristatum and the Toxicologically Testing. Fu-brick tea Eurotium cristatum ferment Sprague-Dawley haematological index ratio of viscera.* Wuhan Polytechnic University
[5] Jung Chang and Jon Halliday. (2006) *Mao, The Unknown Story.* p345. Anchor, London
[6] Kit Chow and Ione Kramer. (1990) *All the Tea in China.* p149. China Books and Periodicals Inc., San Fransisco
[7] Kit Chow and Ione Kramer. (1990) *All the Tea in China.* p132. China Books and Periodicals Inc., San Fransisco

TAIWAN
[1] Kazufumi Yazaki. *Molecular Mechanism of Plant – Insect Interaction via Plant Volatile Compounds and its Application.* (2007) Exploratory Research at the Institute of Sustainability Science, Kyoto University. Retrieved 20 July 2012

JAPAN
[1] Robin Stevens. *Japan's Matcha Tea: A Short Primer.* Tea and Coffee Trade Online. July 2008, Vol 180 Issue 7
[2] *Ibid*
[3] *Ibid*

MYANMAR
[1] *Annual Bulletin of Statistics.* (2015) International Tea Committee, London

INDIA
[1] *A Nice Cup Of Tea by George Orwell (Copyright © George Orwell, 1946).* Reprinted by permission of Bill Hamilton as the Literary Executor of the Estate of the Late Sonia Brownell Orwell
[2] The UK Tea and Infusions Association. https://www.tea.co.uk/east-india-company. Retrieved July 2015
[3] Elisabeth Jöbstl, J. Patrick, A. Fairclough, Alan P. Davies and Michael P. Williamson. (2005) *Creaming in Black Tea. Journal of Agricultural and Food Chemistry.* pp53, 7997-8002
[4] L. P. Bhuyan, Kula Kamal Senapati, Pranjal Saikia and Mridul Hazarika. *Characterization of volatile flavour constituents of orthodox black tea of twenty-nine Tocklai released cultivars for Darjeeling.* (2012) Department of Biochemistry, Tocklai Experimental Station, Tea Research Association, Jorkat 785 008, Assam, India (*Two and a Bud* 59(2):112-118)

SRI LANKA

1 John Weatherstone. (1986) *The Pioneers: Early British Tea and Coffee Planters and Their Way of Life, 1825-1900.* p117. Quiller Press
2 David Robson. (2002) *Geoffrey Bawa: The Complete Works.* Thames & Hudson, London

TURKEY

1 Mehmet Arif Ozyazıcı, Orhan Dengiz, Mehmet Aydogan. *Reaction Changing and Distribution of Agricultural Land for Tea Cultivation.* Retrieved April 2016. http://www.topraksudergisi.gov.tr/index.php/toprak/article/viewFile/1430/42
2 www.todayszaman.com. Retrieved 27th November 2011
3 Salih Kafkas, Sezai Ercişli, Yıldız Doğan, Yaşar Ertürk, Ayhan Haznedar, and Remzi Sekban. *Polymorphism and Genetic Relationships among Tea Genotypes from Turkey Revealed by Amplified Fragment Length Polymorphism Markers, Journal of the American Society for Horticultural Science.* Retrieved April 2016. http://journal.ashspublications.org/content/134/4/428.full

GEORGIA

1 William Ukers. (1935) *All About Tea Vol. 1* p463. The Tea and Coffee Trade Journal Company, New York
2 *World Tea Statistics 1910-1990.* The International Tea Committee

IRAN

1 Reza Azadi Gonbad, Adlin Afzan, Ehsan Karimi, Uma Rani Sinniah. *Phytoconstituents and antioxidant properties among commercial tea (Camellia sinensis L.) clones of Iran.* Electronic Journal of Biotechnology. Volume 18, Issue 6, November 2015, pp433-438. Retrieved April 2016

OTHER CAUCASIAN PRODUCERS

1 Farman Guliyev. (2010) *Tea-growing in Azerbaijan: The Present and Prospects. Visions of Azerbaijan.* Retrieved July 2015. http://www.visions.az/en/news/196/8872cf85/

UGANDA

1 Giles Bolton. (2008) *Aid and Other Dirty Business*, p24. Ebury Press, London
2 Dr Peter Laderach, Anton Eitzinger. *Future Climate Scenarios for Uganda's Tea Growing Areas.* p7. International Center for Tropical Agriculture

OTHER AFRICAN TEA PRODUCERS

1 William Ukers. (1935) *All About Tea Vol. 1* p209. The Tea and Coffee Trade Journal Company, New York
2 *Ibid*
3 *Annual Bulletin of Statistics.* (2015) International Tea Committee, London
4 Charles R. Obatolu and Ayoola B. Fasina. *Features of tea production in Nigeria.* Cocoa Research Institute of Nigeria

ARGENTINA

1   H. Panda. (2011) *The Complete Book on Cultivation and Manufacture of Tea.* p219. H. Panda. Asia Pacific Business Press Inc.

OTHER AMERICAN PRODUCERS

1   Yirka E. Duenas Cavero. (September 1997) *Tea in Peru.* Tea & Coffee Trade Journal

2   Charleston Tea Plantation. Accessed 10th December 2015. https://www.charlestonteaplantation.com/

GLOSSARY

1   J. Werkhoven (1974) *Tea Processing. Agricultural Services Bulletin* No. 26. FAO

2   D. Baruah, L. P. Bhuyan, M. Hazarika. (2012) *Impact of moisture loss and temperature on biochemical changes during withering stage of black tea processing on four Tocklai released clones.* Retrieved July 2015. *http://tocklai.net/wp-content/uploads/2013/07/TwoBud5922012/Impact%20of%20moisture%20loss%20and%20temperature*

3   *Ibid*

ACKNOWLEDGEMENTS

Thanks to the following for their help, sometimes amounting to extended periods away from loved ones in my cause. I hope these words of thanks can in some small way convey the appreciation I feel for their assistance.

EAST AND SOUTH ASIA

In China thanks to Liu Zhiming and his team at Shan Shan; Dick Lao for driving me around Guangxi; Gary Song for hosting an extended stay in Yunnan; Yanfei Kang; Rose Zhang, Madame Yao and Lola Luo in Hunan. In Taiwan to Peter Lee at Kien Yu; Jackson Huang at abc. In Japan to the indefatigable Shirakata family in Shizuoka, and Masanori Den Shirakata at Den's Tea for days checking and verifying my text and map which was greatly valued. In Korea to Kay Lee at Vision Korea for suggestions and images. In Vietnam to Tran Bach Duong at Van Rees for arranging and accompanying a visit to the more remote tribal lands. Alexander Zhiryakov at laostea.com. In Myanmar to Kyisoe Yauk for extensive tasting samples and lengthy weekend discussions. In Thailand to Thomas Kasper for his checking of my facts; Sariya Elle Phataraprasit at Araksa for her photographs. In Indonesia to the late Sandi Sopiyan. In Papua New Guinea to Sidath Perreia and Mike Jackson for arranging and supporting a fascinating visit.

SUBCONTINENT

In India I must thank Puran Tewari at Purba; Ajay Kichlu at Chamong; Shiv Bhasin at Goodricke; Jaydeep Shah and Iftikhar Alam at M.K.Shah; Durga Hegde at Unitea. In Sri Lanka thanks to Shamal da Sylva for corrections and images; Nathaniel Umesh for his tireless ferrying of me around low-, mid-, and up-country gardens; Shiraj Da Silva and his family on later trips; Dushy Perera for applying a planter's eye to my passages on cultivation and manufacture.

WEST ASIA

Thanks to Sevda Buetev for her clear and practical demonstrations of Turkish tea drinking habits; Nigel Adams for having brought his Turkish tea factory experience to bear in my cause; and Eda Eryilmaz for Rize information and images. In Georgia, to Gocha Dzneladze for having driven me around most of West Georgia, and for the vinuous evenings with family cousins that were enjoyed by all.

EAST AFRICA

In Kenya I must thank Mark Peters who helped me understand the rudiments of tea-making when in Kericho. In Mombasa to George Ngugi Waireri, James Gachau Kirathe and Robert Mwatha for helping me learn the trade. In Uganda to Baldeep 'Billy' Singh for having hosted me on his gardens; Fred Ssegujja was a tireless guide during my visit; and Chandri Wijesekere for his ideas and insight whilst there. In Congo thanks to Jaydeep Shah and Iftikhar Alam for their checking of facts and provision of photos to enhance the chapter. In Rwanda thanks to Tresham Graham and Andrew Wertheim for their information and suggestions.

CENTRAL AND SOUTH AFRICA

In Malawi thanks to Jim Melrose; Chip Kay and Alex Kay. In the Eastern Highlands of Zimbabwe to Pratap Pareekh for his time and hospitality despite suffering from the early stages of a malarial relapse. In Mozambique to Dave Saywood for a weekend expedition across the border from Malawi in a *bakkie* well-provisioned with biltong; in Gurue, Almeida Lee made us feel at home in his guest house. In South Africa to David Wishart and Lionel de Roland-Phillips.

AMERICAS

In Argentina thanks to Miguel Newell for text advice, and Roberto Navajas for his superb images. In Brazil thanks to Dario Yamamoto. In Colombia thanks to Juan Guillermo Gonzalez for images and samples.

EUROPE

In Cornwall I must thank Jonathon Jones for welcoming me to Tregothnan. In Scotland to Tam O' Braan for taking the time to explain his bold project.

Thanks to Katy Tubb for having supported my research sabbatical and for engendering an environment that is keenly protective of the importance of expertise, directly acquired at origin on estates, buying in auctions and doing the hard miles of tasting batch upon batch of tea. I must also thank Mark Lawson together with Giles Oakley, Claire Mackintosh, Jo Evans, Philippa Lazenby, Sebastian Michaelis and Paul Jefferies for performing my day job during my extended absences. At JDE sincere thanks to Luc Volatier, Dan Martz and Jan Lühmann for all their support.

More generally thanks to Ed Foster; Philippa Tickle; Stephen Hart; Brian Writer; Michael Adams; Bob Palmer; Cren Sandys-Lumsdaine; Mike Bunston; Nick Robinson; Jem McDowall; Sarah Roberts; Jordy van Honk; David Henderson; Ian Gibbs; Robin Harrison; Ottilie Cunningham; Roeland Stomp; Ronald Bruggeman; Gert ter Voorde; Martin Hodler; Mohammad Beyad; Yahya Beyad; John Snell; Kalle Grieger; Rinus Spijkerman; Walter Vaes; Dirk Irmer; Jan Sloothaak; Franz Tapken; Viral Sheth; and Arend Vollers for their help and advice on various elements of the book.

IMAGES AND MAPS

Jamie Whyte has been a patient, skilled and willing cartographer for whom another draft was never too much, no feature too small to overlook, and who I owe a deep thank you for having produced such detailed maps.

Hannah Hudson's artwork embellishes a number of the pages and she was tireless in re-drafting iteration after iteration. Thanks to Julian Davies at James Finlay, Linda Appelman at Mevrouw Cha and Mathias Kloth of Kloth & Koehnken for permitting the use of their photographs.

Of course all of the help I have received has been distilled into a final text for which I bear responsibility. Any errors are exclusively mine, just as any criticism directed at one or another part of the trade is my own opinion and does not represent the views of the individuals who have assisted me, or my previous employers.

At Troubador my thanks to Jennifer Parker, Chelsea Taylor and Joe Shillito for having forged a book from a text in a creative and long-suffering fashion.

Lastly all my love and thanks go to my children Henry and Sophie, and Annabel my wife. Annabel has always supported the project despite its self-indulgence and extended gestation, and remained a solid support whether at 2am in a cold rural Taiwanese factory five hours beyond her normal bedtime, in a sweltering village B&B in the tribal hills of North Vietnam with an insect populous in the millions, or affecting an interest in tea factory engineering whilst a typhoon raged outside. It certainly would not have reached the shelves without her love and support.

PHOTOGRAPHIC AND DESIGN CREDITS

p204: istock; p211: McLeod Russel India Ltd; p212: Godricke Group Ltd; p213: McLeod Russel India Ltd; p218: McLeod Russel India Ltd; p219: Author; p220: Miracle Tea & Spices; p223: Chamong Tea (Pvt) Ltd; p226: Chamong Tea (Pvt) Ltd; p227: Goodricke Group Ltd; p232: Dharmsala Tea Company; p234: Harrisons Malayalam SBU A; p235: United Nilgiri Tea Estates Ltd; p236 Harrisons Malyyalam SBU A; p238: K C Ponappa; p239: istock; p242: Nabin Koirala; p243: Nabin Koirala; p244: Nabin Koirala; p245 Teatulia Ltd; p246: Teatulia Ltd; p248: istock; p253: Watawala Plantations PLC, p254: Watawala Plantations PLC; p255: Author; p257: Author; p258: Shamal da Sylva; p260: Author; p262: Zealong; p266: Two Rivers Green Tea; p267: Zealong; p268 Eda Eryilmaz; p273: Eda Eryilmaz; p275: Author; p277: Author; p279: Author; p286: Linda Appelman, Mevrouw Cha; p288: Mathias Kloth; p293: Mathias Kloth; p296: James Finlay Ltd; p297: Mmathias Kloth; p299: Viral Sheth; p300: istock; p304: McLeod Russel Uganda Ltd; p306: Rift Valley Tea; p308: East Usumbara Tea Company; p309: (above): Rift Valley Tea; (below): East Usumbara Tea Company; p311: M:K:Shah; p312: M:K:Shah; p314: Borelli Tea Holdings/Gisovu Tea Company; p318: Mathias Kloth; p319: Mathias Kloth; p321: Office de The du Burundi; p324: istock; p329: Author; p331: Anette Kay; p332: Anette Kay; p334: Sto Antonio; p338: Sto Antonio; p339: istock; p340: Pratap Pareekh; p346: Craig Wishart; p347: istock; p348: Tregothnan; p350: istock; p353 (both images) The Wee Tea Company/Tam O´Braan; p354: istock; p358: Ronald Bruggeman; p359 (both images) Establecimiento Las Marias; p363 Agricola Himalaya; p364: Sangay Tea Estate; p365: Agricola Himalaya.

ENDPAPERS

Fletcher Fine Art/Author.

INDEX